GENERAL HISTORIES

The Development of Ballistic Missiles in the United States Air Force 1945–1960

Jacob Neufeld

OFFICE OF AIR FORCE HISTORY
UNITED STATES AIR FORCE
WASHINGTON, D.C., 1990

Library of Congress Cataloging-in-Publication Data

Neufeld, Jacob.
  The development of ballistic missiles in the United States Air Force,
1945–1960 / Jacob Neufeld.
    p. cm.—(General histories.)
  Includes bibliographical references.
  ISBN 0–912799–62–5
  1. Ballistic missiles—United States—History. 2. United States. Air
Force—Weapons systems—History. 3. Atlas (Missile)—History. 4. Thor
(Missile)—History. 5. Titan (Missile)—History.
I. Title. II. Series.
UG1312.B34N48 1989
358.1′7182′0973—dc20   89–71109

For sale by the Superintendent of Documents, U.S. Government Printing Office,
Washington, D.C. 20402

Foreword

Following World War II, the onset of nuclear weapons, long-range jet bombers, and ballistic missiles radically changed American foreign policy and military strategy. The United States Air Force, led by men of far-sighted vision and uncommon dedication, accepted the challenge of organizing and leading a massive research and development effort to build ballistic missiles. In the quarter of a century since, these weapons have constituted one of the three legs of the strategic triad—the basis of America's strategy of deterring nuclear war—yet they have received less attention from the public and within the Air Force than the more glamorous manned bombers of the Strategic Air Command or the missile-launching submarines of the U.S. Navy. This volume attempts to correct the imbalance by telling the story of the development of Air Force ballistic missiles. It concentrates on the first generation of ballistic missiles: the intercontinental Atlas and Titan, and the intermediate range Thor. Although the effort to develop rockets has a longer history than commonly assumed, the modern history spans the relatively short era from 1945 to 1960. During this brief interval, missiles advanced from drawing board to alert status, where the next generation now remains poised to deter war.

The author describes the difficulties involved in the technological competition with the Soviets to be first to develop and deploy a ballistic missile force. With innovative leadership, the Air Force succeeded also in overcoming conflict with the Army and Navy, budgetary constraints, administrative complications, and of course formidable engineering problems. Jacob (Jack) Neufeld has done a thoughtful, thorough job of research in an immense amount of documentation. He came to the task with broad experience in the subject matter. He first joined the history program at Eighth Air Force, Westover Air Force Base, Massachusetts; his initial assignment was to cover the command's ICBMs, including the Titan II and Minuteman, in the annual history. When he came to Washington and joined the Office of Air Force History in 1970, he produced monographs on missiles and space. He also had other diverse assignments, usually in the area of the history of research, development, and technology generally. Before long he earned a well-deserved reputation as an expert in these fields. In the course of his extensive research, Mr. Neufeld also met and interviewed many of the leading people involved in Air Force science and technology.

Although the development of ballistic missiles is largely an administrative history, it is also the story of the herculean efforts of several key individuals. The effort could not have succeeded as it did without the fortuitous appearance on the scene of Trevor Gardner, Gen. Bernard A. Schriever, and Dr. John von Neumann. How these men conceptualized, promoted, and directed the program forms the basis of the story. Additionally, the development of ballistic missiles revolutionized the way the Air Force conducted research and development, having a profound and long-lasting effect on how the service acquired weapons of all types. Mr. Neufeld's fascinating history details these important changes in the process of relating how the service conceived, developed, and brought into the arsenal one of the most revolutionary weapons in the long history of warfare.

RICHARD H. KOHN
Chief, Office of Air Force History

Preface

This book was originally conceived in late 1976 when I was assigned by the Office of Air Force History to "write a twenty-five year history of Air Force ballistic missiles." It soon became apparent that such a monumental task was unlikely to be completed by one individual within a normal lifetime. Moreover, the indicated twenty-five year span had no special historical significance, and the term "ballistic missiles" was too broad. Consequently, I set out to narrow the subject and proposed to write a history of the development of the Air Force's first generation, long-range, strategic ballistic missiles: the Atlas, the Titan, and the Thor. This seemed far more manageable and more useful, and the study could serve as a basis for succeeding histories on the Titan II and Minuteman missile series. Most important, by narrowing the focus and time span, I could produce a work of sufficient depth to be of real value in reconstructing the evolution of the Air Force's research and development history.

Anyone who has worked in a government history office will appreciate the delays a major book can encounter when more pressing assignments or projects fall to an author. While I completed a draft of the book in the spring of 1981, that fall I agreed to accept a management position, supervising the Special Histories Branch, which consumed most of my time. A few years later, I became Chief of the office's Editorial Branch and since 1985, of its Air Staff Branch. After I revised and refined the manuscript, a final seminar panel recommended additional changes, which also took considerable time. Further delays were the product of security and policy review by agencies outside the Air Force and by budget reductions in the Office of Air Force History, which slowed the editing and printing of the work.

There are a great many people I want to thank for helping me with the research and writing of this book. First my family, my wife Shari and children Michelle, Neil, and Jessica, deserves praise for its consistent support. My colleagues at the Office of Air Force History provided much constructive criticism during chapter seminars: Maj. Gen. John W. Huston, Stanley Falk, Max Rosenberg, the late Carl Berger, Warren A. Trest, the late Thomas A. Sturm, Herman S. Wolk, Marcelle S. Knaack, Henry O. Malone, Walton S. Moody, and Edgar F. Raines. Several key figures in the history of missile development were kind enough to share their experiences in interviews. Their names are listed throughout the notes. However, I wish to thank especially Gen. Bernard A. Schriever and Col. Vincent J. Ford. William Heimdahl, Chief of the Reference Branch, was a tremendous help with many of my research problems. At the National Archives, I was assisted by William H. Cunliffe, Timothy K. Nenninger, and John E. Taylor.

I was also fortunate to receive help from several historians at Air Force major commands: at Strategic Air Command John T. Bohn, Sheldon A. Goldberg, J. C. Hopkins, and Frederick J. Shaw; at Air Force Logistics Command Bernard J. Termena; at Air Force Systems Command John T. Greenwood, Charles J. Gross, Walter L. Kraus, Raymond L. Puffer, Robert J. Smith, Thomas S. Snyder, and Malcolm Wall. All of the researchers at the USAF Historical Research Center, at Maxwell AFB, Alabama, assisted at one time or another; I especially want to thank Hugh N. Ahmann, James C. Hasdorff, and R. Cargill Hall. Two people at the Center for Military History provided valuable documents: Vincent C. Jones and Hannah Zeidlick. I benefited considerably from comments by members of the "final" review panel, including Lt. Col. Harry Borowski of the Air Force Academy, Brooke Hindle of the Smithsonian Institution, Richard H. Kohn, Bernard C. Nalty, Alfred Rockefeller, and Col. John F. Shiner. Steven L. Rearden of East Incorporated provided some valuable insights while reading the final draft. Finally, I must commend the splendid work of several editors whose labors improved the volume immeasurably: Vanessa Allen and Alfred M. Beck, who prepared the editorial contract; Joan Compton of Comptron, who edited the book under contract; Anne E. Johnson, who monitored the project, took over the editing, and saw the volume through to completion; and the late Eugene P. Sagstetter, who provided much sound advice and encouragement. If, by the passage of time, I have forgotten to express my appreciation to any deserving individual, my omission is strictly unintentional.

JACOB NEUFELD
April 1989

United States Air Force
Historical Advisory Committee

(As of January 1, 1990)

Charles G. Boyd
Lieutenant General, USAF
Commander, Air University

Norman A. Graebner
The University of Virginia

Dominick Graham
University of New Brunswick,
Canada

Ira D. Gruber
Rice University

Charles R. Hamm
Lieutenant General, USAF
Superintendent, USAF Academy

John H. Morrow, Jr.
University of Georgia
(Chairman)

Ann C. Petersen
The General Counsel, USAF

Marc A. Trachtenberg
University of Pennsylvania

Gerhard L. Weinberg
The University of North
Carolina at Chapel Hill

The Author

JACOB NEUFELD began his service with the Air Force in July 1967 as an historian at Headquarters, Eighth Air Force, Westover AFB, Massachusetts. He has been a member of the Office of Air Force History since February 1970. After working in the General Histories Branch for eleven years, Mr. Neufeld served as Chief of the Special Histories Branch and then Editorial Branch. He is currently Chief of the Headquarters USAF Branch. He holds BS and MA degrees from New York University and has done postgraduate work at the University of Massachusetts, Amherst, and the University of Maryland, College Park. Mr. Neufeld is an author or contributing author of: *The Makers of the United States Air Force* (1987), *Life in the Rank and File* (1986), *The Air War over Vietnam: Aircraft of the Southeast Asia Conflict* (1981), and *The Vietnam War* (1979). He is also the author of numerous monographs, studies, and articles on the history of Air Force technology.

Contents

Photographs

Charts and Tables

The Development of
Ballistic Missiles
in the
United States Air Force
1945–1960

Introduction

Ballistic missiles have revolutionized our national policy, strategy, and military organization. When, how, and why these weapons were built are questions that demand our attention. Many studies are needed to capture the enormous size, complexity, and expense of the missiles program. As an administrative history, this book focuses on the role of the U.S. Air Force. Only the first "generation" of ballistic missiles—Atlas, Titan, and Thor—is considered, for it shaped the nature of succeeding missile types. Minuteman, the mainstay of the U.S. arsenal for the past quarter century, deserves a separate volume. It is my contention that the ballistic missiles program succeeded only because the fortuitous confluence of events and men overcame past obstacles.

Mutual distrust between the United States and the USSR governed the Cold War period following World War II. Both sides engaged in an unbridled arms race in which an action by one side quickly elicited a reaction by the other. The United States had demonstrated its atomic power at the close of World War II; in 1949 the Soviets exploded their own atomic bomb. Three years later the United States tested a hydrogen device; the USSR followed suit in 1953. Although the Russians had a head start in developing ballistic missiles, the United States did not undertake a crash program until the 1950s. By the end of the decade both sides had demonstrated their ability to launch missiles and during the 1960s started to deploy them in significant numbers. Since then the United States and the USSR have continuously improved the types, numbers, and capabilities of their missile forces.

The terms ballistic missile, cruise missile, and rocket have crept into our vocabulary, but relatively few people understand their precise meanings. A missile used as a weapon can be any object propelled to strike a distant target. It may be as primitive as a stone or as advanced as a multiple stage rocket. Missile performance is measured in range, accuracy, and explosive power. A guided missile is an unmanned vehicle whose course may be altered in flight by a self-contained mechanism controlled via a radio signal, built-in target seeking radar, inertial guidance, or (in the broadest sense) on-board preset controls.

In this book I treat just two types of very long-range or strategic

1

missiles. One is the jet-propelled aerodynamic missile (now called the cruise missile) closely resembling an airplane, except that it is unmanned. The second is the ballistic missile that is boosted outside the atmosphere, into space, by a rocket engine. At the end of powered flight the latter missile follows a ballistic path, the propulsion units drop off, and its warhead reenters the atmosphere en route to the target.

Ballistic missiles must carry their own supply of oxygen to traverse the space environment. (Indeed, it is the oxygen in the fuel that chiefly distinguishes the rocket engine from the jet engine.) Ballistic missiles may burn either liquid or solid fuel. The liquid fuel is more powerful and easier to control; however, liquid-fueled ballistic missiles are not only harder to maintain on prolonged alert status but are dangerous to handle.

As far back as 1917, predecessor organizations of the U.S. Air Force, the Army air arm, had experimented with remotely controlled aerodynamic missiles. That interest was always considered in the context of specialized weapons, with the primacy of piloted airplanes remaining intact. Ballistic missiles, by contrast, belonged in the province of the Army's Ordnance Department. The Army Air Forces (AAF) began to explore ballistic missiles only after the German V-2 rocket in World War II showed strategic potential if it could be mated with atomic bombs. Following the war, the Army, Army Air Forces, and Navy all undertook a variety of missile projects to preserve their individual "roles and missions."

Interservice rivalry over who would develop, operate, and control ballistic missiles postponed final decisions and unnecessarily delayed the programs. From World War II through the end of the Korean War, little progress was made in missile development. The Air Force ballistic missiles program was conducted on a modest scale until it was canceled in 1947 for a number of reasons, but primarily due to budgetary constraints. The effort also foundered, lacking an institutional advocacy group when it competed for funds.

Thus, the Air Force relied primarily on its manned bombers, the so-called "force in being." In the missiles arena the Air Force gave preference to the Snark and Navaho aerodynamic missile projects. (These programs continued despite the fact that neither missile was capable of effectively penetrating enemy defenses. Navaho was canceled in July 1957, whereas Snark was briefly deployed and then dismantled early in the Kennedy Administration.) This void was filled in 1950 when the Air Force established the Air Research and Development Command (ARDC) and added a Deputy Chief of Staff for Development at USAF Headquarters.

With the advent of the Eisenhower Administration, Trevor Gardner was named Special Assistant (later Assistant Secretary of the Air Force) for Research and Development. Gardner became the chief protagonist for an intercontinental ballistic missile (ICBM), especially after he learned that

2

low-weight, high-yield nuclear warheads were feasible. He appointed Dr. John von Neumann, a renowned mathematician, to chair a select committee on strategic missiles. In February 1954 von Neumann's Teapot Committee recommended, and the Air Force initiated, a crash program to develop an ICBM (called the Atlas) within six years. Dr. von Neumann continued as chairman of the ICBM Scientific Advisory Committee, a body that dispensed impartial advice to both the Defense Department and the Air Force. In May the Air Force chose Brig. Gen. Bernard A. Schriever, a technically oriented officer, to head the Atlas program. His office, the Western Development Division (WDD) at Inglewood, California, belonged organizationally to ARDC.

The Teapot Committee believed that the Air Force's conventional aircraft development approach would not work for ballistic missiles. Because these new weapons posed considerable technical uncertainty, their development required a unique, highly competent scientific organization. Thus, Schriever was granted broad powers in running the Atlas program. He engaged the Ramo-Wooldridge Corporation to provide WDD with systems engineering and technical direction. Schriever also held contracting authority through a special field office of the Air Materiel Command (AMC) collocated with WDD.

Another significant innovation was the establishment of simplified administrative channels, leading directly from Schriever's office to the Air Force's top leadership. Called the Gillette Procedures, these channels streamlined reporting and review and cut through unnecessary red tape to expedite the missiles program. A single, comprehensive plan was developed annually for approval. Two Ballistic Missiles Committees—one under the Secretary of the Air Force, the other under the Secretary of Defense—provided timely and authoritative decisions. Finally, Schriever transformed the acquisition process from a functional to a systems approach. He adopted concurrent management in building the ballistic missiles, thereby compressing the lead time from development to operational status.

The foresight, dedication, and persistence of these three men—Gardner, von Neumann, and Schriever—won the ICBM program top national priority from President Eisenhower in September 1955. The WDD emerged as a full-fledged missiles complex, whose projects included the Atlas and Titan intercontinental ballistic missiles and the Thor intermediate range ballistic missile (a competitor of the Army's Jupiter). In November 1956 the Air Force won exclusive rights to operate intermediate range ballistic missiles (IRBMs).

Just as the Air Force's missiles program seemed on the verge of success, however, it met Army and Navy competition for scientists, facilities, and funding. Moreover, the Eisenhower Administration had embarked on an austerity drive, known in the Air Force as the "Poor Man's

Approach." It reduced the number of ICBMs to be deployed by one-third (from 120 to 80), cut the IRBM complement in half (from 120 to 60), and planned to stretch out the missiles' deployment. Trevor Gardner had earlier resigned to protest the large reductions in research and development. By March 1957 the Administration had lowered the missile program's priority, now calling for operational readiness at the earliest practical—instead of the earliest possible—date. Additional reductions continued until October 4, 1957, when the Soviets electrified the world by launching into orbit Sputnik, the world's first artificial satellite.

In the wake of Sputnik emerged the so-called "missile gap," a notion that the USSR was poised to surpass the United States in numbers of strategic missiles. As Democrats exploited the issue, the Administration denied any cause for alarm. Nonetheless, the Sputnik scare served to defer spending cuts and accelerated the missiles program. Ironically, it also led to a rapid introduction of space projects which interrupted orderly missiles development.

Meanwhile, a new class of solid-fueled missile programs had appeared, including the Navy's Polaris IRBM and the Air Force's Minuteman ICBM. Both programs showed tremendous military potential and won eager acceptance at nearly all command levels. Between 1958 and 1960 the Air Force began deploying Thor and Jupiter missiles in Europe and started making Atlas operational.

As the Kennedy Administration took office, the more advanced Atlas and Titan ICBMs were installed. In all, 12 Atlas squadrons (126 missiles), 6 Titan I squadrons (54 missiles), and 4 Thor squadrons (60 missiles) were deployed. Soon the much publicized "missile gap" narrowed, then disappeared altogether. In April 1961 the Air Force Systems Command (AFSC) and Air Force Logistics Command (AFLC) replaced ARDC and AMC. General Schriever had finally achieved one of his long-term aims, to consolidate research, development, and acquisition. Schriever, then head of ARDC, retained command of AFSC.

Secretary of Defense Robert S. McNamara readily endorsed the Minuteman because it offered greater simplicity and ease of operation than the liquid-fueled ICBMs. In October 1962, at the time of the Cuban Missile Crisis, ten Minuteman missiles stood on operational alert. Over the next two years, the first generation missiles—the Atlas, Titan I, and Thor—were inactivated. Only the Titan II, an advanced liquid-fueled ICBM that entered the inventory in 1963, survived.

In retrospect, the first-generation missiles had served merely as interim weapons. Considering the context of the times, no responsible official could have foreseen their rather limited roles. Critics are fond of pointing out the missiles' huge developmental costs and spectacular initial failures, without considering the enormous technical and organizational challenges involved.

4

Initially the Air Force had required Western Development Division to provide only flyable missiles, but later decisions added responsibilities to make the missiles operational. For example, prelaunch survival originally meant the ability to launch within a specified warning time. Later the problem was made far more complex: missiles had to be hardened to withstand nuclear explosions and mobile enough to escape being targeted by enemy nuclear forces. Under these circumstances, it is remarkable that the first generation missiles were built and deployed within their scheduled time limits and prescribed performance requirements.

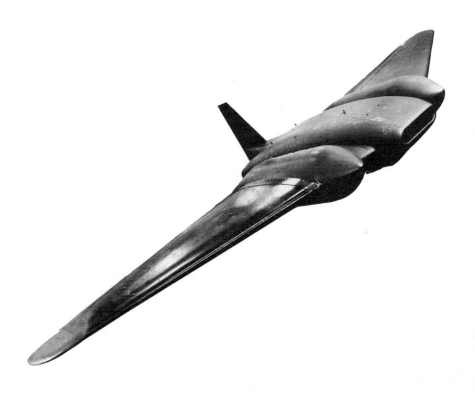

The jet-propelled JB–1, a "flying wing" type missile.

Chapter I

Pilotless Aircraft

> . . . in technical pursuits, the first idea put into
> practice can never be perfect—and can never
> mean the end of the work.
>
> Walter R. Dornberger, 1964

U.S. military aviators first demonstrated interest in guided missiles in 1917 by conducting experiments with pilotless aircraft. These efforts continued sporadically through the 1920s and 1930s. At that time, attention was centered on the pilot and funding was scarce, so guided missiles remained a minor effort.

During World War II, guided missile development—largely involving remotely controlled bombs and aircraft—was conducted by a special weapons group at Wright Field, Ohio. In view of the ample supply of men and planes available, guided missiles had only marginal appeal. Nevertheless, at Headquarters AAF the Air Communications Officer, Brig. Gen. Harold M. McClelland, believed that missiles suffered from lack of serious attention. In September 1943 he instigated a reorganization that made him responsible for missile development.

In June 1944 the Germans started firing their dreaded V (for vengeance) weapons. Although highly inaccurate and soon easily defeated, the V–1 cruise missile terrorized the Allied civilian population, and a clamor went up for the United States to match the enemy's technology. Consequently, the AAF shifted its research to concentrate on jet-propelled missiles. Headquarters AAF also reverted to a functional arrangement in managing missile development. The most important result of these changes was that they forced missiles to vie with aircraft for money and technical expertise.

Competition grew in the U.S. military as the Navy embarked on a very broad and expensive missile development program; the AAF and Army Ground Forces also competed in missile research and development. The rivalry really concerned roles and missions—the lifeblood of the military—

because it was expected that the organization that won responsibility for missile development would gain operational control as well. The War Department faced a difficult decision, given the revolutionary nature of guided missiles. In October 1944 the War Department divided missiles into two categories, aerodynamic lift (cruise) and momentum (ballistic), and assigned the development of these two types to the AAF and Army Ordnance Department respectively.

Convinced that missiles would revolutionize warfare, the Commanding General of the Army Air Forces, Gen. Henry H. "Hap" Arnold, tried to point the AAF to the future. It was Arnold who commissioned Dr. Theodore von Kármán's seminal study, *Toward New Horizons*. In 1945 Arnold also appointed Maj. Gen. Curtis E. LeMay as Deputy Chief of Air Staff for Research and Development, hoping thereby to "protect" the AAF's interest in technology. As an outgrowth of these efforts the Air Force established the Scientific Advisory Board and the Rand Corporation, its most forward-looking institutions.

Following World War II, in October 1945, Wright Field engineers drew up a comprehensive plan for guided missile development, including four varieties of missiles: air-to-air, air-to-ground, ground-to-air, and ground-to-ground. Twenty-eight study contracts were awarded through April 1946, but the program fell victim to fiscal retrenchment in December. Thus, the $29 million budgeted for missiles in FY 1947 was slashed to $13 million and ten studies were dropped. Wright Field was forced to pursue the most promising technologies and chose to develop only those it expected to become operational the soonest. Fiscal problems continued in the spring of 1947, demanding even more cuts. In July the Air Staff decided to prioritize the air-to-air and air-to-ground missiles because these would enhance the capabilities of manned aircraft. Long-range ground-to-ground missiles fell to fourth place because they were expected to take the longest to develop.

Early Experimental Guided Missiles

The Aviation Section of the Signal Corps* first became involved with missiles shortly before America's entry into World War I when it sponsored Charles F. Kettering's research on a remotely controlled aircraft dubbed the "Bug." A renowned engineer, Kettering collaborated on the project with several associates, including Orville Wright, Elmer A. Sperry, Edwin S. Votey, and Childe H. Wills. Also called a flying bomb, an aerial torpedo, and Project Liberty Eagle, the small craft was built by the Dayton Metal

---

*Established on August 1, 1907, the Aeronautical Division (Signal Corps) became the Aviation Section (Signal Corps) on July 18, 1914. The Air Service was created in May 1918.

Products Company. It performed well enough after several flight tests for the Air Service to order 100 of the pilotless aircraft in October 1918. Col. Henry H. "Hap" Arnold, another of those involved in the project, then decided to persuade Gen. John J. Pershing, Commander of the American Expeditionary Forces, to organize tactical missile units in Europe. Unfortunately for missile enthusiasts, Arnold became ill and before he could see General Pershing the war had ended. With the cessation of hostilities, production was canceled and the project abandoned. The Navy, which had started a similar program in 1916, continued its research until about 1919, but then it too scrapped the work.[1]

In 1923 the Chief of the Air Service Engineering Division at McCook Field, Ohio, recommended adapting radio controls to the aerial torpedo and the following year obtained funds for the project. Despite such signal achievements as preset flights to a distance of 30 miles and radio-controlled flights of up to 90 miles, the project was canceled a second time for a lack of funds. Then, in 1928, it was revived as part of a scheme to adapt remote control and guidance, with various-sized bombs, to commercial aircraft and to file the data for future reference in the event of war. After a promising start, however, the effort foundered in 1932 and then lay dormant until the eve of World War II.

Interest was next renewed with the August 1937 demonstration of a completely automatic radio-controlled flight and landing of an aircraft.* This event prompted Maj. Gen. Oscar Westover, Chief of the Air Corps,† to establish a requirement for an unmanned aircraft with a range between 20 and 50 miles, carrying 200 to 300 pounds of explosives and capable of striking a 2-square-mile target. A design competition was initiated in April 1939 but failed to elicit an acceptable proposal. Nonetheless, the effort resumed in February 1940, with even more demanding specifications for the aircraft to fly up to 100 miles and strike within one-half mile of a target.

This phase culminated in April 1941 when Charles F. Kettering, now a General Motors Corporation executive, won a contract to fabricate ten aerial torpedoes. Designated as Guided Missile A-1 (GMA-1), or "controllable bomb, power-driven," the project was supervised by Col. George V. Holloman, Chief of Air Materiel Command's Special Weapons Unit at Wright Field, Ohio.[2]

The new Bug was expected to carry between 2,000 and 4,000 pounds of explosives over a preselected 20-mile range and then dive into its target. The Special Weapons Unit grappled with the requirement for about 2 years without appreciable success and was especially stymied by the craft's

---

*Capt. George V. Holloman, Capt. Carl J. Crane, and Raymond K. Stout developed the automatic landing system and flew aboard the test aircraft on its historic flight.

†The Air Corps was established on July 2, 1926.

inaccuracy. Moreover, during the course of the war, the Bug's capabilities in terms of speed, range, and bomb load seemed increasingly inadequate as those of standard combat aircraft increased. Consequently, in August 1943 the AAF* considered other small, power-driven pilotless aircraft for special bombing missions, including the Fleetwings XQB-1 and XQB-2 and the Fairchild XQB-3. But these conventional aircraft also proved inadequate because they were expensive and because they needed clear visibility, fighter protection, and highly skilled crews.[3]

A more promising approach, begun in 1944, involved the use of obsolescent B-17 and B-24 aircraft as power-driven bombs. The project, nicknamed War Weary, employed a large number of these aircraft. On a typical mission, the pilot would take off in an airplane laden with about 20,000 pounds of explosives, set a course, and then bail out. (Navy Lt. Joseph P. Kennedy, Jr., President John F. Kennedy's older brother, died on such a mission when the bomb load exploded prematurely.) War Weary aircraft carried a predetermined fuel load to stop the engines over the target. The bombers could also be controlled by accompanying "director" aircraft or from the ground. Like the Bug, these experimental aircraft were beset by serious problems in accuracy and therefore proved most useful against large area targets.[4]

Another category of missiles developed during the war included the air-launched glide bombs (GB), which had numerical designations from 1 to 15. Interest in these weapons stemmed from the work done by the British, and from General Arnold's 1941 directive to the AAF to develop them. The glide bombs were nothing more than standard 1,000-, 2,000-, and 4,000-pound bombs fitted with wings and gyrostabilizers. The GB-1, for example, was a general-purpose bomb to which was attached a simple monoplane structure, including a wing assembly with twin booms extending rearward to a horizontal surface with 2 square fins and a movable elevator. Most glide bombs were preset on a course and could not be controlled after being released from their aircraft.

Although these missiles experienced problems in achieving acceptable accuracies, the AAF was determined to prepare them for combat. The effort began in October 1942, and by the end of 1943 the GB-1 and its B-17 launch aircraft were declared ready. The initial combat mission, however, was not flown until March 25, 1944, when a squadron of 58 B-17s, each carrying 2 GB-1s, attacked Cologne. Fewer than one-half of the bombs hit their intended targets, and the Eighth Air Force, noting that manned bombers could do better, gave up on the project. At war's end the AAF had 200 glide bombs in storage but did not plan any further research with them.[5]

A variant of the GB series was the air-launched glide torpedo, which involved the AAF and Navy in a dispute over which service should develop it.

---

*The AAF was created on June 20, 1941.

The AAF also experimented with the radio-controlled and television-guided GB–8 missile. While the AAF encountered accuracy problems with the GB–8, the Navy used a similar missile, the Bat, with some success. The AAF also experimented with a larger bomb, the television- and radio-guided GB–4. Between July and September 1944 the GB–4 was launched against German U–boat pens at Le Havre, France, with generally disappointing results.[6]

Another category, called high-angle or vertical bombs (VB series), also consisted of standard-size bombs equipped with special controls. Developed by the National Defense Research Committee, the apparatus was mounted in a square-shaped tail at the rear of the bomb. Also included on the tail were a flare, radio receiver, antenna, gyrostabilizer, and rudders. Launched from B–17 aircraft, the vertical bombs were controlled through part of their earthward dive by the bombardier. The most useful of these weapons—and the only one used in combat in more than experimental quantity—was the Azon (VB–1) missile. Azon (short for azimuth only) was a 1,000-pounder that could be controlled to the right and left of a target and, therefore, might prove effective in attacking roads, tunnels, bridges, and railways. The first Azon model appeared in 1943, and 150 of the missiles were initially ordered for testing. Test results proved so encouraging that the AAF placed quantity orders for the missile.

In early 1944, a specially trained squadron attached to the Fifteenth Air Force in Italy unveiled the VB–1 in attacking the Brenner Pass and river locks on the Danube. Despite some early successes, Azon performed erratically in subsequent missions and saw only limited action in Europe during the balance of the war. The weapon proved more successful, however, in the China–Burma–India Theater. In 1944 and 1945 the 7th Bombardment Group used Azon missiles to destroy nearly all of the bridges in Japanese-held Burma. During a 2-month period, 10 Azon-equipped B–17s destroyed 27 bridges with an expenditure of 459 missiles and had direct hits with 10 to 15 percent of the weapons.[7] At the end of the war there were 12,000 Azons on hand and another 10,000 on order. Nonetheless, the AAF abandoned Azon when it achieved better test results with more technologically advanced vertical bombs.[8]

Even as the AAF flew the Azon, the Massachusetts Institute of Technology (MIT) was devising a more advanced missile called the Razon (for range and azimuth). This 2,000-pound vertical bomb entered development in 1942 but was not ready for combat before the war ended. At that time the service had a stockpile of 3,000 Razon bombs.* Other bombs in the

---

* In 1946 the Air Proving Ground Command at Eglin Field, Florida, ran extensive tests on Razon, contemplating using the missile aboard all-weather bombers. Nothing materialized, however, until the Korean War, when the Far East Air Forces ordered and used the Tarzon, a Tallboy-Razon combination. [Mary R. Self, *History of the Development of Guided Missiles, 1946–1950* (Wright-Patterson AFB, Dec 1951), pp 32–34.]

VB series included the Felix (VB–6), a heat-seeking missile, and the Roc, a television-guided bomb with radio-controlled variants. The AAF also fitted television guidance to the 12,000-pound British Tallboy bomb; called the VB–13, it was used to attack German submarine pens.[9]

The most important category of pilotless aircraft developed by the AAF during the Second World War was the jet-propelled missile. In July 1944, one month after Germany began launching its V–1 Buzz Bombs against England, Materiel Command obtained parts of the weapon from the battlefields and within two weeks succeeded in copying the V–1's pulse jet engine. By September 8, less than sixty days after they had begun, Wright Field and Republic Aviation engineers had produced a copy of the German V–1 for testing.

Although the V–1 had caused a sensation when it was first launched by the Germans, the AAF and Royal Air Force (RAF) quickly learned to master the missile with their fighter aircraft and antiaircraft guns. Gen. Carl A. Spaatz, Commanding General of the United States Strategic Air Forces in Europe, and Gen. Ira C. Eaker, Commanding General, Mediterranean Allied Air Forces, foresaw "no immediate requirement for the use of pilotless aircraft." [10] Dr. Vannevar Bush, Director of the Office of Scientific Research and Development, also opposed developing an American version of the V–1, because he considered it uneconomical. Among those favoring development were General Arnold and Robert A. Lovett, the Assistant Secretary of War for Air. Lovett believed that the AAF should match the enemy, if only to counter the V–1's potential for damage.[11]

Called the JB–2 (for jet bomb), the American copy of the V–1 experienced launch difficulties and problems with inferior components and unreliable autopilots, but the AAF was satisfied enough to order the missile into mass production. Lt. Gen. Barney M. Giles, AAF Chief of Air Staff, wanted to produce JB–2s in sufficient quantity to permit launching 500 missiles per day by February 1945. The War Department General Staff approved JB–2 production at a reduced level of 5,000 missiles. After applying a number of general improvements, the AAF contracted with the Ford Motor Company for the engine and the Willys Overland Company for the airframe.

Although the JB–2 was not ready in time for employment against its inventors,* the AAF made good use of the missile in testing and training of personnel. By August 1945 the AAF had test-launched more than 200 of the missiles and by mid-September, when the contracts were terminated, had accepted 1,391 JB–2s. Development continued until 1946, when emphasis shifted to the Snark and Navaho missiles.[12]

---

*Shortly after the end of the war in Europe, the War Department considered launching German V–1 and V–2 missiles against Japan. [Ltr, Gen Marshall to Gen Eisenhower, no subj, May 6, 1945. RG 341, AAG File (TS), NA.]

Besides copying the V-1, the AAF also contracted with Northrop Aircraft to develop a new jet-propelled missile called the JB-1. This was a flying wing structure beset by shortcomings similar to those of the V-1, including low speed, small payload, limited range, and poor accuracy. First launched in December 1944, the JB-1 encountered an incompatibility problem between its airframe and engine. This difficulty led to several modifications and a redesignation as the JB-10. The new version, however, proved little better than the original, and the service dropped the project altogether in March 1946.

In addition to the JB-10, only the JB-3 air-to-air missile remained under development at the end of the war. Research on the JB-3 was performed by Hughes Aircraft and the National Advisory Committee for Aeronautics.[13]

Interservice Rivalry

Early in World War II, guided missile programs were the responsibility of the Assistant Chief of Air Staff, Materiel and Services, with development performed by Materiel Command's Special Weapons Group at Wright Field, Ohio. The slow pace of missile development disturbed Brig. Gen. Harold M. McClelland, the Air Communications Officer * on the Air Staff. He attributed the problem to the existing organization which, because of its preoccupation with wartime aircraft requirements, was unable to devote enough attention to missiles. General McClelland also argued that the Special Weapons Group did not have sufficient influence to promote missiles properly, and he campaigned to create a central missile authority. Having prepared a study outlining these conclusions, McClelland won the support of Maj. Gen. Laurence S. Kuter, the Assistant Chief of Air Staff, Plans. Consequently, in September 1943 the Air Staff reorganized its missile management. Although the Assistant Chief of Air Staff, Materiel and Services retained formal responsibility for guided missiles, the Air Communications Officer was assigned to "monitor, coordinate and expedite" the program and was also made responsible for "requirements, development, experiment and procurement."[14]

The reorganization disconcerted some Air Staff members, and throughout 1944 opposition grew to the Air Communications Officer's role in the missile program. The Assistant Chief of Air Staff, Operations, Commitments, and Requirements seems to have led the drive to return

---

* The Air Communications Officer determined requirements for radar and other electronic aids. [Wesley F. Craven and James L. Cate (eds.), *The Army Air Forces in World War II*, Vol VI: *Men and Planes* (Chicago, 1955), p 234.]

Jet Missiles Developed During World War II

Test flight of the JB-2, an American copy of the German V-1.

A static test firing of the JB-2 guided missile at Eglin Field, Florida, November 1944.

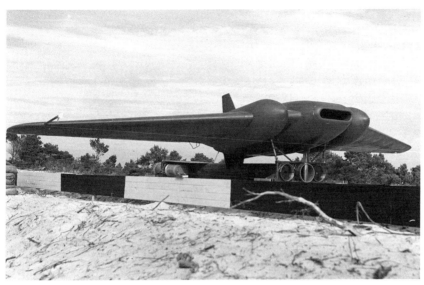

As an alternative to the JB–2, the AAF developed a "flying wing" missile—the JB–1.

The JB–10, an improved version of the JB–1, being prepared for a test flight at Eglin AFB.

The JB–3, among the most promising missiles at the end of World War II.

Lt. Gen. Barney M. Giles, Chief of the Air Staff, AAF, advocated mass production of the JB–2.

missiles along functional staff channels (i.e., under the Assistant Chief of Air Staff, Materiel and Services). He noted that the Air Communications Officer's original interest in coordinating with the Signal Corps on radar and electronics had been overtaken by new developments. As missile technology broadened during the course of the war, it spilled into such areas as aircraft fuselages, propulsion and ordnance—all functional staff matters. The opposition to the Air Communications Officer's control strengthened in June 1944 when German V-1 missiles started to rain on London and in September as the V-2 ballistic missile attacks began. These events triggered a frantic search to match the enemy's new terror weapons.[15]

By January 1945 the opposition prevailed, and missile functions were restored along regular Air Staff channels. Operations, Commitments, and Requirements assumed responsibility for setting new missile requirements. Materiel and Services was assigned to oversee missile research and development, whereas the Air Communications Officer was relegated to an advisory role and retained responsibility only for the remaining unpowered missiles developed during the war.

The issue of central versus functional control surfaced briefly in the postwar period. Proponents of centralization, including Maj. Gen. Curtis E. LeMay, Deputy Chief of Air Staff for Research and Development, believed that it was the best approach to meeting interservice competition, but two Assistant Chiefs of Air Staff—for Operations, Commitments, and Requirements and for Materiel and Services—each laid claim to the missile field. Over most of the next decade, however, functional proponents within the AAF (and later the Air Force) defeated all attempts at centralization. They argued successfully that technological and financial limitations dictated orderly, sequential missile development.[16]

Meanwhile, the advent of the German V weapons in 1944 had widened interest in guided missiles within the U.S. Army. Recognizing the potential of missiles, the AAF, Army Ground Forces (AGF), and Army Services Forces (ASF) maneuvered to win developmental and operational control. The nature of guided missiles, however, provided no clear basis for decision. The AAF claimed that missiles were simply advances in aircraft technology with control and guidance equipment replacing the pilot. The AGF and ASF, by contrast, regarded missiles as evolutionary extensions of artillery. These conflicting views on guided missile antecedents and their proper role in supporting assigned missions soon had the Army's three coequal forces at odds.

Basically, the issue concerned the enlargement or preservation of service roles and missions. The AAF wanted to preserve its air defense, interdiction, close support, and strategic bombardment roles as well as to obtain AGF's antiaircraft artillery function. The AGF, in turn, eyed part of the AAF mission, and control of guided missiles appeared as a means toward that end. The principal questions were: who would develop missiles and who would operate them? The AAF and ASF became engaged in a dispute over missile development. Also, since the combat forces both prepared military characteristics statements based on their requirements and conducted training and operational planning in advance of weapon availability, the AAF and AGF clashed over operational responsibility.[17]

In January 1944, ASF's Ordnance Department contracted with the California Institute of Technology (Caltech or CIT) to develop a long-range surface-to-surface rocket.* That August the AGF asked Ordnance to develop an antiaircraft guided missile. These two actions prompted Robert A. Lovett, Assistant Secretary of War for Air, to alert General Arnold to the possible duplication of AAF programs by the Ordnance Department. General Arnold and his staff minimized the possibility, noting that Ordnance was primarily involved with rockets, whereas AAF's Materiel Command concentrated on air-breathing missiles. Where the two programs overlapped, Arnold believed that CIT provided a common meeting ground. Others, including Maj. Gen. O. P. Echols, the Assistant Chief of Air Staff, Materiel and Services, however, sensed that duplication—for example, Ordnance's development of surface-to-air missiles—signaled competition, and particularly the intention of the AGF to gain control over the antiaircraft mission. More significantly, Ordnance's long-range rocket work emerged as an apparent threat to the AAF's strategic bombardment mission. It did not take General Arnold long to grasp fully the implications of the coming struggle over guided missiles. In September 1944 the Air Staff asked the War Department General Staff to assign all guided missile research and development, including joint service projects, exclusively to the AAF.[18]

Gen. George C. Marshall, Army Chief of Staff, was about to assign all missile research and development to the AAF when the AGF's latest requests to Ordnance—and Navy complaints about interservice confusion and lack of cooperation—caused the War Department General Staff to reopen the subject. In September 1944 the New Developments Division, headed by Brig. Gen. William A. Borden, an Ordnance officer, drafted a policy statement. It noted that the AAF held developmental responsibility for guided missile projects because they involved guided bombs, torpedoes, and aircraft. But with the growing interest in long-range, self-propelled missiles of both the flying (winged) and rocket (wingless) types, the situation had changed entirely. Thus, while missile technology was not far enough advanced to require assigning operational responsibility, a definite need existed for an orderly and coordinated development program.[19]

On October 2, 1944, Lt. Gen. Joseph T. McNarney, the Army Deputy Chief of Staff (and an AAF officer), issued an official policy statement.

---

*Called Project ORDCIT. See page 42.

Known as the McNarney Directive, it assigned to the AAF responsibility for developing all missiles launched from aircraft, as well as those surface-launched missiles that depended upon aerodynamic lift for sustaining flight. The ASF (Ordnance Department) would develop those surface-launched missiles that depended upon momentum for flight sustenance. Propulsion and control systems were considered integral elements of the missile and, therefore, the responsibility of the developing agency. Warheads, fuzes, non-integral launching devices, and ground portions of the control system were to be developed by the Army branch possessing the greatest technical competence in that line.[20]

Under the McNarney Directive, the AGF could establish missile characteristics and then ask either the ASF or AAF to develop the missile. Similarly, the AAF could prepare missile statements and undertake development or ask ASF to do it. The Army branches were expected to coordinate their efforts and to exchange technical information so that as a developmental missile neared operational status, the AAF and AGF could determine the missile's potential for their needs. Until then, the Army Chief of Staff would not make any operational assignments. In practice, however, the McNarney Directive proved to be a vaguely worded compromise which led to divergent interpretations of its provisions.[21]

An early test of the McNarney Directive arose in late 1944. As the JB-2—the American copy of the German V-1—approached production status, both the AAF and AGF stated operational requirements for its use and planned to form and train JB-2 combat units. Although General Marshall favored the AAF in this instance, he directed the War Department General Staff to study the general issue more extensively. In June 1945, the General Staff decided that it was still too early to consider making operational assignments for missiles.[22]

In August 1945 the AAF learned that the Ordnance Department planned to make its Nike surface-to-air missile maneuverable in flight by adding airfoils. The AAF regarded this plan as a clear violation of the McNarney Directive, because it meant converting the missile to an interceptor aircraft. Ordnance also sought to extend the range of its ORDCIT* surface-to-surface missile by adding fins. The AAF called the fins "wings" and, again, saw the action as a violation of the McNarney policy. Because of a pending War Department reorganization, however, the AAF did not pursue the issues.[23]

New impetus for reopening the missile question was next provided in November 1945 when Maj. Gen. Lauris Norstad, Assistant Chief of Air Staff, Plans, issued a broad policy statement of future AAF actions and responsibilities. It noted that the AAF, as the primary force for the defense

---

*See page 36.

of the nation, had to be prepared to repel all attacks—land, sea, and air. Hence, the AAF should have unlimited freedom to obtain any type of weapon, whether aerodynamically sustained or self-propelled in flight.[24]

Norstad's statement came before the General Staff and, in February 1946, led Gen. Dwight D. Eisenhower, the new Army Chief, to order a review of the McNarney Directive. General Spaatz again recommended assigning all missile development to central AAF control. He argued that missiles required autopilots, remote control devices, and airfoils—all items developed and procured by the AAF. Moreover, continuing War Department disagreement in the missile field might result in an uncontested victory for the Navy. Ordnance, however, adamantly refused to relinquish its interest in developing missiles maneuverable in flight.

The AAF then offered to prepare military characteristics for all air-launched missiles and for those surface-launched missiles employed in strategic and air defense missions, whereas the AGF would prepare statements for all close support and unguided air defense missiles. Therefore, the AAF would develop all missiles controllable in flight and the ASF would govern in the area of non-controllable missiles. Under the proposal, each organization would use the technical capabilities of the other. Both would encourage joint contracting and submit missile projects to the New Development Division in order to avert duplication. The AAF planned to

Gen. Joseph T. McNarney. In October 1944, as Army Deputy Chief of Staff, he assigned the AAF responsibility for developing all air-launched missiles and certain surface-launched missiles.

Gen. Henry H. (Hap) Arnold, Commanding General of the Army Air Forces.

demonstrate its abilities through a 1,000-mile remote-controlled flight of a B–29 aircraft nicknamed Project Banshee.[25]

General Spaatz* submitted the AAF proposal in April 1946, but because of the pending War Department reorganization, it was delayed for some time before being rejected. Maj. Gen. Henry S. Aurand, an Ordnance officer who was named the Army General Staff's Director of Research and Development in the summer of 1946, expressed the view that missiles were basically rockets. He reasoned that, since the AAF was concerned with pilots, it had a dubious claim on the missile field.[26] Although AAF leaders acknowledged the primacy of flying, they also recognized that "the long-range future of the AAF lies in the field of guided missiles."[27]

The AAF–Navy rivalry had its roots outside the missile arena in long-standing controversies concerning roles and missions. The Navy's air arm, for example, served as a major irritant, contradicting the AAF's doctrine of the indivisibility of air power. The AAF also considered the Navy a serious threat to its air defense and strategic bombardment missions. Conversely, the Navy resented the AAF's monopoly on delivering the atomic bomb and the challenge it posed to the future of sea power. At the close of World War II, however,

---

*He succeeded General Arnold as Commanding General, AAF on March 1, 1946.

guided missiles constituted an insignificant part of the difficulties facing the services. Therefore, the issue attracted little public attention.[28]

After the war, in its pursuit of operational control over missiles, the Navy expanded its considerable missile program and pursued development aggressively. Air Staff officials observed that the Navy seemed intent upon grabbing the air defense mission by conducting an extensive antiaircraft guided missile program. In November 1945 General Arnold learned that the Navy had requested $50 million to build and operate a missile test range at Point Mugu, California. Arnold interpreted this large request to mean that the Navy intended to dominate the missile field. His subsequent opposition to the request increased tensions between the services.[29]

Another aspect of the rivalry concerned responsibility for missile development. In February 1946, when General Eisenhower directed a review of the McNarney Directive, he asked Adm. Chester W. Nimitz, Chief of Naval Operations, to consider dividing missile responsibilities between the Army and Navy. General Spaatz suggested that the Navy might adapt Army-developed missiles for its ships and aircraft. Anticipating that the Navy would reject this suggestion, Spaatz urged closer interservice cooperation. As expected, the Navy concluded that it was best for missile development to rest with the using service. Moreover, Admiral Nimitz advised—and General Eisenhower accepted—that a division of missile responsibility was premature.[30]

In the fall of 1946 scientific and industrial leaders complained that the military was wasting money, personnel, and resources because of duplication in the missile field. The complaints drew top civilian and military leaders into the controversy and led to a swift settlement within the Army. General Spaatz, Lt. Gen. Thomas T. Handy,* and W. Stuart Symington, the Assistant Secretary of War for Air, narrowed the solution to several possibilities: (1) establish an independent missile development agency; (2) assign development control to the General Staff Research and Development Division; or (3) assign development to one of the branches. The consensus favored the last possibility and chose the AAF as the most logical and best equipped to assume management of the Army's missile development program. Maj. Gen. Everett S. Hughes, the Chief of Ordnance, reluctantly accepted this decision, but only on the condition that his department would retain development of some "guided objects or projectiles." Moreover, to ensure that the AAF would not favor its own developments above those of other agencies, General Aurand, the Army General Staff's Director of Research and Development, would referee all disputes.[31]

---

*Lt. Gen. Thomas T. Handy succeeded General McNarney as Army Deputy Chief of Staff.

The new policy, which rescinded the McNarney Directive, became official on October 7, 1946. An amendment, issued on October 10, stipulated that the Ordnance Department and the Signal Corps would continue their current development projects under AAF cognizance, but this activity would not involve any transfer of funds, personnel, contracts, or facilities. The AAF was also assigned to examine the War Department's missile program and to prepare a plan for its administration. On November 26, following considerable debate over where certain programs belonged, General Aurand approved the AAF plan.[32]

The AAF plan recommended continuing the existing Army missile program until the AAF Technical Committee*—on which the other two branches had representatives—analyzed it. New development requests would be processed by the AAF through the General Staff. The AAF Technical Committee would then prepare a priority list, select an agency to conduct development, pass on contracts, and, beginning in Fiscal Year 1949, coordinate budgetary requests of the Technical Services.† Finally, the developing agency would conduct acceptance tests and procure test missiles.

This management system continued until March 1948, six months after the establishment of the Air Force. (Immediately after achieving independence, the Air Force wanted to maintain cooperation with the Army on missiles.) Considering the acrimony which had preceded it, the arrangement worked reasonably well. Seldom was General Aurand asked to referee an issue, and only once did the AAF Technical Committee complain of a lack of cooperation from the Technical Services. [33]

While the War Department worked out a satisfactory compromise on missile development, the vexing problem of operational responsibility remained unsettled. In August and October 1946 the Army Ground Forces asked for operational control over all surface-launched missiles. The AAF, however, was willing to concede only short-range, or close support missiles. Throughout 1946, operational control of surface-to-air missiles—a by-product of the AAF–AGF dispute over the air defense mission—remained in dispute. In the summer of 1947, just before the AAF separated from the Army, officials incorporated a loosely worded paragraph on missile operations in the transfer agreement. The statement glossed over the controversy, indicating that the parties were mainly interested in effecting a gigantic task peaceably and speedily and in letting the future take care of itself.[34]

---

*The AAF Technical Committee was established in February 1946 to coordinate AAF research and development programs with other services and industry. [Mary R. Self, *History of the Development of Guided Missiles, 1946–1950* (Wright-Patterson AFB, Dec 1951), pp 111–112.]

†The ASF became the Technical Services in June 1946.

BALLISTIC MISSILES

The Postwar Program

The development of guided missiles was not a significant factor in America's victory in World War II. Despite the hullabaloo attending the advent of missiles, jet aircraft, the atomic bomb, and a host of esoteric weapons, the war was fought and won with large stocks of conventional armaments. Until 1944, when the Germans demonstrated the potential of guided missiles, the AAF had treated missiles as gadgets and assigned them a low priority. By September 1944 the AAF had intensified its interest in guided missiles and shifted the focus of its development from controlled bombs to self-propelled missiles. The change eventually laid the foundation for the postwar program, but at that time the AAF still retained most of its existing projects and emphasized developing those missiles that might become operational before the war ended.[35]

In the closing days of the war, General Arnold asked Dr. Theodore von Kármán, Director of the California Institute of Technology's Guggenheim Aeronautical Laboratory and of the AAF Scientific Advisory Group, to survey the war's scientific and technical advances. In August 1945 von Kármán published the findings of his study group in *Where We Stand,* and in December his group released the monumental thirty-three-volume report entitled *Toward New Horizons,* which made recommendations based on the earlier survey. After studying the German missile program in great detail, von Kármán's group concluded that missiles would not be effective until the state of the art had improved considerably. Von Kármán advised the AAF to emulate the Germans in their single-manager type organization and to provide researchers with adequate resources and funds. Moreover, he recommended that the AAF emphasize jet aircraft and pursue an orderly, sequential guided missile development program based on air-breathing jet propulsion. This was precisely the course that the AAF pursued.[36]

General Arnold also believed that the war's scientific and technological advances, especially in guided missiles and atomic energy, would revolutionize the concepts of warfare, and he predicted that the future of the AAF depended on how well it adjusted to these developments. Although a few Air Staff members shared Arnold's vision, the majority—supported by the testimony of leading American scientists and engineers—felt that guided missiles were still many years away from practical utility and that there were more pressing problems demanding attention.[37]

Understanding the need to influence the new technological development, Arnold created the position of Deputy Chief of Air Staff for Research and Development and named Maj. Gen. Curtis E. LeMay, a combat leader in Europe and Asia, to the post. LeMay had only a small staff and few resources for the task, but during his brief two-year tenure two significant technological organizations—the Scientific Advisory Board (SAB) and the nonprofit Research and Development (Rand) Corporation—were created.[38]

Dr. Theodore von Kármán, scientific adviser to the AAF on missiles and technology.

Meanwhile, after readjusting its missile organization at the end of 1944, the Air Staff conducted a complete review of the existing guided missile program, surveying all of the available information on design, construction, and the availability of test facilities. Early in 1945 the Assistant Chief of Air Staff, Operations, Commitments, and Requirements concluded that missile development was hampered by a lack of suitable statements of military requirements. There also had been a tendency to label virtually all missiles as "urgent," with the result that the Air Technical Service Command* did not know where to focus its attention. Over the next several months, in an attempt to solve these problems, the Operations, Commitments, and Requirements office established requirements for guided missiles,† set realistic completion dates, and promoted the construction of additional wind tunnel and test facilities. Believing that guided missile goals exceeded technical capabilities, the Air Staff asked the command to formulate a plan that divided missiles into two groups: those that could be developed immediately and those expected to be completed within five years.[39]

---

*On August 31, 1944, Materiel Command and Air Service Command were combined into the Air Technical Service Command.

†Mindful of the AAF versus AGF–ASF rivalry over roles and missions, the Operations, Commitments, and Requirements office blanketed its requirements over the entire missile field in an attempt to strengthen the AAF's position.

BALLISTIC MISSILES

Despite a great deal of activity, little progress was achieved. At war's end the AAF program was virtually nonexistent in comparison with the more advanced Navy and Army Ordnance Department missile programs. Air Technical Service Command endured the ill effects of the demobilization, personnel reductions, and funding uncertainties while it was attempting to start or enlarge development in several new areas, including atomic energy, jet propulsion, and electronic guidance. However, with some prodding from the Air Staff, the command managed to produce a comprehensive missile development plan that related personnel, funding, and facilities difficulties and described possible remedies to get the program under way. More significantly, starting in October 1945, the technical command invited the nation's leading aeronautical firms to bid on studies and preliminary designs for the projected missiles. During the war these companies, inundated with aircraft production contracts, had not been interested in missile development; they were now eager to participate. In the following months the command's Engineering Division evaluated industry proposals and selected winners. The study program divided missiles into four categories: air-to-air, air-to-surface, surface-to-air, and surface-to-surface. During March and April 1946 the command let a series of one-year study and design contracts for twenty-eight missiles and terminated all except four* of the wartime projects.[40] (See Chart 1-1, April 1946 Program.)

The program proceeded in orderly fashion with only minor changes until December 1946, when President Harry S. Truman suddenly ordered a drastic reduction in research and development funding for Fiscal Year 1947. This decision marked the first of several adverse actions that would disrupt AAF guided missile plans. The Air Staff responded to the cutback by paring its missile development budget from $29 to $13 million. Ensuing discussions between the Air Staff and Air Materiel Command† led to a decision to concentrate on those missiles that showed the greatest promise of early tactical availability and to terminate ten of the original twenty-eight projects. One new air-to-air project (MX-904) was established, leaving nineteen active at this time.[41] (See Chart 1-2, March 1947 Program.)

In the spring of 1947 new funding problems arose. After reviewing the missile program, Air Materiel Command concluded that it was technically sound but too large for the expected Fiscal Year 1948 budget. Even though most projects were still in the study phase, some contractors were ready to begin producing missile components. Therefore, assuming that for the near term the AAF could not expect to receive more than about $22 million

---

*The four wartime missile projects were: JB-3 (MX-570), Roc (MX-601), Tarzon (MX-674), and Hydrobomb (MX-777).

†ATSC was redesignated AMC in March 1946.

annually in missile development money, AMC—in an attempt to salvage the program—proposed to reduce the number of missile projects.

The command first recommended eliminating the "insurance missiles"—primarily subsonic versions of supersonic missiles. Other suggested economies included emphasizing development of those missiles with the greatest promise of early availability, using one contractor to obtain a series of progressively more advanced missiles, and relying on the Navy and the Ordnance Department for certain missiles. The Air Staff concurred, and in June 1947 General Spaatz approved AMC's recommendations. Under the reoriented program, three more missiles were terminated, one project (Hydrobomb) * was transferred to the Navy, and three were reduced to the development of components only.[42] (See Chart 1-3, July 1947 Program.)

In another response to the shrinking peacetime budgets—and based on a study made in connection with the missile program review—the Air Staff in July 1947 issued guidance on developmental priorities. Its major conclusion was that, in the wake of America's rapid and extensive demobilization, the atomic bomb constituted the nation's main source of power and the subsonic bomber its only means of delivery over the next ten years. As these aircraft would have to penetrate enemy air defenses and return safely, top priority went to air-to-air and air-to-surface missiles. Second priority was assigned to short-range (under 150 miles) surface-to-surface missiles, because the Army Ground Forces urgently requested improved support weapons and the AAF expected to have them available by 1952. (These missiles, however, were not under AAF development at this time.) Air defense missiles and detection and warning systems occupied third place, on the assumption that by 1952 the Russians would have long-range bombers and missile-carrying submarines capable of delivering atomic weapons.[43]

The AAF recognized in mid-1947 that long-range surface-to-surface missiles eventually would challenge the strategic bombardment mission. Because of the economic facts of life, however, and an anticipated development period of no less than ten years, these systems were assigned fourth priority. Only the wartime-originated air-to-surface missiles, such as the vertical bombs, occupied a lower priority. It is not surprising that AAF planners, faced with austere budgets and technological uncertainty, placed their trust in the familiar and proven subsonic bomber, and looked to missiles to augment manned aircraft rather than to replace them.[44]

---

* See page 42.

Chart 1-1

Army Air Forces Guided Missile Program as of April 1946

Project	Contractor	Performance Features

SURFACE-TO-SURFACE

Project	Contractor	Performance Features
MX–770	North American Aviation Inc.	175–500 mi, winged rocket—Nativ, Navaho
MX–771A	The Glenn L. Martin Co.	175–500 mi, subsonic—Matador
MX–771B	Glenn L. Martin	175–500 mi, supersonic
MX–772A	The Curtiss-Wright Corp.	500–1500 mi, subsonic
MX–772B	Curtiss-Wright	500–1500 mi, supersonic
MX–773A	The Republic Aviation Corp.	500–1500 mi, subsonic
MX–773B	Republic Aviation	500–1500 mi, supersonic
MX–774A	The Consolidated Vultee Aircraft Corp. (Convair)	1500–5000 mi, subsonic
MX–774B	Convair	1500–5000 mi, supersonic—Hiroc
MX–775A	Northrop Aircraft, Inc.	1500–5000 mi, subsonic— Snark
MX–775B	Northrop Aircraft	1500–5000 mi, supersonic—Boojum
MX–767	AMC	Modification of B–29 to drone—Banshee

AIR-TO-SURFACE

Project	Contractor	Performance Features
MX–601	The Douglas Aircraft Company, Inc.	Vertical bomb controllable in range and azimuth—Roc
MX–674	Bell Aircraft Corp.	Vertical bomb controllable in range and azimuth—Tarzon
MX–776	Bell Aircraft	100 mi, subsonic—Rascal

MX–777	McDonnell Aircraft Corp.	100 mi, supersonic
MX–778	The Goodyear Aircraft Corp.	100 mi, subsonic
MX–779	Goodyear Aircraft	100 mi, supersonic
Mastiff	None	300 mi, supersonic, atomic warhead

SURFACE-TO-AIR

MX–606	The Boeing Airplane Company	35 mi, 60,000-foot altitude—Gapa, Condor
MX–794	University of Michigan	550 mi, 500,000-foot altitude—Wizard
MX–795	General Electric Corp.	550 mi, 500,000-foot altitude—Thumper

AIR-TO-AIR

MX–570	Hughes Aircraft Co.	9 mi, 50,000-foot altitude, subsonic JB–3—Tiamat
MX–798	Hughes Aircraft	Continuation of MX–570, 5 mi, subsonic
MX–799	Ryan Aeronautical Co.	Fighter-launched, subsonic—Firebird
MX–800	M.W. Kellogg Co.	Fighter-launched, supersonic
MX–801	Bendix Aviation Corp.	Fighter-launched, supersonic
MX–802	General Electric	Bomber-launched, supersonic—Dragonfly

Source: Max Rosenberg, *The Air Force and the National Guided Missile Program, 1944–1950,* (USAF Historical Div Liaison Ofc, Jun 1964), p 77.

Chart 1–2

Revised AAF Guided Missile Program as of March 1947

Project	Contractor	Performance Features
		SURFACE-TO-SURFACE
MX–770	North American Aviation Inc.	500 mi, winged rocket
MX–771A	The Glenn L. Martin Co.	500 mi, subsonic, turbojet
MX–772B	The Curtiss-Wright Corp.	150 mi, changed from 500–1500 miles to meet AAF–AGF military characteristics
MX–773B	The Republic Aviation Corp.	1500 mi, supersonic, ramjet or rocket
MX–774B	The Consolidated Vultee Aircraft Corp. (Convair)	5,000 mi, supersonic, rocket
MX–775B	Northrop Aircraft, Inc.	5,000 mi, supersonic, turbojet
MX–767	AMC	Modification of B–29—Banshee
		AIR-TO-SURFACE
MX–674	Bell Aircraft Corp.	Vertical bomb
MX–776	Bell Aircraft	100 mi, subsonic
MX–777	McDonnell Aircraft Corp.	Changed to air-to-underwater missile; planned transfer to Navy
MX–778	The Goodyear Aircraft Corp.	100 mi, subsonic
Mastiff	None	300 mi, supersonic, atomic warhead
		SURFACE-TO-AIR
MX–606	The Boeing Airplane Company	35 mi, 60,000-foot altitude, vs aircraft

MX-794	University of Michigan	550 mi, 500,000-foot altitude, vs ballistic missiles
MX-795	General Electric Corp.	550 mi, 500,000-foot

AIR-TO-AIR

MX-799	Ryan Aeronautical Co.	Fighter-launched, subsonic
MX-800	M.W. Kellogg Co.	Fighter-launched, supersonic
MX-802	General Electric	Bomber-launched, supersonic
MX-904	Hughes Aircraft Co.	Bomber-launched, subsonic, replaced MX-798, a generalized study

PROJECTS CANCELED

MX-771B	Glenn L. Martin	500 mi, supersonic, surface-to-surface missile (SSM)
MX-772A	Curtiss-Wright	1,500 mi, subsonic, SSM
MX-773A	Republic	1,500 mi, subsonic, SSM
MX-774A	Convair	5,000 mi, subsonic, SSM
MX-775A	Northrop	5,000 mi, subsonic, SSM
MX-601	The Douglas Aircraft Co.	Vertical bomb, air-to-surface missile (ASM)
MX-779	The Goodyear Aircraft Corp.	100 mi, supersonic, ASM
MX-570	Hughes Aircraft	Generalized air-to-air missile (AAM) study
MX-798	Hughes Aircraft	Generalized AAM study, reoriented to bomber-launched version & redesignated MX-904
MX-801	Bendix Aviation Corp.	Fighter-launched, supersonic, AAM

Source: Max Rosenberg, *The Air Force and the National Guided Missile Program, 1944–1950*, (USAF Historical Div Liaison Ofc, Jun 1964), p 81.

Chart 1-3

Revised AAF Guided Missile Program as of July 1, 1947

Project	Contractor	Performance Features

SURFACE-TO-SURFACE

Project	Contractor	Performance Features
MX–770	North American Aviation Inc.	500 mi, supersonic, winged rocket—Navaho I
MX–771A	The Glenn L. Martin Co.	500 mi, subsonic, turbojet—Matador
—	North American	1,500 mi, supersonic, ramjet to follow development of MX–770—Navaho II
MX–775B	Northrop Aircraft Inc.	5,000 mi, supersonic, turbojet—Boojum
—	North American	5,000 mi, supersonic, nuclear ramjet, to follow development of 1,500-mi missile—Navaho III
MX–767	AMC	Modification of B-29—Banshee

AIR-TO-SURFACE

Project	Contractor	Performance Features
MX–674	Bell Aircraft Corp.	Vertical bomb—Tarzon
MX–776	Bell Aircraft	100 mi, supersonic—Rascal
Mastiff	None	300 mi, atomic warhead to follow development of MX–776

SURFACE-TO-AIR

Project	Contractor	Performance Features
MX–606	The Boeing Airplane Company	Defense vs aircraft—Gapa
MX–794	University of Michigan	Defense vs ballistic missiles, continued as "prolonged study"—Wizard

MX–795	General Electric Corp.	Defense vs ballistic missiles, continued as "prolonged study"— Thumper

Air-to-Air

MX–799	Ryan Aeronautical Corp.	Fighter-launched, subsonic— Firebird
—	Ryan Aeronautical Corp.	Fighter-launched, supersonic, to follow development of MX–799
MX–802	General Electric Corp.	Bomber-launched, supersonic

Projects Canceled or Downgraded to Component Development

MX–772B	The Curtiss-Wright Corp.	150 mi, SSM, terminated by WDGS directive
MX–773B	The Republic Aviation Corp.	1,500 mi, SSM, terminated
MX–774B	The Consolidated Vultee Aircraft Corp. (Convair)	5,000 mi, SSM, terminated
MX–777	McDonnell Aircraft Corp.	Hydrobomb, ASM, transferred to Navy
MX–778	The Goodyear Aircraft Corp.	100 mi, ASM, reduced to guidance development
MX–800	M.W. Kellogg Co.	Fighter-launched AAM, reduced to guidance development
MX–904	Hughes Aircraft Co.	Bomber-launched AAM, reduced to guidance development

Source: Max Rosenberg, *The Air Force and the National Guided Missile Program, 1944–1950* (USAF Historical Div Liaison Ofc, Jun 1964), p 83.

Dr. Robert H. Goddard stands beside his liquid-fuel rocket prior to its historic launch on March 16, 1926, at Auburn, Massachusetts.

Chapter II

Ballistic Missiles Research

. . . someday, not too far distant, there can come streaking out of somewhere (we won't be able to hear it, it will come so fast) some kind of a gadget with an explosive so powerful that one projectile will be able to wipe out completely this city of Washington. . . . I think we will meet the attack alright [sic] and, of course, in the air. But I'll tell you one thing, there won't be a goddam pilot in the sky! That attack will be met by machines guided not by human hands, but by devices conjured up by human brains.

Gen. Henry H. Arnold, 1943

Early in the twentieth century European, Russian, and American scientists investigated rockets as a means of reaching outer space. The foremost American pioneer, Dr. Robert H. Goddard, experimented with rocket engines and fuels. At the close of World War I he tried, but failed, to interest the Army in the military utility of rockets. Continuing his experiments, Goddard fired the world's first liquid-fueled rocket in March 1926. At the California Institute of Technology during the 1930s, Dr. Theodore von Kármán encouraged a group of students, including Frank Malina, to pursue rocket research. Then, during World War II, Goddard and von Kármán contributed to the war effort by developing rockets (for the Navy and Army respectively) that were attached to aircraft to help with heavyweight takeoffs. Although this application provided limited benefits, it led to the discovery of new principles and to the development of techniques governing rocket engines and fuels.

Meanwhile, German scientists had seized on Goddard's investigations and eagerly applied them. Rockets had special appeal for the Germans because the new technology was not covered by the Versailles Treaty, which restricted their development and procurement of artillery. Thus the Germans opened a large research center at Peenemünde on the Baltic coast, where they developed the V–1 cruise missile and the V–2 ballistic rocket. In October 1942 Germany launched the first man-made vehicle to reach the edge of space, and in September 1944 the V–2 made its combat debut. Through the end of the war, the Germans fired some 3,700 V–2s and made remarkable progress in the field of rocketry, including plans for an intercontinental ballistic missile.

In the United States, the Ordnance Department commissioned Dr. von Kármán's laboratory to develop ballistic missiles. Known as ORDCIT (an acronym combining Ordnance and CIT), the project tested V–2s assembled from captured rocket parts. Using American versions of German rockets, ORDCIT also built on the German research. Right after World War II, in December 1945, the U.S. Army launched Operation Paperclip, under which the service recruited some 200 German rocket scientists and engineers who had worked at Peenemünde. Located first at Ft. Bliss, Texas, and later at the Redstone Arsenal at Huntsville, Alabama, this program was led by the former head of research at Peenemünde, Dr. Wernher von Braun. The Russians also "recruited" German rocket experts in areas under Soviet control. They exploited the Germans' knowledge and conducted a rocket program that paralleled American efforts. The Russian approach, marked by its emphasis on the rapid development of rocket facilities and large rockets, leapfrogged the sluggish American program.

U.S. efforts to create a "national" missile program began during World War II and continued through the 1940s without much success. Instead, American research and development was split into four separate military programs: the AAF (later the Air Force), the Ordnance Department (later the Army), the Navy Bureau of Aeronautics, and the Navy Bureau of Ordnance. As stated previously, the governing factor was the postwar conflict over roles and missions, with each agency believing that developmental responsibility would later lead to operational control as well.

Among the early attempts to develop ballistic missiles was the study commissioned by Wright Field in April 1946: Consolidated Vultee's* Project MX–774B. This study called for a supersonic ICBM to carry a 5,000-pound atomic warhead over a distance of 5,000 miles and to strike within a mile of its intended target. Convair's project manager, Karel Bossart, based his design on the V–2 but made major alterations and concentrated on improving the rocket's guidance system. In December 1946, however, MX–774B funding was reduced, and in July 1947 the project was canceled altogether.

At that time the AAF decided to pursue ground-to-ground aerody-

---

*The Consolidated Aircraft Corporation and Vultee Aircraft, Inc., merged on March 17, 1943. The new Consolidated Vultee Aircraft (Convair) Corporation became the Convair Division of the General Dynamics Corporation on April 29, 1954.

namic (cruise) missiles, including Navaho and Snark, on the grounds that the cruise missiles would be available sooner than the ten-year development expected for the MX-774B. Also, cruise missiles offered superior payload and range, whereas the ballistic types were considered too expensive and beset by technical uncertainties. Nevertheless, Convair was permitted to complete its MX-774B flight tests during 1948 and succeeded in verifying the rocket's design.

Louis Johnson became Secretary of Defense in March 1949 and ushered in a new round of cost reductions that exacerbated the roles and missions controversies. Johnson ordered a thorough review of missile programs. Led by Air Force assistant Harold C. Stuart, the review produced little agreement. Each service was assigned a missile test range, and a joint group was created to establish requirements. Consequently, the Joint Chiefs of Staff (JCS) created a consolidated priority list of missiles to be developed. More importantly, the review recommended assigning long-range strategic missiles to the Air Force, an action Johnson approved in March 1950.

The Air Force's missile program dwindled as lean funding continued. This situation required the Air Force to choose between existing aircraft programs and long-term missile development. With an eye toward the immediate goal of improving the nation's ability to deliver atomic weapons, the Air Force chose to develop aircraft and those missiles that enhanced aircraft. Long-range strategic missiles were placed eighth on the JCS list of missiles to be developed. In July 1949, the Matador and Firebird missiles were canceled and other missile projects were downgraded to component developments or studies, or were canceled altogether. The Soviets' first atomic bomb test in August shook U.S. complacency but failed to generate progress in the missile program. At the start of the Korean War the Air Force had only three missiles in development: Navaho, Rascal, and Falcon.

In addition to economic problems, missile development was hampered by technological difficulties. Air Force efforts to mate atomic bombs with ballistic missiles suffered from a lack of cooperation on the part of the U.S. Atomic Energy Commission (AEC). Atomic weapons were still scarce. The implosion-type atomic bombs showed promise because they could be produced more readily than the gun type. Unfortunately, implosion bombs were heavier and would require larger missiles to carry them. On an optimistic note, the AEC predicted the feasibility of smaller nuclear warheads, thus implying that U.S. missiles could be made smaller than anticipated.

Meanwhile, the military services were engaged in a roles and missions controversy over missiles. In an effort to establish a truly national program, Secretary of Defense Johnson had tried to standardize requirements. Then, in October 1950, his successor, George C. Marshall, appointed Chrysler's K. T.

Keller as the "missiles czar." Although Keller occupied this position for three years, he concentrated on production rather than on development, and his close association with Army officers made his objectivity questionable.

Whereas Keller and the Army sought to separate the production of missiles and aircraft, the Air Force was opposed. The Air Force argued that missiles were simply "pilotless aircraft" and both were built by the same manufacturers. The Air Force conducted missile research and development functionally, using the same procurement and development channels and procedures employed for aircraft. The service even went so far as to assign aircraft nomenclature to missiles. Ironically, the Air Force's efforts to integrate missiles and aircraft worked against its interests. The service's fragmented missiles program appeared small by comparison with the centralized Army and Navy programs. Clearly, the Air Force needed a strong missiles program under a single manager if it was to compete with its sister services.

Modern Rockets

Invented by the Chinese in the twelfth century A.D., rockets were not introduced into Europe until two centuries later. Thereafter they were used only sporadically until William Congreve developed advanced rockets in 1805. The British launched Congreve rockets during the Napoleonic wars and the War of 1812. In 1847, during the Mexican War, American batteries fired Hale rockets, and both the Union and Confederacy used rockets in the Civil War. The employment of these early rockets, however, proved more spectacular than decisive, and with improvements in artillery toward the end of the nineteenth century, these weapons lost their military appeal.[1]

America's leading exponent of rocket technology at the start of the twentieth century was Robert H. Goddard, a physics professor at Clark University, Worcester, Massachusetts. Goddard began to experiment with rockets and fuels in 1908, thus making him a contemporary of leading pioneers in the space field, including Robert Esnault-Pelterie of France, Hermann Oberth of Germany, and the Russians Valentin P. Glushko and Sergei P. Korolyev. Goddard experimented largely on his own, although aided by grants from the Smithsonian Institution and the Guggenheim Foundation. During World War I, he proposed to develop rockets for the Army and Navy. On November 6, 1918, at the Aberdeen Proving Ground, Maryland, he demonstrated successfully a series of tube-launched, solid-fueled rockets that could be fired from the ground, or from airplanes. But, five days later, the war ended and with it the military's interest in rockets. Between 1922 and 1924 Goddard performed numerous experiments for the Navy but was unable to obtain sufficient funding to conduct a substantial rocket research program.[2]

Despite this lack of public support, the American engineer went on to make significant progress in the field. On March 16, 1926, Goddard fired the world's first successful liquid-fueled rocket from a farm near Auburn, Massachusetts. The 10-foot long rocket accelerated to 60 miles per hour and traveled a distance of 184 feet. During the 1930s, thanks to the help of Charles A. Lindbergh, Goddard was able to continue his work at the Mescalero Ranch, Roswell, New Mexico, where he, his wife, and 4 assistants lived and worked. In May 1935 Goddard fired a rocket to 7,500 feet. Among his numerous achievements in rocketry were: using gyroscopes for stabilization; proving that rockets could operate in a vacuum; employing movable exhaust vanes for steering; and using staged rockets. In addition, Goddard engineered many major rocket components, including the airframe, fuel pumps, valves, and guidance devices. He was granted more than 200 patents in the field. Although his publications were widely read and respected abroad, Goddard was virtually ignored in the United States.[3]

Also in the 1930s, Dr. Theodore von Kármán, a Hungarian emigré who directed the Guggenheim Aeronautical Laboratory (GAL) at the California Institute of Technology, was investigating jet propulsion. Apart from his own work, von Kármán encouraged a group of students to pursue their interest in rockets. The students, including Hsue Shen Tsien, Apollo M. O. Smith, John W. Parsons, Edward S. Forman, and Weld Arnold, were led by Frank J. Malina, a doctoral candidate who began experimenting with rockets in 1936.*

Through his association with Maj. Gen. Henry H. Arnold, von Kármán won the backing of the Army Air Corps for the project at Caltech. The Air Corps was especially interested at that time in developing rockets for use as aids in the takeoff of heavily laden aircraft. Because the term "rocket" connoted something futuristic and impractical, however, it was decided to call them jet-assisted takeoff (JATO) devices instead. In January 1939 the Air Corps provided $1,000 for this jet propulsion research project, nicknamed Project GALCIT, after von Kármán's laboratory. Based upon the promising findings of the study, von Kármán won a $10,000 contract in July to design and construct small solid- and liquid-fueled rocket engines.[4]

Initially sponsored by the National Academy of Sciences, Project GALCIT came directly under the Air Corps in July 1940. At about this time the Malina team made a momentous breakthrough, demonstrating that it was theoretically possible to develop a constant-pressure, long-duration, solid-propellant engine, and began to draft the basic criteria for JATO units.[5]

---

*Caltech and Harry Guggenheim approached Goddard several times, proposing cooperation between the experimenters. Goddard guarded his work jealously, fearing that the "students" wanted to cash in on his years of toil.

From this work emerged GALCIT 27, a compressed solid propellant used to power JATO units, each delivering 28 pounds of thrust for 12 seconds. Flight testing of JATO-launched aircraft began in early 1941. Wright Field engineers selected a low-wing monoplane, called the Ercoupe, for the tests and designated Capt. Homer A. Boushey, Jr., as the test pilot. On August 12, 1941, Boushey became the first American to pilot a plane boosted by rocket power as he flew over March Field, California. Later that month Boushey made history again as the first American to fly on rocket power alone. Based on the results of these experiments, the Navy contracted with GALCIT in early 1942 for a supply of JATO units that could provide 200 pounds of thrust for 8 seconds to help launch heavily laden carrier-based aircraft.[6]

Despite their remarkable achievements, the GALCIT researchers were unable to interest industrial firms in manufacturing rocket motors. Consequently, von Kármán and Malina formed their own company in March 1942, calling it the Aerojet Engineering Corporation (which eventually became Aerojet General, a division of General Tire and Rubber Company). Later that year they made significant progress in the construction of rocket engines and in the discovery of new rocket fuels. In April the GALCIT team developed an engine that was fueled by red fuming nitric acid (RFNA)* and gasoline. Two months later the researchers introduced GALCIT 53, an asphalt-potassium perchlorate castable solid propellant.[7]†

During World War II Goddard also experimented with JATO devices and variable-thrust rocket motors for the Navy's Bureau of Aeronautics at Annapolis, Maryland. In 1942 Goddard developed a LOX-gasoline JATO unit which was further improved by Reaction Motors Incorporated (later a division of Thiokol Chemical Company) to provide 3,000 pounds of thrust for 60 seconds. There was, however, no direct collaboration between Goddard and the GALCIT researchers, primarily because von Kármán required a complete exchange of technical information on all problems under cooperative study, while Goddard was unwilling to share the details of his lifelong work. Goddard died on August 10, 1945.[8]

Ironically, while Goddard's early research was ignored in the United States, the Germans built on the American's ideas as well as the work of Hermann Oberth and the German Rocket Society. Prohibited under the terms of the Versailles Treaty from producing conventional weapons, the

---

*Because JATO units were required to be mobile, the researchers discarded liquid oxygen (LOX) as the oxidizer. Goddard had used LOX and gasoline to fuel his rockets, whereas German V–2 scientists favored a LOX-alcohol combination.

†GALCIT's theory and invention of castable solid propellants paved the way to the development of the engines that power today's long-range missiles and rockets used to boost vehicles into outer space. The project is also credited with perfecting storable liquid propellants still used in military rockets.

German Army turned its attention to rockets as a means of extending long-range artillery. By the early 1930s the Germans were constructing the A–series of rockets. Under the direction of Capt. (later Maj. Gen.) Walter R. Dornberger, the rocket program expanded steadily, and between 1937 and 1938 the Germans built the large experimental rocket station at Peenemünde on the Baltic Sea. Here they developed and tested the A–4 model of the rocket series. It was better known as the V–2, the term given to the rocket by Joseph Goebbels' propaganda ministry to denote the Nazis' second "vengeance weapon." Standing 46 feet high and 5 feet in diameter, the 14-ton rocket flew about 200 miles and delivered a 1,650-pound amatol* warhead. Although it was beset by the same deficiencies as the V–1 in terms of range, payload, and accuracy, the V–2 possessed one major advantage: it was unstoppable. Once it was launched, no one could predict when and where it would land.[9]

On October 3, 1942, after two unsuccessful launch attempts, the V–2 completed a flight test of 120 miles and became the world's first long-range ballistic missile. Despite this encouraging result, the missile test program was erratic and Hitler did not approve production until August 1943. Even then the V–2 was far from being fully operational. Moreover, German planners held up the rocket's introduction to combat until they had built up large stocks. Allied intelligence first learned of the existence of the "V" weapons in late 1942 and had the fact confirmed during the spring of 1943. Their response was Operation Crossbow, a bombing campaign directed against Peenemünde and all "V" weapon production and launch sites. The bombing attacks, however, served mainly to disperse the missile facilities, while also diverting Allied sorties away from their primary effort—the combined bomber offensive against the Third Reich. At last the V–2 made its combat debut on September 8, 1944,† when the Germans began to fire the rockets against England, particularly London. By the end of March 1945, when the last V–2 was deployed, the Germans had launched 3,745 V–2s, with more than 1,100 directed at England and the remainder fired on continental targets, including Antwerp, Brussels, and Liege.[10]

How effective were the German missiles? Gen. Dwight D. Eisenhower later wrote that if the "V" weapons had been introduced earlier in the war, they might have prevented the Normandy invasion. Some observers speculated that the V–2 might have affected the outcome of the war. Others, including Vannevar Bush, pointed to the costliness of the German rocket program, in which a single V–2 was used to deliver less than one ton of explosives.‡ Accuracy remained a problem. Through the course of the

---

*An explosive consisting of ammonium nitrate and trinitrotoluene (TNT).
†On September 6, 1944, two V–2s were fired against newly liberated Paris.
‡The much cheaper V–1 also delivered a one-ton warhead.

"rocket blitz" the Germans managed to hit London only 500 times. The most remarkable achievement, however, was how far the V-2 research had advanced the field of military rocketry. By the war's end the Germans had also drawn plans for a two-stage (A-9 and A-10 combination) transatlantic rocket, which they intended to launch against New York City.[11]

Germany's wartime progress caught the attention of U.S. military leaders. During the summer of 1943, GALCIT scientists in the United States were asked to study and comment upon British intelligence reports concerning certain "reaction devices for projectiles and aircraft" that were being developed in Germany. Of course, the devices turned out to be the pulse-jet V-1 and the ballistic rocket V-2. Completing their investigation in November, GALCIT scientists concluded that rockets held great military promise and urged their development by the AAF Materiel Command. But, perhaps because of its preoccupation with filling the immediate demands of the war, Materiel Command hesitated. The Army's Ordnance Department, on the other hand, expressed a strong interest in rocket development. In January 1944, with the acquiescence of Materiel Command, the Ordnance Department contracted with Caltech's rocket team to undertake Project ORDCIT and develop a series of solid-fueled and liquid-fueled rockets.* Later in 1944, GALCIT was reorganized as the Jet Propulsion Laboratory (JPL) and undertook the following research projects:[12]

> JPL-1 (MX-121)—JATO devices for Materiel Command Aircraft Lab
>
> JPL-2 (MX-363)—Hydrobomb † for Materiel Command Armament Lab
>
> JPL-3 (MX-527)—Ramjets for Materiel Command Propulsion Lab
>
> JPL-4—Project ORDCIT for the Ordnance Department

During the summer of 1944, JPL tackled the ORDCIT project, using work already started on solid- and liquid-fueled engines. In the solid category were two designs: the Private A missile, fitted with fins, and the Private F model, a winged version. In December 1944, only eleven months after the project began, ORDCIT successfully launched the Private A. The

---

*Also in January 1944, Maj. Gen. Gladeon M. Barnes of Ordnance asked GALCIT to study a long-range (75 to 100 miles), jet-propelled missile capable of carrying 1,000 pounds of high explosives. The AAF considered this action an infringement on its roles and missions by the Ordnance Department. See Chapter I.

†An air-to-underwater, jet-propelled missile. Chief questions concerned firing below the surface, the effects on missile stability, and cavitation. A 2,200-pound thrust motor burned GALCIT 65, a solid-propellant variation of GALCIT 61-C. Later tests demonstrated launching speeds of 385 miles per hour.

liquid rockets were represented by the Corporal E and F missiles. In this area the Americans built on the work done by the German V–2 scientists.[13]

In June 1944, at about the time that Germany began to fire the V–1 against England, a V–2 test missile strayed off course and crashed in Sweden. It was subsequently recovered and scrutinized by the Allies. After the V–2 entered combat, recovered components were shipped home by the U.S. Army for study and testing. Under the Hermes Program, begun in November 1944, the Ordnance Department initiated a research and development effort for ballistic missiles and signed a prime contract with the General Electric Company. Within two years some twenty-five V–2 rockets were assembled, and a flight test program was initiated. The tests provided invaluable data on missile design, fabrication, handling, and launching, and materially advanced the state of liquid rocket technology in the United States.[14]

Also during 1944, just before the end of the year, Frank Malina returned from an inspection trip to England and France and recommended the development of sounding rockets* aimed at carrying a 25-pound payload to a 100,000-foot altitude. Malina obtained approval for his recommendation as a first step in producing an antiaircraft missile. The development of sounding rockets was also an area of interest to the Army Signal Corps and the program built on Project ORDCIT.[15]

In the closing days of World War II, the Americans and Russians raced to capture and exploit German weapons and scientists. The most prominent of the Germans—including Wernher von Braun, chief scientist on the V–2, and Walter Dornberger, who commanded Peenemünde—traveled westward to surrender to the Allies. The American effort, called Project Paperclip, brought some 600 German scientists, including about 130 rocket specialists, to the United States. The Ordnance Department—because it operated under an "arsenal system," where development was done within the service's own plants—benefited most directly from Paperclip. In December 1945 Ordnance established a team of German rocket scientists at Ft. Bliss, Texas, to continue refining the V–2.† They worked in conjunction with the Hermes Program.[16]

While the Americans "recruited" the cream of the Peenemünde scientists, the Russians brought back hundreds of German scientists and engineers. U.S. officials associated with Paperclip were confident that, with the help of the foreign experts, the United States would handily outpace the

---

*Rockets used solely for measurements within the atmosphere, including temperature, pressure, density, composition, structure, and movements of the atmosphere. The Navy was first to enter upper atmospheric research, beginning its program in 1945.

†Between April and November 1950 the von Braun team was relocated to the Redstone Arsenal, Huntsville, Alabama.

Soviet Union in rocketry. But contrary to the popular western stereotype of the technologically backward Russians, the latter had decades of experience in missile research. By the end of the nineteenth century, Konstantin E. Ziolkovsky had begun to investigate space flight. By 1930 the Soviets had achieved considerable progress, and during World War II they made extensive use of their famous Katyusha rockets.*

After the war, therefore, the Soviets were prepared to conduct their own rocket research program.† They put the Germans to work on advancing the V-2, exploited their knowledge, and used the foreigners' work to gauge their own progress. The Germans were not permitted to observe the Soviet missile program. According to the Air Force Systems Command historian, "Their [the Soviets'] principal advantage lay in their early decisions, a relatively simple program, and maximum support in facilities and funds." In contrast to the slow, sequential missile development approach that the Americans were to adopt, the USSR "leapfrogged" development by concentrating from the start on building very large rockets while also working on atomic and hydrogen warheads. In the early 1950s, after having learned all they needed from the Germans, the Soviets released them.[17]

Project MX-774

Unlike the Ordnance Department, the AAF did not assemble a team of German rocket scientists. Instead, it placed its faith in the aircraft industry. By 1945 several companies—notably North American Aviation, Bell Aircraft, General Electric, and Consolidated Vultee—had formed missile divisions that were continued after the war. Although these were individually small, the aggregate effort represented a relatively large investment in terms of money and talent.

Starting on October 31, 1945, the Air Technical Service Command (ATSC) invited industry proposals for studies and preliminary designs on a 10-year research and development program in 4 categories of missiles with ranges of up to 5,000 miles. Considering that the range of the V-2 was about 200 miles, this represented a staggering requirement. Nonetheless, aircraft manufacturers were receptive because the postwar retrenchment in military spending had reduced their business sharply. The Consolidated Vultee

---

*The Katyushas could be fired either from the ground, or from truck-mounted racks containing 2 rows of 8 rockets each. Usually employed in barrages against German troops, these solid-fuel rockets were 6 feet long and 5 inches in diameter, weighed about 100 pounds, and had a 3-mile range.

†In the postwar period the Russians produced a single-stage, liquid-fueled rocket called the T-1, an improved version of the V-2.

Aircraft Corporation (Convair for short), for example, had turned out about 31,000 airplanes during World War II. Its peacetime business fell to almost nothing as production contracts were canceled. Moreover, weapons research was given a boost when the War Production Board urged the Army and Navy to do whatever they could to help relieve industrial dislocations.[18]

Although Convair was preoccupied with the B–36 aircraft program, its Vultee Field Division, at Downey, California, had developed a Navy short-range rocket called the Lark and felt qualified to pursue missile development. By January 1946 Convair engineers provided the AAF with 2 proposals for a long-range missile. One was a subsonic, winged, jet-powered missile; the other was supersonic, ballistic, and rocket-powered. In April the AAF accepted the proposals and awarded Convair a $1.4 million study contract.* Both designs aimed at a missile capable of delivering a 5,000-pound warhead over ranges between 1,500 and 5,000 miles, and within 5,000 feet of the target.[19]

The award of this contract marked the birth of a quiet, unpublicized effort nicknamed Project MX–774. Convair's project manager was Karel J. (Charlie) Bossart, a Belgian-born structural engineer whose only missile experience had been with the Lark program. Bossart's major problem was a lack of data, especially concerning missile weights. In order to collect the needed information, he secured permission to build ten test vehicles of three designs.† MX–774 Design A represented a subsonic vehicle which was later abandoned due to the sharp funding cutback that occurred in December 1946.‡ Design B was a supersonic ballistic missile intended to prove the concepts of the final article—Design C. The vehicles were later dubbed as follows: Teetotaler (A), because it did not use alcohol fuel; Old Fashioned (B), because it resembled the V–2; and Manhattan (C), because it would carry the atomic warhead. In June 1946 the AAF added $493,000 to the Convair contract, raising its total to $1.893 million.[20]

The point of departure for the MX–774 was the V–2. As a structural engineer, Bossart immediately concerned himself with tackling the problem of the V–2's weight. He removed the double wall arrangement from the German missile and stored its propellant in two individual metal enclosures mounted inside the missile. In a single stroke, Bossart increased the missile's fuel capacity while also eliminating the internal tanks. What emerged was a

---

*Contract Number W33–038–AC–14168, April 2, 1946.

†The test vehicles provided design information on stabilization, guidance, and power plant problems involved in storing, handling, and launching the missiles. Also called RTV–2–As or Hirocs, the test vehicles were single-stage missiles 31 to 34 feet long by 30 inches in diameter. They were powered by 4 Reaction Motors Inc. LOX-alcohol engines, producing a combined thrust of 8,000 pounds. The design payload was 100 pounds to an altitude of 670,000 feet, or 300 pounds to 530,000 feet. The guidance system was a prototype of the Azusa system.

‡See page 26.

Test-firing of an MX-774 at White Sands Proving Ground, New Mexico.

sort of flying propellant tank with a power plant in the rear and an instrumentation package up front.[21]

The V-2 also was deficient in that the entire missile was designed to reenter the atmosphere and, therefore, had to withstand considerable heat. Bossart, however, reasoned that after the missile was launched the only part needed to complete the mission was the warhead. Thus, if the warhead could be separated from the missile after burnout, it alone would have to be protected against heat. The result would be another savings in weight. Another advantage in devising a separating nose cone (which housed the warhead) was that it would reduce the drag on the missile, thereby improving its range.

Bossart and his team also removed the stiffeners that had supported the interior of the V-2's conventional airframe. They obtained structural rigidity in an ingenious manner, by utilizing nitrogen gas * pressure to support the airframe. When all these innovations were taken together, Bossart's weight reduction program improved the V-2's airframe-to-propellant weight ratio by a factor of three.[22]

The fourth, and perhaps the most important, MX-774 design innovation was Bossart's swiveling engines. Although the Germans had first conceived the idea and discarded it, Bossart was unaware of their work and arrived at his design independently. Previously, the only way to control the direction of flight of a rocket had been through insertion of movable vanes in the exhaust system. This method, however, retarded the exhaust flow and thereby reduced thrust by about 17 percent. By swiveling the engines, Bossart obtained better control of the rocket's flight. Bossart also kept the missile's fins (inspired by the V-2) as a form of insurance, although he was confident that the swiveling engines would suffice to keep the MX-774 stable.[23]

Shortly after the AAF approved building the 10 MX-774 test vehicles, Convair solicited candidates to produce a suitable power plant. The firm chosen was Reaction Motors Inc. (RMI), a young company created by members of the American Rocket Society and located in Rockaway, New Jersey. RMI was already building a 1,500-pound thrust engine for the Bell X-1 rocket plane. It was decided that a cluster of 4 such engines, with the thrust of each engine raised to 2,000 pounds, could be adapted to the MX-774. A hydrogen peroxide turbopump, in combination with pressure feeding, was devised to upgrade the thrust by increasing the LOX-alcohol fuel supply.[24]

Through the latter half of 1946 and early 1947, Project MX-774 moved ahead quietly with the construction of the test vehicle, design of the advanced missile (both tasks were accomplished at Downey, California), and the buildup of the RMI engines in New Jersey.[25]

---

* The nitrogen was used to push the LOX-alcohol fuel out of the tanks.

BALLISTIC MISSILES

The MX-774 guidance system was a relatively simple device based on a gyrostabilized autopilot. From 1946 on, Convair conducted more advanced work on a precise phase comparison system called Azusa.* In the latter system signals transmitted from the missile in flight were received at two pairs of ground stations. Phase variation, due to differences in distance between the stations and the missile transponder, were fed into a ground-based computer, thus enabling the missile's flight to be compared to an ideal trajectory up to the point of nose cone separation. Corrective signals were then relayed to the missile guidance system. Although the Azusa system was not used in the MX-774, more man-hours were expended on the guidance electronics than on the overall missile design, and the Air Force continued to support Convair's guidance work even after the MX-774 contract ended.[26]

As noted in the preceding chapter, there had been a sharp reduction in missile development funds in December 1946 when President Truman initiated his economy drive. Consequently, the AAF dropped Convair's subsonic missile design, electing to continue a similar program under way at Northrop which eventually resulted in production of the Snark missile.† The AAF also advised Convair to stretch its MX-774 project funds—calculated to support one year's development work—to 1948. But, in July 1947, after reassessing its missile program once more, the AAF canceled MX-774 altogether.[27]

The choice between the aerodynamic (now called cruise) missiles— Navaho (MX-771) and Snark (MX-775)—and the ballistic MX-774 missile was a tough one, and General Spaatz directed his staff to emphasize this point in its upcoming Congressional testimony. Gen. Hoyt Vandenberg and Gen. Thomas Power—the Assistant Chief of Staff (Operations, Commitments and Requirements) and his deputy respectively—explained that the decision between the two types of missiles was based upon which one could be expected to become available the soonest. Because ballistic missiles did not promise "any tangible results in the next 8 to 10 years," they were sacrificed.[28]

Also, several areas associated with ballistic missiles required further technical investigation, including the problems of reentry, range, more accurate guidance, more efficient and higher powered motors, and higher specific impulse fuels than could be provided by a LOX-alcohol combination. Other factors cited in the decision were that the cost per missile—

---

*Named after a small town near Los Angeles, California. Ironically, Azusa became headquarters of a Convair competitor, the Aerojet General Corporation, the eventual builder of the engines for the Titan missile.

†The AAF relied on the development of Northrop's jet-propelled, subsonic Snark (and its contemplated supersonic version, Boojum) and later on North American's ramjet-powered Navaho for its future strategic missile requirements.

$500,000—was too high; that $50 million would be needed to complete the program; and that aerodynamic missiles offered superior payload and range and seemed nearer to completion.[29]

Nevertheless, Convair was permitted to use its unexpended project funds to complete and flight-test three vehicles, which were then under construction, and to continue its studies on guidance and nose cone reentry. Convair economized by moving its operations from Downey to San Diego, California. It selected a static test site at Point Loma,* California, a peninsula on the Pacific Ocean which was hidden from public view. The captive tests were run between November 1947 and May 1948, after which the first MX-774 test vehicle was transported to the Army's White Sands Proving Ground, New Mexico.

The flight plan called for launching the missile to an altitude of about 100 miles, jettisoning the nose cone at peak altitude, and recovering the missile by means of a 40-foot parachute. Minor problems delayed the launch until July 13, 1948. The first missile launched rose to an altitude of 6,200 feet in less than 1 minute, but something choked the engines and it fell back to earth and exploded. Because of a crew member's error, the parachute failed to deploy, but the on-board camera survived and was recovered. Although no definite conclusion was reached about the cause of the engine shutdown, the flight was recorded as partially successful, and the rocket's stability during its brief ascent was encouraging.[30]

The second flight test occurred on September 27, with similar results. The engines shut down again, but at ten miles altitude rather than one mile. This time battery failure, not human error, was responsible for preventing deployment of the recovery parachute, and excessive pressure in the LOX tank caused the missile to break apart during the descent. Somehow, the camera survived and provided bits of flight data, but still there were no positive clues as to the engine problem.[31]

On December 2 the third vehicle lifted off successfully and flew for 51 seconds before it, too, exploded. Once more the camera and film survived, and a study of the photographic data showed that a valve which controlled the LOX flow had closed unexpectedly. Convair engineers concluded that vibration was the likely culprit, but with their funds expended, this knowledge was of no immediate practical use.[32]

Although the flight tests were only partially successful, they demonstrated the correctness of Bossart's designs, including the swiveling (gimbaling) rocket engines that provided directional control; the lightweight airframe structure achieved through pressurization; the autopilots and command system; and the separation of the nose cone from the missile in flight. In late 1948 the Air Force proposed that the MX-774 be used as a

---

* The first test stand was a converted oil derrick.

49

high-altitude research vehicle. (The Fiscal Year 1948 supplemental budget provided funds for procuring fifteen such vehicles.) But the Research and Development Board's Committee on Guided Missiles compared the capabilities of the MX-774 with those of the Navy's Viking and decided to retain the Viking for the high-altitude mission and terminated MX-774 in February 1949.[33]

The National Guided Missile Program

Because of their potentially revolutionary impact on several fronts, including wartime force employment, roles and missions, procurement costs, and technology, guided missiles received special treatment from the defense establishment. Certainly, no other weapon was so constantly beset by outside interference from higher military and political authorities; the results were not good.

The Joint Chiefs of Staff first perceived a need for central coordination of guided missiles early in World War II but were too preoccupied with waging the war to take action. In June 1942 the JCS Committee on New Weapons and Equipment reviewed the military missile efforts, and in December recommended establishing a joint service program with the help of the Office of Scientific Research and Development (OSRD). As a result, Division 5 (New Missiles) of OSRD was created. The division operated throughout the war but, instead of coordinating the missile program, served primarily as a research body.[34]

In January 1945, motivated by the advent of the German "V" weapons and in the wake of the McNarney Directive,* the JCS displaced Division 5 with its own Guided Missiles Committee (GMC)† in a renewed attempt to achieve a coordinated program. Composed of two representatives from OSRD, one from the National Advisory Committee for Aeronautics (NACA) and three each from the Army and Navy, the GMC was expected to coordinate research and development among the services, evaluate projects and priorities, recommend a single development program, and propose responsibility assignments. However, despite this broad area of responsibility, the committee occupied itself almost exclusively with formulating broad policy.[35]

Convinced that the United States possessed a limited pool of scientific and engineering talent, the GMC urged combining resources into a single national guided missile program. The military services, however, split on the

---

*See page 19.

† Redesignated frequently over the course of the next ten years, it was popularly called the Guided Missiles Committee.

Vannevar Bush, head of
the Joint Research and
Development Board.

issue. The AAF sought to gain exclusive control over all missile development, while the Navy favored the creation of a national program to silence
critics of the military's handling of missile projects. The Army leadership
sided with the Navy, and on April 1, 1946, the two service secretaries issued
a joint statement supporting a comprehensive national guided missile
program, including joint procurement, testing, and training. Despite this
declaration, interservice conflicts over development responsibility continued, and no national program was implemented.[36]

Two months later came a further step toward interservice program
management. On June 6, 1946, the Joint Research and Development Board
(JRDB) was chartered with Vannevar Bush, the wartime head of OSRD, as
its chairman. The JRDB formed a Committee on Guided Missiles in
August, and two weeks later the JCS dissolved its GMC. Composed of two
Army and Navy representatives and three civilians, the JRDB missile
committee reflected the partisan tendencies and vested interests of its
members.

During its existence the committee resisted attempts to apportion
missile projects among the contending services. Wherever possible, the
committee avoided controversy and sought compromise. Consequently, the
committee concentrated on reviewing and questioning technical approaches
pursued on various projects. Given an uninterested JCS and a weak JRDB,
it was inevitable that the services would exploit the situation, unconcerned
with accountability. The only restraint on service duplication and waste, it

51

seemed, was the lack of funding. In place of a "National Guided Missile Program," there were actually four separate missile programs: those of the AAF, the Army Ordnance Department, the Navy Bureau of Aeronautics, and the Navy Bureau of Ordnance. Unification of the military services in 1947 did nothing to remedy the situation.[37]

On July 26, 1947, the National Security Act created the National Military Establishment. The act retained the Navy Department but abolished the War Department, replacing it with a Department of the Army and an independent Department of the Air Force. As subsequent events demonstrated, however, the act failed to define roles and missions and failed to resolve the ongoing intense interservice rivalry.[38]

Meanwhile, on September 15, 1947, in a set of transfer agreements with the Army, the Air Force obtained operational control over surface-to-surface pilotless aircraft and strategic missiles.* The latter were defined as missiles employed against targets whose destruction would not directly affect Army tactical operations. The Army would control tactical missiles, that is, missiles supporting land operations and those used against targets affecting Army tactical operations. Additionally, the Air Force would control surface-to-air missiles for area defense, and the Army was assigned those surface-to-air missiles that would protect field forces from air attack.

In effect, the agreements permitted both services to operate surface-to-surface as well as surface-to-air missiles, but only for specific purposes. The negotiations were concluded by purposely keeping the terms of reference broad, omitting controversy, and making distinctions that did not establish new precedents. For better or worse, the Army–Air Force agreements served as basic policy until mid-1949, because the Air Force and Army did not concern themselves with the divisive issue of operational responsibility until that time.[39]

Two weeks after the Army–Air Force transfer agreements were concluded, on September 30, 1947, the Research and Development Board (RDB) replaced the JRDB, prompting yet another examination of missile development. The new organization possessed broader authority than its predecessor by virtue of becoming a statutory body under the National Security Act. As a result, it was empowered to consider all research and development matters, not only those of a joint service nature. Vannevar Bush, who retained direction of the RDB, announced his intention to create "a single coordinated [missile] program for all the services without duplication or R&D gaps."[40]

Late in 1947 the RDB established a new Guided Missiles Committee, which undertook to resolve the missile development responsibility issue. The

---

*The agreements, subject to later adjustment, were approved by Secretary of Defense James Forrestal on October 14, 1947.

GMC was composed of three civilians and six military men, two from each service. Again, because of its political composition, the GMC concentrated on studying and questioning the technical aspects of individual missile projects. Its lack of leadership was especially evident in March 1948, when the Air Force revamped its missile program without directly notifying the committee. The Army and Navy, too, blatantly disregarded the GMC.[41]

In March 1949, Louis A. Johnson succeeded James V. Forrestal as Secretary of Defense and ushered in a new round of cost reductions. At this time the Army and Air Force were embroiled in a dispute over missile roles and missions. The quarrel erupted in May when the Army, in a "once and for all" stab at settling the issue, recommended that the Army be assigned development responsibility for all surface-launched missiles; that the Navy control all ship-launched missiles; and that the Air Force all air-launched missiles. Secretary Johnson referred the proposal to the JCS for evaluation.

The JCS deliberated until the fall, arriving at a split decision with the Army and Navy teamed against the Air Force. Later, under pressure for results, the JCS offered a plan to (1) assign to the Army and Navy all surface-to-air missiles that extended the range of antiaircraft artillery; (2) assign to the Air Force and Navy all surface-to-air missiles that supplemented interceptor aircraft; and (3) assign to the Army and Navy all short-range surface-to-surface missiles, which replaced field artillery.

Although the JCS omitted to mention long-range surface-to-surface missiles, it was understood that, so long as the Air Force retained responsibility for strategic bombardment, it remained the logical user. The plan, approved by Johnson in March 1950, did not seem to resolve the issue. Because it defeated the Army's attempt to gain control over all surface-launched missiles, however, some Air Force officials viewed the new policy as a significant victory.[42]

Meanwhile, the matter of missile development remained open, with the Research and Development Board delaying a recommendation until the JCS had resolved the operational assignment issue. The Soviet atomic test of August 1949 helped somewhat to overcome the inertia that had precluded progress in U.S. missile development. In November 1949 the RDB's Guided Missiles Committee reviewed the Air Force missile program and declared it consistent with JCS operational criteria, except for the Gapa air defense missile, which was being canceled. The GMC, in a March 1950 report, observed that all the services were conducting satisfactory missile programs, that interservice coordination was excellent, and that no changes were necessary or desirable. The committee further recommended that missile development assignments follow the direction established by the Joint Chiefs for operational assignments.

Secretary Johnson, however, rejected the GMC's recommendation because he considered the JCS operational guidelines too broad to apply in the development area. He reasoned that, although more than one service might demonstrate a legitimate requirement for a missile, it was not necessary for all the services to develop that missile. When asked how it hoped to avoid the duplication inherent in the GMC's proposal, the RDB responded in August 1950 with a review of all its weapons policies, not just missiles. Thus, after five years the problem of missile development responsibility remained unsettled.[43]

In December 1949, with the question of budget cuts still unresolved, Johnson assigned Air Force Secretary W. Stuart Symington to conduct a detailed review of all Department of Defense (DOD) missile projects and to propose a joint services missile program. Symington formed the Special Interdepartmental Guided Missiles Board (known as SIB or SIGMB) with his assistant, Harold C. Stuart, as its head.

The Stuart Board was stymied from the first by the issue of operational responsibility. The Air Force charged that the Army and Navy were illegally developing surface-to-surface missiles with ranges beyond 500 miles. Properly, these missiles belonged in the strategic class and, therefore, to the Air Force. The services also traded accusations of unwarranted duplication and waste, with the Air Force noting the Navy's development of three air-to-air missiles as gross examples, while the Army and Navy

**Secretary of Defense
Louis A. Johnson.**

Harold C. Stuart, Assistant Secretary for Civil Affairs, headed the Special Interdepartmental Guided Missiles Board.

characterized the Air Force's Snark and Navaho surface-to-surface projects as wasteful and costly. The Air Force proposed that each service be limited to developing only one missile in any category in which it had operational responsibility. Had this policy been adopted, it would have reduced the entire national missile program to thirteen projects.[44]

When finally completed in January 1950, the Stuart Report was a complex document containing long lists of disagreements. The services agreed on only two points: (1) the operation of a missile range by each service, which would be used jointly; and (2) the desirability of reestablishing an interdepartmental operational requirements group for guided missiles. The Stuart Report, including comments by the service secretaries, was submitted to Johnson in February.

The Secretary of Defense was still dissatisfied by the lack of consensus among the services and considered appointing an outsider to bring order to the missile program. Stuart Symington, however, persuaded Johnson to allow the JCS to undertake another review. This time the JCS created a set of priorities for missile projects that covered weapon development, component development, design study, and research study. The JCS also agreed to conduct annual reviews of the missile program, beginning in September 1950. Finally, it assigned to the Air Force formal and exclusive responsibility

for developing long-range strategic missiles and short-range tactical missiles.*
Submitted in March 1950, the JCS plan was approved by Secretary
Johnson.[45]

Although this decision seemed to give the Air Force exclusivity, its
significance should not be exaggerated. Thus, the Army and Navy continued to sponsor missile "studies and designs," hoping through this evolutionary approach to develop complete missile systems. Once these missiles
were developed, the services would have powerful arguments to retain the
weapons because of their unique experience and technical know-how.

With the impact of Johnson's economy drives and the threat of even
deeper budget cuts, the services grew increasingly restless over the question
of missile priorities, because only the highest priorities would survive the
constant onslaught on the research and development budget. In July 1949
each service had drawn up a list of its priorities and submitted it to the JCS.
At the time, the Air Force assigned top priority to those missiles which
would enhance the capabilities of its strategic bombers and second priority
to air defense missiles. But, when the consolidated JCS list first appeared in
October, long-range strategic missiles occupied a lowly eighth place. The Air
Force was shocked by what it considered to be a misplaced priority, but
expected that this would be corrected by the Guided Missiles Interdepartmental Operational Requirements Group (GMIORG). The problem dragged
on unchanged until June 1950 when, with the onset of the Korean War,
additional appropriations obviated the need for direct action.[46]

USAF Missile Program, 1947–1950

When the United States Air Force was established in September 1947,
its missile program comprised eighteen projects: seven missiles under
development, four follow-on missiles, two in the study stage, two continu-
ations of World War II projects, and three in component development. In
a briefing before the USAF Aircraft and Weapons Board in early 1948, Air
Materiel Command representatives observed that, if existing trends continued, missile research and development would be subjected to serious
funding shortages for the next five years. In order to salvage the basic
program, they recommended canceling or reducing several missile projects.
Some members of the Air Staff opposed this strategy, arguing that it would
create a void in several developmental areas—including ramjet and rocket
propulsion for air defense and ballistic missiles—and that certain advanced
developments then under way might be abandoned, or reduced sharply.[47]

---

*The short-range tactical missiles corresponded to the Air Force missions of air
interdiction and close air support.

56

The Aircraft and Weapons Board and the Chief of Staff endorsed AMC's recommendations but stipulated that, if money became available later, it would be applied to retain some of the projects that had to be canceled. The final decision, made in March 1948, approved fourteen missile projects: seven missiles in development, four follow-ons, one study, and two carry-overs from World War II. Six system or component developments were canceled.* Although the number of projects remained stable, the program objectives were considerably realigned. (See Chart 2-1, March 1948 Program.) [48]

For Fiscal Year 1948 the Aircraft and Weapons Board approved military characteristics statements for thirteen missiles and initial programming of production funds. The FY 1948 budget provided $13 million for missile production and $20 million for missile development. For Fiscal Year 1949 $10.3 million was allocated to production and only $7 million for development. [49]

The adjustments in program objectives and trimming of funds stemmed from President Truman's May 1948 budget policy (for FY 1950), which precluded the services from initiating in any fiscal year a project requiring larger annual investments in subsequent years. Truman's policy was undoubtedly influenced by the Finletter Commission report, "Survival in the Air Age." Issued in January 1948, the report urged maintaining strong forces in being because the commission expected that there would be no time to mobilize for the next war. It also assumed that no nation other than the United States could wage atomic warfare before 1952. This formulation, in effect, matched forces in being against long-range developments. Forced to choose between the two, the Air Force opted for forces in being. Developmental projects were most severely affected because of their needs for specialized experimental and test facilities. [50]

In late 1948 and early 1949 the Board of Senior Officers—which replaced the Aircraft and Weapons Board—reviewed the Air Force missile program. The AMC representatives did not propose any significant changes and the Board postponed making a decision pending an Office of the Secretary of Defense (OSD) budget review. Conducted between January and May 1949, the review, in large part, dictated the Air Force's program realignment. By the time the realignment was completed in July 1949, the Matador and Firebird missiles had been canceled and the USAF missile program was down to twelve projects: five in development, one study, four follow-ons, and two World War II carry-overs. (See Chart 2-2, July 1949 Program.) [51]

A year later, at the start of the Korean War, the USAF missile program shrank further. The Snark intercontinental missile, a major project, was

---

*The totals do not balance because the March 1948 program added two follow-on projects for the Navaho.

Chart 2-1

Revised Air Force Guided Missile Program as of March 1948

Project	Contractor	Performance Features & Remarks

SURFACE-TO-SURFACE

MX-770	North American Aviation Inc.	Navaho; changed from 500-mi winged rocket to 1,000-mi test vehicle to be followed by a 3,000-mi test vehicle and a 5,000-mi operational missile. Rockets dropped as cruise propulsion.
MX-771A	The Glenn L. Martin Co.	Matador; 500-mi subsonic, turbojet
MX-775A	Northrop Aircraft, Inc.	Snark; 5,000-mi subsonic, turbojet; to be followed by the Boojum supersonic version
MX-767	AMC	Banshee; modification of B-29

AIR-TO-SURFACE

MX-674	Bell Aircraft Corp.	Tarzon vertical bomb
MX-776	Bell Aircraft	Concentration on Shrike test vehicle (and possible 50-mi tactical version); the 300-mi Rascal version to follow

SURFACE-TO-AIR

MX-606	The Boeing Airplane Co.	Gapa; 35-mi defense vs aircraft
MX-794	University of Michigan	Wizard; defense vs ballistic missiles; continued as a study

AIR-TO-AIR

MX-779	Ryan Aeronautical Co.	Firebird; fighter-launched, subsonic
MX-904	Hughes Aircraft Co.	Falcon; bomber-launched; upgraded from guidance component development

PROJECTS CANCELED

Mastiff	None	300-mi, ASM, atomic warhead
MX–795	General Electric Corp.	Thumper; defense vs ballistic missiles, SAM, study
—	Ryan	Firebird; fighter-launched, AAM-supersonic, follow-on to MX–779
MX–802	General Electric	Dragonfly; bomber-launched, AAM, supersonic

COMPONENT DEVELOPMENTS

MX–778	The Goodyear Aircraft Corp.	Dropped
MX–800	M.W. Kellogg Co.	Dropped

Source: Max Rosenberg, *The Air Force and the National Guided Missile Program, 1944–1950* (USAF Historical Div Liaison Ofc, Jun 1964), p. 117.

---

downgraded to component development.* Project Banshee, the long-suffering effort to demonstrate the remote control flight of a B–29 aircraft, was finally abandoned. And Bomarc replaced Gapa, but only as a study. Only three development projects remained under this emasculated program: Navaho, Rascal, and Falcon. In the surface-to-air category, there were no projects under development. (See Chart 2–3, July 1950.)[52]

Atomic-Equipped Missiles

Immediately following the A-bomb explosion on Hiroshima, Air Staff officials suggested equipping missiles with atomic warheads. Convert-

---

*Robert L. Perry, *The Development of the Snark Guided Missile, 1945–1953*. Wright-Patterson AFB, Ohio: Historical Branch (WADC, 1956), p. 72: "Something in the neighborhood of $250,000,000 had gone down the gullet of the Snark by 1953."

ing the idea into practice, however, proved extremely difficult. After two years of frustrating negotiations with the Manhattan District and its successor, the Atomic Energy Commission, the AAF conceded its inability to carry out the proposal. In October and November 1947 the Air Force included a requirement for atomic warheads in several missile characteristics statements, but nothing came of this. Not until 1949, when the AEC was satisfied that enough progress had been made in missiles and atomic energy, did that agency begin a feasibility study on combining the two technologies.

The Air Force, made cautious by experience, approached the matter with circumspection. The Army, by contrast, acted boldly, seeking to break the Air Force's monopoly on atomic weapon delivery. On May 24, 1949, at the time that it proposed to assume responsibility for all surface-launched missiles,* the Army asked the JCS to approve its requirement for a short-range surface-to-surface missile with an atomic warhead. The Navy supported the Army, while promoting its own atomic weapon ambitions. Noting the complex issues of operational responsibility involved, the Air Force opposed the Army recommendation. Instead, the Air Force requested that the JCS resolve the question of missile priorities and determine the targets and the circumstances under which atomic weapons would be used. In July 1949 the JCS agreed to address operational assignments within the broader context of priorities.[53]

Independent of the JCS proceedings, Defense Secretary Louis A. Johnson, in June 1949, established a committee to study the mating of atomic warheads to missiles. The committee, headed by the Director of the Weapon System Evaluation Group, Army Lt. Gen. John E. Hull, concerned itself only with the question of development possibilities over the next five to ten years. It left the matter of the missiles' military worth to other "appropriate" Defense Department agencies.[54]

Issued on September 14, 1949, the Hull Committee Report contained the stated requirements of the three services alongside expert scientific opinion that both types of atomic bombs—gun and implosion—could be adapted as missile warheads. The services were advised that they could obtain two or three times as many implosion warheads as gun-type warheads for the same quantity of fissionable material. Implosion weapons, however, were heavier and bulkier and would, therefore, require larger missiles.

According to the report, four missiles then under development—the Army Hermes A-3, the Navy Regulus, and the Air Force Snark and Rascal—might be operational in either late 1953 or early 1954, at which time there would be enough fissionable materials to fill all military needs for atomic warheads. The Hull Committee also concluded that several missiles under development were justifiable, economically and militarily, only if

---

*See page 53.

Chart 2–2

Air Force Guided Missiles Program as of 1949

Project	Contractor	Performance Features & Remarks
		SURFACE-TO-SURFACE
MX–770	North American Aviation Inc.	Navaho, 1,000-mi test vehicle, to be followed by 3,000-mi and 5,000-mi operational missiles
MX–775A	Northrop Aircraft Inc.	Snark, 5,000-mi subsonic, to be followed by Boojum supersonic version
MX–767	AMC	Banshee, modification of B–29
		AIR-TO-SURFACE
MX–674	Bell Aircraft Corp.	Tarzon vertical bomb
MX–776	Bell Aircraft	Concentration on Shrike test vehicle (and possible 50-mi tactical version); 300-mi Rascal to follow
		SURFACE-TO-AIR
MX–606	The Boeing Airplane Co.	Gapa; 35-mi defense vs aircraft
MX–794	University of Michigan	Wizard; defense vs ballistic missile, study
		AIR-TO-AIR
MX–904	Hughes Aircraft Co.	Falcon; bomber-launched
		PROJECTS CANCELED
MX–771A	The Glenn L. Martin Co.	Matador
MX–799	Ryan Aeronautical Co.	Firebird

Source: Max Rosenberg, *The Air Force and the National Guided Missile Program, 1944–1950* (USAF Historical Div Liaison Ofc, Jun 1964), p 118.

Chart 2-3

Air Force Guided Missile Program as of 1950

Project	Contractor	Performance Features & Remarks

SURFACE-TO-SURFACE

Project	Contractor	Performance Features & Remarks
MX-770	North American Aviation Inc.	Navaho, 1,000-mi air-launched missile to be followed by 1,700-mi air-launched and 5,500-mi surface-launched versions
MX-775A	Northrop Aircraft Inc.	Snark, downgraded to development of guidance subsystem and guidance test vehicle

AIR-TO-SURFACE

Project	Contractor	Performance Features & Remarks
MX-674	Bell Aircraft Corp.	Tarzon vertical bomb
MX-776	Bell Aircraft	Rascal I with 100-mi range; to be followed by Rascal II with 150-mi range

SURFACE-TO-AIR

Project	Contractor	Performance Features & Remarks
MX-1599	The Boeing Airplane Co.	Bomarc, study only, 100-mi range replacement for terminated Gapa
MX-794	University of Michigan	Wizard, defense vs ballistic missiles, study

AIR-TO-AIR

Project	Contractor	Performance Features & Remarks
MX-904	Hughes Aircraft Co.	Falcon, fighter-launched; to be followed by bomber-launched version

PROJECTS CANCELED

Project	Contractor	Performance Features & Remarks
MX-767	AMC	Banshee
MX-606	Boeing	Gapa was replaced by Bomarc

Source: Max Rosenberg, *The Air Force and the National Guided Missile Program, 1944-1950* (USAF Historical Div Liaison Ofc, Jun 1964), p 150.

A Navaho cruise missile test-launched. The piggyback arrangement would be used years later by the space shuttle.

The Air Force invested heavily in Northrop's jet-propelled, subsonic Snark missile.

they carried atomic warheads. Finally, the report recommended closer technical liaison between the services and AEC and continued study by the Department of Defense on the use and effectiveness of atomic weapons.[55]

Secretary Johnson transmitted the Hull Report to the Joint Chiefs and asked: (1) Which missiles should be designated to carry atomic warheads? (2) What channels of communication were needed between DOD and the AEC? and (3) How should the Defense Department evaluate the military worth of the missiles selected? There followed a period of indecision by the JCS and an Army–Air Force misunderstanding which deferred the JCS answer for two months.[56]

Meanwhile, on November 22, 1949, General Vandenberg observed that the selection of atomic warheads depended upon the dimensions of the missile rather than on the warhead features. He also noted that the gun-type atomic warheads were nearly out of production and were being removed from the stockpile. Thus, a sizeable requirement for gun-type warheads would necessitate either an expansion of AEC production facilities or a reduction of the stockpile.[57]

By the end of 1949 the JCS had endorsed the Hull Committee Report, including a call for closer liaison between the AEC, the RDB, and the services. Secretary Johnson, on January 16, 1950, approved the report and directed the RDB to emphasize the four missiles expected to carry atomic warheads. The decision prompted the services to launch a drive to obtain still more atomic warheads. The services soon expanded their requirements greatly and asked for the development of two additional, smaller versions of atomic warheads. When the Army asked permission to develop an atomic artillery shell, the Air Force acquiesced but clung to its belief that tactical aircraft would be more efficient. The Air Force's aim here was to ensure that, in the enthusiastic search for alternate means to deliver atomic weapons, the Department of Defense would retain an adequate inventory to support the strategic Air Force. General Vandenberg and the Air Staff counseled caution, emphasizing the need to gauge carefully the effects of new demands on the atomic stockpile in terms of use, cost, and effectiveness.[58]

Chapter III

The Contest for Control

> . . . the separation of research and development
> from Air Materiel Command was like surgery
> involving Siamese twins. The operation was ex-
> tremely risky because it could result in the death
> of both parties.
>
> Lt. Gen. Benjamin Chidlaw, 1950

Beginning in 1947, funding for missiles dropped as part of the general decline in military research and development. Several Air Force notables believed that this trend could be stemmed if R&D had a formal advocacy group. These men, including Jimmy Doolittle, Theodore von Kármán, and Donald Putt, campaigned to upgrade the status of R&D in the Air Force. By mid-1949 they had persuaded the Air Force Chief of Staff, Gen. Hoyt S. Vandenberg, to commission a study on the subject. Eventually two studies were undertaken. Both reached the same conclusions: (1) that Air Force R&D should be separated from Air Materiel Command and placed under a separate command; and (2) that R&D should be assigned high-level representation on the Air Staff. Both recommendations were subsequently adopted.

Other world events served to promote the case for restoring funds for R&D, especially for missiles. One was the Soviet atomic bomb test of August 1949, and another was the onset of the Korean War in July 1950. In December 1950 RAND reported to the Air Force that it was now technically feasible to build long-range missiles. Proceeding cautiously, the Air Force awarded a study contract to Convair, builder of the MX-774. The new study, called MX-1593, would decide which was preferable—a ballistic or a glide-type missile. The general requirements envisioned a missile with a range of 5,000 nautical miles, capable of carrying an 8,000-pound warhead and striking within 1,500 feet of its target.

In September 1951 Convair's ballistic missile design, 160 feet long by 12 feet in diameter, was contemplated to require as many as 7 rocket engines. Meanwhile, U.S. intelligence reported that the Soviets were building a large variety of missiles and had developed an engine generating 265,000 pounds of thrust—twice as powerful as any existing American power plant.

A debate raged within the Air Force concerning what to do next. When the Atomic Energy Commission predicted that lighter warheads, weighing as little as 3,000 pounds, would be feasible, Air Research and Development Command officials argued for proceeding with full-scale development of an intercontinental ballistic missile that would be half the size of the Convair design. But Air Staff officers feared that this approach might jeopardize the ongoing development of aerodynamic missiles, the Snark and Navaho, and that claims for the ICBM were fraught with technical uncertainty. The question of a preferred approach was submitted to the Air Force Scientific Advisory Board in December 1952. A committee chaired by Dr. Clark B. Millikan concluded that it was reasonable to reduce the requirements for the ICBM to carry a 3,000-pound warhead and to relax the accuracy requirement to 1 nautical mile. Also, the committee favored a measured, incremental approach to missile development.

During the spring of 1953 a flurry of meetings among the contending Air Force factions produced a compromise position. The new ICBM remained a formidable vehicle. It would be 110 feet long by 12 feet in diameter, weigh 440,000 pounds, carry a 3,000-pound warhead to 5,500 nautical miles, and possess a 1,500-foot accuracy. The Atlas would be powered by 5 engines generating a total thrust of 656,000 pounds.

Throughout this period, missile development was ostensibly under the direction of the so-called National Guided Missiles Program. In practice, however, there was virtually no coordination among the Research and Development Board, the Munitions Board, the military services, and the Joint Chiefs of Staff. An interdepartmental coordinating group created in March 1950 did little to eliminate the waste and duplication attending missile development. Similarly, President Truman's appointment of K. T. Keller as "missiles czar" in October 1950 failed to resolve interservice disagreement.

The Air Staff itself could not agree whether missiles ought to be treated separately or integrated with aircraft. In 1945 there were separate missile offices under both the operations and materiel deputies. In the operations area, missiles were combined with air defense and then dropped altogether. From June 1952 until December 1954, missiles were integrated with aircraft under the Deputy Chief of Staff for Development (DCS/D).

The Air Force believed that integrating missiles with aircraft development was the more efficient approach because both types of vehicles used the same industrial contractors. Perhaps more important, the Air Force could thereby lay a clear claim to missile roles and missions. In May 1951 the

Air Force Council went so far as to assign aircraft designations to guided missiles. The Air Force began calling missiles "pilotless aircraft" in July 1952. Naturally, the Army challenged this position. Efforts to resolve Air Force–Army differences foundered over mutual distrust.

Ironically, while the Air Force sought to integrate missiles into its aircraft structure, it became apparent that missile development required a separate, concerted effort. Otherwise, the Army and Navy, with their heavy emphasis on missiles, would prevail in the roles and missions competition. The Air Force's position was particularly dangerous because, with the advent of the Eisenhower Administration, missiles were certain to undergo another review.

Guided missiles represented but one manifestation of a general decline in Air Force research and development since the 1947 economy drive. Curiously, Vannevar Bush, Chairman of the Research and Development Board, recommended limiting all military research and development for FY 1949 to $500 million. Dr. Bush contended that all basic research should be performed strictly by civilian agencies, such as the National Advisory Committee for Aeronautics and the National Science Foundation (NSF).

As was seen earlier, Truman's economy drive had forced a choice between augmenting forces in being and long-term research and development. Within Air Force organization, the engineering function was subordinate to the Air Materiel Command and, therefore, had little influence on policy. This neglect of R&D became apparent to General Doolittle and Dr. von Kármán and to several scientifically minded Air Staffers, including Major Generals Gordon P. Saville, Donald L. Putt, and David M. Schlatter. Doolittle and Putt helped instigate two studies of Air Force R&D organization. In late 1949 these studies, conducted by the Ridenour Committee and the Anderson Committee, arrived at similar conclusions. They recommended creation of a separate command and a new Air Staff deputate for research and development.

The Air Force adopted the recommendations of the Ridenour and Anderson Committees, and in 1950 created the Air Research and Development Command and the Deputy Chief of Staff for Development. Although their "materiel" counterparts—Air Materiel Command and the Deputy Chief of Staff for Materiel—retained control of the research and development budget, the new organizations succeeded in promoting long-term projects.

General Schlatter, as Air Staff Assistant for Atomic Energy in 1948, had proposed establishing both a separate command for weapon system development and a Deputy Chief of Staff for Development ("Development of the Air Force for Atomic Warfare," October 15, 1948). He became the first Commander of ARDC. Maj. Gen. Gordon P. Saville, the Director of Requirements, was appointed Deputy Chief of Staff for Development.

Saville absorbed into his new office both his former directorate as well as the Directorate of R&D from the Deputy Chief of Staff for Materiel.

Project MX–1593 Atlas

Following the cancellation of Project MX–774,* in July 1948, the Guided Missiles Committee of the Research and Development Board urged the Air Force to continue studying long-range rockets as an expansion of its work on artificial earth satellites. The Air Force then directed Project RAND to monitor the field and to recommend initiation when the military utility of rockets appeared feasible. This event occurred during 1950, and in December of that year RAND reported that significant advances in rocket engines and guidance systems made long-range missiles technologically feasible. Some Air Force officers, however, remained skeptical about what they labelled as RAND's "highly theoretical" conclusions and proposed to investigate long-range rockets from an engineering point of view. To that end the Air Force signed a contract on January 23, 1951, with Convair—the contractor on the MX–774. The Korean War had prompted increased military spending, so supplemental FY 1951 funds were available to support several missile projects.[1]

---

*See pages 44–50.

First Commander of the Air Research and Development Command—Maj. Gen. David M. Schlatter.

Maj. Gen. Gordon P. Saville was Deputy Chief of Staff for Development.

Designated Project MX–1593, the Convair effort involved a 2-phase study. The first phase would decide whether a ballistic rocket or a glide rocket was preferable for a long-range missile. This 6-month study cost $500,000 and required Convair to define a vehicle that could carry an 8,000-pound atomic warhead a distance of 5,000 nautical miles and strike a target with a Circular Error Probable (CEP) of 1,500 feet.* A minimum speed of Mach 6 over the target was desired. Phase I included (1) a determination of time and cost to develop both ballistic and glide rockets, (2) a configuration analysis, and (3) an assessment of problems anticipated with each type of rocket. An intense study of these problems would be performed in Phase II.[2]

Actually, the RAND reports questioned by the Air Force were not entirely theoretical. After Project MX–774 was canceled, Convair invested its own funds in missile research, including the solution of problems related to pressurized tanks, separation of the warhead (or reentry vehicle) from the missile airframe prior to reentering the atmosphere, and thrust vector steering.† Throughout this period Convair's engineers, led by Karel J. Bossart and William Patterson, lobbied the Air Force to resume sponsoring research on rockets. Moreover, while the Air Force had canceled MX–774, it had continued to support Convair's research in missile guidance. As a

---

*Circular Error Probable (CEP) is the radius of a circle within which half of all the weapons targeted for the center of that circle can be expected to land.

†Another term for gimbaling rocket engines.

result, Convair's Project Azusa, a "long base leg radio guidance system," reportedly improved existing radar guidance by a factor of two.[3]

Like Convair, North American Aviation had spent its own money for rocket engine research when funding cutbacks occurred in 1947. North American claimed to have spent $1 million and purchased the Santa Susana, California, site at which it built the nation's first high-energy engine test stand. The Air Force subsequently funded North American's LR-45 rocket engine program which produced the mechanical components leading to the safe operation of nitric acid hydrocarbons.[4]

In September 1951 Convair reported on the progress of the MX-1593 study. Now called Project Atlas,* the long-range missile could be designed either as a ballistic or glide rocket missile. The ballistic version would measure 160 feet long and 12 feet in diameter and the glide version would run 110 feet in length and 8 feet in diameter. Convair planned to use North American's 120,000-pound thrust alcohol-LOX engine, and 20,000-pound thrust engines produced by Reaction Motors Inc., in either a 7- or a 5-engine configuration. The glide rocket was expected to weigh half that of the ballistic version and be much easier and less expensive to build. Additionally, Convair's Bossart expressed concern over the ballistic rocket's anticipated problems involving warhead reentry and indicated that more study was necessary on hypersonic speeds. Finally, Convair proposed to modify the MX-1593's requirements to carry only a 7,000-pound bomb and to have a CEP of 1 mile (instead of the called-for 1,500 feet).[5]

ARDC's Brig. Gen. John W. Sessums, Jr., an ardent advocate of long-range missiles, favored the ballistic approach and so recommended to the Air Staff. Sessums noted that there had been considerable progress in thermonuclear warhead technology since Project Atlas began.† He argued that mating Atlas with the lighter-weight, more efficient bombs would be a revolutionary step. It was a development that the Air Force could not ignore. Sessums proposed a $4.5 million Fiscal Year 1952 budget aimed at solving Atlas's anticipated technical problems.[6]

Brig. Gen. Donald N. Yates, the Director of Research and Development, Office of the Deputy Chief of Staff for Development, acknowledged the necessity for solving the technical problems. But contrary to Sessums, Yates favored a slower, more systematic approach and recommended ARDC extend research and development for Atlas over a five-year period while demonstrating the technology. The demonstrations would be conducted on smaller test vehicles and would include accuracy, guidance and control, and

---

*The name Atlas, said to represent Convair's parent company, the Atlas Corporation, was approved in August 1951. [Memo, S. D. Cornell, Exec Sec GMC (RDB), to Dir/R&D, subj: Approval of the Popular Name "ATLAS" for USAF Guided Missile Project MX-1593, Aug 6, 1951.]

†The thermonuclear breakthrough and related developments are discussed in Chapter IV.

propulsion. Under this approach, Atlas would not have become operational until about 1965.[7] ARDC, fearing that this approach would be an irreparable one, on its own reprogrammed $350,000 of its FY 1952 funds to start Atlas development.[8]

Technological considerations alone did not prompt ARDC's recommendation to pursue Atlas development. Alarming intelligence reports in late 1951 and early 1952 indicated that the Soviets had developed a huge rocket engine (said to generate 265,000 pounds of thrust) and that another engine, twice as powerful, was under development.[9] Moreover, if the Soviets achieved advances in the field of air defense missiles—similar to the Air Force's Falcon, the Army's Nike, and the Navy's Terrier and Lark—U.S. manned bombers would be increasingly vulnerable in the future.[10]

During the spring of 1952 ARDC continued to press for a full-scale development effort on Atlas. General Sessums believed that, if the project were adequately funded and supported in terms of priority, it could be operational as early as 1960. He noted that Snark and Navaho—the Air Force's air-breathing strategic missiles—were consuming a large portion of the research and development budget. For $3 million in FY 1953 funds the Air Force could build an experimental Atlas rocket capable of transporting a 3,000-pound warhead a distance of 2,000 miles, or a 1,500-pound warhead over a 3,000-mile range. Citing Soviet activity in long-range ballistic missiles, Sessums argued that the Atlas would prove useful in an "emergency." In addition, he believed that the future of long-range missiles depended largely upon progress in making atomic warheads smaller and lighter.[11]

General Yates, on the other hand, claiming to have a broader perspective on matters, continued to caution against asking for full-scale development of the Atlas. He believed such a request would elicit an unfavorable reaction from the Research and Development Board's Guided Missiles Committee. Not only would the Atlas clash sharply with the Army's interest in ballistic rockets, but Yates feared that Atlas's stringent accuracy requirements would not withstand scrutiny. Finally, he asserted that the RDB would undoubtedly question the Air Force's ability to fund simultaneously both the Atlas and the extremely expensive Snark and Navaho missile developments.[12]

The Atlas issue came to the attention of the Guided Missiles Committee in May 1952, when Col. R. L. Johnson, Chief of the Weapon Systems Division of the Wright Air Development Center, briefed the committee on the latest thinking. The proposed "1952 Atlas" would carry a warhead weighing only 3,000 pounds and, significantly, would only be about half the size and cost of the 1951 design. Colonel Johnson emphasized that ballistic missiles were inherently simpler to build than the aerodynamic types, such as Snark and Navaho. Finally, ballistic missiles were considered invulnera-

Brig. Gen. John W. Sessums, Jr., pushed for accelerated development of long-range ballistic missiles.

As Director of R&D on the Air Staff, Donald N. Yates advocated a slower developmental path for the Atlas missile.

ble against any known defenses and would cost less—when measured by the number of targets destroyed—than any other weapon system. The GMC was sufficiently impressed to approve Project Atlas as "a study and/or development project." In other words, continued development would depend upon the rate of demonstrated progress.[13]

This support of Project Atlas prompted General Yates to endorse $850,000 for FY 1952 and $3 million for FY 1953. At the same time Yates asked ARDC to prepare detailed military characteristics for the Atlas and cautioned that it was still not a full-fledged prototype weapon system project, only a study and component development effort. Many problems had to be overcome involving guidance and control; high heat associated with atmospheric reentry; engine design, staging, and control; and alternate methods of airframe fabrication. More aerodynamic and performance analyses also were needed.[14]

Settling on a mutually acceptable set of military characteristics for the Atlas proved difficult. RAND's analysis indicated that Convair had been too optimistic in its accuracy expectations, achievable weights, and the amount of funding required for the project. RAND also disputed Convair's reservations about starting rocket motors in a vacuum and urged the company to devote more attention in its design to accommodating future atomic warheads. With regard to the latter issue, the Atomic Energy Commission had predicted that smaller warheads would be feasible as fissionable materials became more efficient.[15]

In August 1952 the Wright Air Development Center (WADC)* forwarded proposed Atlas missile characteristics to ARDC. In them, Atlas retained its major performance requirements: a range of 5,500 nautical miles and a CEP of 1,500 feet. But the weight of the atomic warhead was sharply reduced, from the original 8,000 to 3,000 pounds. Speed over target was raised from Mach 6 to Mach 10, an easily attainable figure in the view of scientists who expected the missile to travel at about Mach 18. Other specifications were:

Reliability —95 percent.

Guidance —Pure inertial with radio or radar super vision during powered flight; no mid-course or terminal guidance required.

Temperatures—Expected to withstand extremes between minus 65°F and plus 120°F and winds of 20 knots.

---

*During 1952 Project Atlas came under the supervision of WADC's Bombardment Missiles Branch. Lt. Col. Joseph Heck, Jr., was the project engineer.

Transport —By water, rail, air, and highway.

Readiness —100 missiles during the first 24 hours; assembly, preparation, and checkout within 2 hours.

Longevity —One year storage without maintenance; 24 hours without a recheck.

Finally, WADC requested a 1–A top-priority for the project.[16]

On October 1, 1952, ARDC forwarded the Atlas military characteristics to Headquarters USAF. In its report, the command emphasized the significant advances being made in atomic energy research which promised to produce a 3,000-pound warhead that would have the same kiloton yield and efficiency as existing atomic warheads weighing 7,000 pounds. It recommended immediate approval and top priority for Atlas.[17]

Even as elements within the Air Force anticipated the development of lighter warheads, however, Convair had not given up trying to satisfy the earlier requirements for a missile capable of carrying 7,000 pounds over 5,500 nautical miles. Project engineer Morton Rosenbaum calculated that the 7-engine Atlas design could achieve the required 143,000 pounds of thrust per engine by converting the fuel from alcohol-LOX to gasoline-LOX and by increasing the chamber pressure slightly. He also hoped to bring down the total missile weight from 670,000 to 560,000 pounds.[18]

At last, Lt. Gen. Laurence C. Craigie, Deputy Chief of Staff for Development (DCS/D), submitted the Atlas requirements to the Air Force Scientific Advisory Board for study. The SAB appointed an ad hoc committee for the task with Dr. Clark B. Millikan, head of Caltech's Guggenheim Aeronautical Laboratory,* as chairman. Meeting from December 8 to 13, 1952, the Millikan Committee reviewed the Atlas program in great detail and unanimously recommended to: †

- Retain Project Atlas.

- Relax the warhead weight requirement to 3,000 pounds and 45 inches in dimension and the accuracy to a 1-mile CEP.

- Endorse General Sessums's view that if Atlas failed to meet

---

*This was where Dr. Theodore von Kármán had made his reputation in the U.S. [See pages 39–40.] Other members of the Millikan Committee were H. W. Bode, M. V. Clauser, C. S. Draper, G. B. Kistiakowsky, G. F. Metcalf, H. J. Stewart, and M. J. Zucrow.

†The Millikan Committee met one month after the "Mike" shot at Eniwetok—the first U.S. "wet" bomb—demonstrated the feasibility of thermonuclear weapons. Although the committee must have been aware of the event, the device tested was still regarded as too large for practical application.

its 5,500-nautical mile range requirement, a lesser range would be militarily useful.

- Retain Convair as contractor. But, because it was premature to build large test vehicles, Atlas components could be tested aboard smaller vehicles, such as the Navaho or the Navy's Viking.

- Adopt a "stepwise" development approach under which all components would be fully tested prior to granting production approval.[19]

Air Research and Development Command was displeased with the recommendations of the Millikan Committee. First, the command saw no particular advantage to lowering the accuracy requirements from 1,500 feet to 1 mile; it believed that the more stringent requirement could be met. ARDC was also taken aback by the proposal to test Atlas components aboard Viking and Navaho vehicles, arguing that this approach would entail unnecessary testing and prove far more costly than developing Atlas prototype test models. While agreeing that thorough testing of all major components was desirable, the command (along with Convair) believed that Atlas could be readied by 1963, provided the Air Force set a high priority and supported the project adequately. Finally, ARDC noted that anticipated expenditures of between $15 million and $30 million per year were not out of line when compared with other system developments then under way:

> This command has always believed that the cost estimates of Convair on this program have always been low, and further, that the cost estimates on any development program are almost always underestimated by contractors in general. The cost of developing a modern supersonic weapon system is on the order of half a billion dollars or more, and it is not expected that this program is an exception. If it could be definitely stated that this program is an exception and would cost much less, we would have urged immediate adoption of a development program even more strongly than we have.[20]

To help resolve the differences between the Millikan Committee report and the Air Force, ARDC Vice Commander, Maj. Gen. Donald L. Putt, met with SAB scientists at Wright-Patterson AFB, Ohio, on February 26 and 27, 1953. Dr. Mervin J. Kelly* and his associates from Bell Laboratories, Dr. Hendrik W. Bode and Dr. Walter A. MacNair, were invited to review the Atlas program with General Putt and other Air Force officials. A major

---

*Dr. Kelly had been invited to sit on the Millikan Committee but could not participate because of other commitments. In January 1955 Kelly succeeded von Kármán as Chairman of the Scientific Advisory Board.

point of contention involved the Millikan Committee recommendation on flight-testing Atlas components aboard Navaho and Viking vehicles. Before these meetings, the Air Force had contacted the Navy's Viking Project Office and arranged for an exchange of technical data between the Atlas and Viking programs. (The Naval Research Laboratory was especially interested in Atlas's guidance system.) Dr. Kelly's group was convinced to support the Air Force's solution to the problem.

The scientists also proposed the establishment of a panel of experts in astrophysics, aircraft structures, and mathematics to meet periodically with Convair to help solve unusual problems. Acting on yet another recommendation by Dr. Kelly, Wright Air Development Center directed Convair to study the use of an inertial guidance system for Atlas, while the contractor's own Azusa guidance system was being installed at the Air Force Missile Test Center, Patrick AFB, Florida, for testing at an early date.[21]

Perhaps the most important outcome of these meetings stemmed from an ARDC proposal for Atlas flight testing. First, Convair would build a single-engine Atlas test vehicle using an alcohol-LOX engine developed under the Navaho program. In the second phase a 3-engine Atlas, also burning alcohol-LOX, would be built. The final test phase would be conducted aboard a 5-engine vehicle converted to burn gasoline-LOX; the conversion was expected to improve the thrust per engine from 120,000 to 132,000 pounds. The 5-engine configuration, generating more than 650,000 pounds of thrust, would serve as a prototype for the operational Atlas. ARDC contemplated a 10-year development program, from FY 1954 through 1963, costing about $378 million. Implicit in this plan was the sequential deployment of Snark, Navaho, and then Atlas.[22]

On March 30, 1953, Dr. Millikan reconvened his ad hoc committee at Maxwell AFB, Alabama, to revise its earlier recommendations. The Millikan Committee approved ARDC's development plan involving the one-, three-, and five-engine Atlas test vehicles (designated X–11, X–12, and XB–65, respectively). The X–11 and X–12 described rocket-powered research test vehicles, whereas the XB–65 stood for "experimental bomber." A consensus emerged among USAF leaders, the Millikan Committee, and Convair that this was an opportune time to initiate a full-scale Atlas development program. The question remained: How fast? Millikan's committee continued to favor a slow, "stepwise" approach that aimed at completing research in 1956, development in 1961, and testing in 1963.[23]

By April 1953 the optimism surrounding the Atlas—along with delays in the Snark and Navaho programs—prompted General Yates, USAF's Director of Research and Development, to request a "realistic" appraisal of Air Force strategic missiles. ARDC, the principal advocate of missiles in the Air Force, replied that there would be a definite need for both piloted and "pilotless" aircraft (that is, missiles) over the next twenty years. Col. Arthur

A. Fickel, an assistant to General Sessums, noted the long, uphill battle that ARDC had waged to gain approval for missile development: *

> Under the present administrative and budget conditions which prevail within the Air Force, it can be stated that, in [general] the large piloted bomber developments are supported by Air Materiel Command with its large budget program, while pilotless bomber developments are being financed by this Command [ARDC] under a greatly restricted budget program.

ARDC recommended completing the development of all three strategic missiles—Snark, Navaho, and Atlas.† It favored Atlas, however, because of the invulnerability of ballistic missiles once they were launched.[24]

The USAF Director of Research and Development approved ARDC's development approach "in principle," but asked for a revised plan based on a "relatively slow rate." General Yates also cautioned against proceeding on a ten-year development schedule, arguing that it was more prudent to undertake "a logical series of developments which may later permit speed up."[25]

Over the next several months ARDC and WADC revised the Atlas development plan again. When they submitted the plan in October 1953, it reflected a development budget of $269 million compared with the earlier estimate of $378 million. It was broken down as follows:

R & D Funds

Fiscal Year	$ millions
1951	.549
1952	.878
1953	3.206
1954	10.614
1955	23.719
1956–1964	230.000

Essentially, the revised plan continued to center on development of the major components—airframe, propulsion, guidance, and nose cone. It

---

* Between 1951 and 1954 the Atlas program received $26.2 million, of which $18.8 was FY 1954 funds. By comparison, Snark was allotted $226 million and Navaho $248 million. [Rockefeller, *Atlas,* p 20.]

† The ARDC–AMC power struggle was common knowledge at the top levels of the Air Force. An aide to General Doolittle reported that AMC was undermining ARDC and trying to "screw up" its programs. General Twining noted pressures applied to recombine AMC and ARDC. [Memo, Lt. Col. Peter J. Schenck, Exec to Spec Asst to CSAF, to Gen. Jimmy Doolittle, Spec Asst to CSAF, no subj, Feb 25, 1953; memo, Lt. Col. Schenck to Lt. Gen. L. C. Craigie, SAB Matters, May 22, 1953, in RG 341, Box 19, NA.]

conformed to the Millikan Committee recommendations, which required complete ground testing of the major components and the solution of all problems before proceeding with any of the flight tests; that is, the one-, three-, and five-engine Atlas vehicles. No date was set for completing research and development. Instead, planners indicated it should be finished "sometime after 1964." Program priority was reduced to 1–B, further ensuring the pursuit of the slow-paced, systematic approach. Development planners provided for operational readiness during 1965, but noted that with additional support it was possible to advance that date by two or three years.[26]

Designated Weapon System (WS)–107A, the Atlas "intercontinental ballistic rocket" would be a stainless steel, monocoque airframe (pressurized for stability) 110 feet long and 12 feet in diameter. Fully loaded— including 409,000 pounds of gasoline-LOX propellants—Atlas would weigh 440,000 pounds. It would deliver a 3,000-pound atomic warhead a distance of 5,500 nautical miles* and impact within 1,500 feet of the target. The operational version would have 4 first-stage engines, each rated at 133,200 pounds of thrust, and 1 centrally positioned, gimbaled sustainer rocket providing 123,300 pounds of thrust, for a total of 656,100 pounds. Atlas was dubbed a "1½-stage" vehicle because Convair's launch procedure called for starting all 5 engines on the ground, to avert the possibility of a failure to start the sustainer engine in the vacuum of outer space. An on-board inertial autopilot transponder-receiver and a ground-based station—which included a radio transmitter, radar tracker, and computer— would provide the required guidance.[27]

Convair engineers envisioned a full-length Atlas flight to follow this sequence: The rocket would be elevated to a vertical position on a concrete stand. After takeoff—with all 5 engines operating—the rocket would execute a programmed turn at approximately 15,000 feet altitude, placing it on a ballistic trajectory. Some 200 nautical miles downrange, the ground station would begin tracking the rocket. At 120 seconds after launch, the first-stage engines would be jettisoned. Next, the ground station would assume control of the stabilization system (as Atlas contained no aerodynamic control surfaces), while its computer analyzed the flight data and applied corrections to keep the rocket on target. At 266 seconds the sustainer engine would shut down and a pair of small thrust rocket motors (verniers) would "trim" the final velocity for the remaining 30 seconds of powered flight.

Approximately 296 seconds after launch the verniers would cut off, the nose cone would separate from the airframe, and, by a final command

---

*With a 4,500-pound payload, the rocket would travel between 3,250 and 4,250 nautical miles; with a 7,000-pound warhead, between 2,000 and 3,250 nautical miles.

from the ground, the warhead would be armed. The heat-dissipating copper heat-sink nose cone * containing the warhead then would follow an elliptical free-fall path at a velocity of approximately 23,000 feet per second. Decelerating to Mach 6, it would strike the target at a 20-degree angle to the surface. For 95 percent of the time the rocket would travel outside the earth's atmosphere, reaching a peak altitude of 525 nautical miles.[28]

Reorganizing for Missiles

No one could predict with any certainty the end products of guided missile research and development, nor how missiles would be used. Consequently, the military services could generally pursue whatever development projects they wanted and could find money for. It was understood that a missile developed by one service could be used by another if the particular missile fit the latter's "roles and missions" requirements. Thus, as noted earlier, the so-called National Guided Missiles Program became a facade for separate military efforts and abounded in waste and duplication.†

The Guided Missiles Committee of the RDB proved ineffectual in coordinating missile research and development, in part because of the partisanship of its members. Secretary of Defense Louis Johnson recognized the problem and appointed the Stuart Board to solve it. One of the board's recommendations, adopted in March 1950, was to establish GMIORG, the Guided Missiles Interdepartmental Operational Requirements Group, for the purpose of improving coordination of research, development, and procurement among the military services, the Joint Chiefs of Staff, the RDB, and the Munitions Board. (The latter performed industrial mobilization planning for guided missiles.) Air Force members of GMIORG,‡ however, regarded it suspiciously as simply another forum for the Army and Navy to combine and frustrate Air Force missile aspirations.[29]

In August 1950 John A. McCone, Undersecretary of the Air Force, complained that guided missiles were not getting sufficient attention because of the military's preoccupation with the Korean War. As a corrective measure, he proposed creation of an independent missiles office

---

* In June 1952 H. Julian Allen, of NACA's Ames Laboratory, conceived the principle that a blunt-shaped nose cone would absorb only one-half of one percent of the heat generated during atmospheric reentry. The official report, coauthored with Alfred J. Eggers, Jr., did not appear until the following spring, and the Air Force did not consider Allen's principle until 1956.

†See pages 50–56.

‡Originally the group included Maj. Gen. Gordon P. Saville (USAF), RAdm. G. B. Hall and Gen. S. R. Mickelson (USA). Their successors were Maj. Gen. Robert M. Lee (USAF), Adm. John H. Sides, and Gen. Harry M. Roper (USA) respectively. Air Force assistants were Col. Fred H. Fairchild and Col. John R. Sutherland.

to manage a crash program modeled along the lines of the Manhattan Project. Although the Air Staff did not take kindly to the reorganizational proposal, Air Force Secretary Thomas K. Finletter and the Senior Officers Board agreed to approve additional funds to accelerate missile procurement and production.[30]

In time the apparent waste and duplication besetting the National Guided Missiles Program attracted the attention of President Truman himself. Mr. Truman called on an old friend, K. T. Keller, the head of Chrysler Motors, to effect reforms. Keller was promised "wide authority" with which to accomplish the job. In October 1950 Keller formally accepted the challenge, but only on the condition that he serve as a part-time consultant. And, while Keller assumed the imposing title of Director of Guided Missiles, Office of the Secretary of Defense, he in fact maintained a small (eleven-member) staff of "fact finders." Keller permitted the military services to continue their separate administration and planning of missile programs, and viewed his primary task as getting missiles out of research and development and into operation as quickly and economically as possible.[31]

Earlier, in September 1949, the question of production facilities and materials had joined other portions of the missile program as subjects for interservice dispute. The Munitions Board proposed to begin planning the allocation of facilities and materials for missiles and sought guidance from the JCS. As they had not developed any short-term plan, and their long-term considerations were only at the "study" stage, the Joint Chiefs suggested that the Munitions Board ask the services directly for their estimates. The board then asked that the services provide lists of required missiles and components for which planning and production should be initiated. By May 1950, a mobilization plan was in draft form and the GMIORG had formulated a statement of missile requirements for the JCS. Because of some unexpected complications, however, the Air Force did not submit its components listing until July. Meanwhile, the whole matter was overtaken by events, most specifically the outbreak of the Korean War.[32]

In August 1950 the Army proposed that the Munitions Board separate guided missile production from aircraft production in its planning operations. The Army argued that the time had come for missiles to have their own production, compatible with their assigned functions. Keller, who also served as a consultant to the Munitions Board, approved the proposal in February. The decision displeased the Air Force because it distinguished between missiles and aircraft, but no action to reverse it was instituted at that time.[33]

Roswell L. Gilpatric succeeded John A. McCone as Undersecretary of the Air Force in October 1951. Because this change coincided with the Air

John A. McCone, Undersecretary of the Air Force, believed that guided missiles deserved a higher priority.

Secretary of the Air Force Thomas K. Finletter.

Force's submission of JCS Paper 1620/42,* Gilpatric postponed recommending a revision of the Munitions Board's separation of missile and aircraft production. He believed that it would be advantageous to settle the JCS issue first. Finally, in May 1952—with JCS 1620/42 no nearer to solution—Gilpatric complained to the Munitions Board. He noted that, because aircraft and missiles used the same manufacturers, the lack of coordination between the two had begun to impinge on aircraft production. He proposed to reassign missile production to the Aircraft Committee and to the Aircraft Production Resources Agency.[34]

The issue dragged on unresolved for months with K. T. Keller and his deputy, Army Maj. Gen. K. D. Nichols, opposed to the Air Force's proposal. Preoccupied with guided missile operational assignments, the JCS elected not to comment. In November 1952, the Munitions Board took the position that, since guided missiles were nearing but had not yet reached the mass production stage, and since guided missile research and development was being handled adequately by the RDB, the Munitions Board could table Gilpatric's recommendation for six months without any adverse results.[35]

The creation of Keller's office in October 1950 had prompted changes in the Air Staff's organization for missiles. At the end of World War II, guided missile research and development responsibilities resided in the Special Weapons Section of the Assistant Chief of Air Staff. Renamed the Guided Missiles Branch in November 1945, the unit continued under the successor Deputy Chief of Staff, Materiel until January 1950, when it was transferred to the newly created Deputy Chief of Staff for Development.

Almost concurrently with Keller's appointment to the Office of the Secretary of Defense, the Air Force Deputy Chief of Staff for Development established an office of the Assistant for Guided Missiles in December 1950. The appointee, Brig. Gen. Pearl H. Robey, headed this office until May 1951, when he left to join Keller's staff as Deputy for Production.

Meanwhile, the Guided Missiles Branch continued to function until June 1952, when there was an organizational realignment in the Directorate of Research and Development. At that time, the guided missile duties were divided into air defense, tactical, and strategic categories and placed alongside their piloted aircraft counterparts. The Deputy Chief of Staff for Development did not regain its separate and distinct guided missiles office to oversee research and development until December 1954.[36]

In August 1945 the Office of Guided Missiles,† under the Assistant Chief of Air Staff for Operations, Commitments and Requirements, was redesignated the Guided Missiles Division, with responsibility for "establishing military characteristics and computing quantitative requirements."[37] The

---

* See page 86.
† See page 17.

division continued unchanged until January 1947, when it was combined with the unit overseeing the antiaircraft requirements function to form the Guided Missiles and Air Defense Division.

In October, however, the Assistant Chief of Air Staff for Operations, Commitments and Requirements became the Deputy Chief of Staff, Operations. The Guided Missiles Group was established with subordinate missile and air defense divisions. In July 1948 the Air Defense Division was transferred to the Directorate of Plans and Operations. The Guided Missiles Group continued until July 1, 1949, when it was redesignated as the Office of the Assistant for Guided Missiles. The latter was abolished in December and its functions were distributed among several Deputy Chief of Staff, Operations offices. Development of guided missile policy and objectives, however, was assigned to the newly established Special Weapons Team of the War Plans Division, Directorate of Plans and Operations.[38]

Although authorized only a small staff, the Special Weapons Team soon acquired numerous responsibilities, including guided missile programming, budgeting, operating concepts, and monitoring missile activities. In addition, the Special Weapons Team was assigned coordination of chemical, biological, and radiological (CBR) weapons. In April 1952 the Office of Assistant Deputy Chief of Staff, Operations (Guided Missiles) was created to ease the team's heavy workload. The new office coordinated guided missile activities within the Deputy Chief of Staff, Operations and with other Air Staff agencies. Intended only as a temporary office without operational responsibilities, the Assistant Deputy Chief of Staff, Operations (Guided Missiles) lasted until February 1954, despite its own chief's recommendations to phase out the office earlier.[39]

Roles and Missions Controversy

Ironically, even as the Air Force attempted to integrate guided missiles into its aircraft structure, it faced the need to centralize guided missile activities. The primary impetus for strengthening its missile organization was the challenge that the Army and Navy posed to Air Force missions, as exemplified by the usual two-to-one votes of the JCS, RDB, GMIORG, and the Munitions Board during missile deliberations. While the Army and Navy devoted large staffs to administer their missile programs, the Air Force effort seemed fragmented and badly undermanned. Another reason to improve representation was the need to educate both headquarters and field commands about Air Force objectives and the status of its missiles. An illustrative example of this lack of knowledge occurred in January 1952, when the Air Force narrowly avoided the "disaster" of losing the mission to the Army. Maj. Gen. Robert M. Lee, Director of Plans, had to prevail upon

The Air Force's Matador short-range missile.

Secretary of the Air Force Finletter not to cancel the Matador short-range (200–500 miles) missile, because the Army was certain to claim it or the close air support mission as a consequence.[40]

On May 14, 1951, the Air Force Council recommended assigning aircraft designations to guided missiles, corresponding to the functions that the missiles would perform. The Chief of Staff agreed and provisions were also included to make the missiles "integral parts of the major combat forces." Thus, for instance, the Matador surface-to-surface missile was later designated as the B-61 bomber, and a wing of Matadors was included among the total number of Air Force wings.[41]

By August 1951 USAF guided missiles bore designations for bombers, fighters, and experimental vehicles: [42]

Matador	XB-61
Snark	XB-62
Rascal	XB-63
Navaho	XB-64
Atlas	XB-65
Falcon	XF-98
Bomarc	XF-99
Ramjet Research Test Vehicle (MX-883)	X-7
Aerobee High Altitude Research Vehicle	X-8
Shrike Research Test Vehicle	X-9
RTV-A-5 Atlas Test Vehicle	X-10

During the summer of 1951, Gen. Robert M. Lee directed his Special Weapons Team to clarify service responsibilities for guided missiles as well as related problems in the atomic energy field. The directive coincided with the preparation of the GMIORG's second annual report and resulted in JCS Paper 1620/42,* dated October 29, 1951, which evolved as the official Air Force position on guided missiles.[43]

By this time, the Air Force noted, many of the past uncertainties regarding guided missiles had been overcome. Parallel developments could be identified more readily and operational programs formulated. Several of the Army and Navy guided missile programs seemed to the Air Force to represent violations of assigned roles and missions, with significant wasteful overlap and duplication. The Air Force built its roles and missions case on legal provisions, specifically the National Security Act of 1947, as amended, and JCS Memorandum 1478/23, "Functions of the Armed Forces and the Joint Chiefs of Staff," April 21, 1948. These documents, the service argued, prescribed responsibilities for guided missile research based on assigned

* See page 86.

missions, not on missions that a service anticipated receiving. Testing and operational programs conformed to the same guidance. (For a list of specific missiles under development by the services, see Chart 3-1.)

The Air Force also believed that the post–World War II categorization of guided missiles into four segments had been a mistake. These categories (air-to-air, surface-to-air, air-to-surface, and surface-to-surface) created considerable confusion because they described missiles that might be used by several services in carrying out their assigned missions. Instead, the Air Force proposed two new designations: robot aircraft and guided rockets. Under these categories, the Air Force and the Navy would have primary interest in robot aircraft, whereas all three military services could employ guided rockets.[44]

Specifically, Air Force interest centered on the air defense of the United States and "other land areas," one of its primary responsibilities. The Air Force sought to have air defense missiles assigned first priority for national defense, rather than to place in first priority some other weapon on the basis of promised early performance. To that end, air defense required centralized control of "all maneuverable weapons," including robot aircraft and guided rockets. According to this proposal (JCS Paper 1620/42), the Army would retain responsibility for artillery (called "predicted fire weapons"), and the Navy would assume responsibility for the air defense of naval forces at sea. Moreover, the Air Force recommended limiting the range of Army rockets to a depth of 75 miles to the front and rear of a combat line.[45]

The Air Force also pointed out the potential for conflict in the aircraft industry because of that industry's involvement with guided missiles. Competition between aircraft and missiles seemed certain with regard to the development and production of airframes, jet propulsion, instrumentation, and electronics. Because the Air Force considered the problem critical, it proposed the application of two controls. First, the Air Force offered to act as the sole procurement agent for itself and the Army in the aircraft industry. Second, in the field of atomic energy, the Air Force advanced the idea of basing the design of atomic warheads on target requirements, thereby ensuring for itself an adequate supply for strategic operations.[46]

In November 1951 the Army countered with its own proposals in the form of JCS Paper 1620/44. Briefly, the Army argued that any missile launched from the ground should be the responsibility of the Army. The contest was joined, and over the next two years the Air Force and Army clung adamantly to their stated positions.[47]*

If Air Force apprehensions regarding the Army's encroachment on

---

*GMIORG's 1951 annual report was never published, and the 1952 report was not issued until May 1953. The latter contained so many qualifications that its usefulness became questionable. The Air Force and Army did not withdraw their memoranda until September 14, 1954.

Chart 3–1

National Guided Missile Program
June 30, 1953

Air Force	Army	Navy
Snark (R&D)	Nike	D–40
Navaho (R&D)[a]	Hawk	Gorgon V
Falcon (Flt Test)	Corporal	Meteor I & II
Matador (Flt Test)	Lacrosse	Sparrow I, II, III
Rascal (R&D)[b]	Hermes	Sidewinder
Bomarc (Flt Test)	Redstone	Oriole
Crossbow (R&D)	Honest John[c]	Terrier I & II
Atlas (R&D)		Talos
Wizard (Design)		Petral
		Omar
		Regulus
		Triton

[a] Navaho designs explored both air-launched and surface-launched versions.
[b] An outgrowth of the Shrike.
[c] A 762-mm heavy unguided rocket.

Source: Chart, USAF Guided Missiles, ca Jun 53, RG 340, File 557–50, Vol 5, NA; Draft brief, Col J. R. Sutherland, Dep Asst DCS/0 (GM) to Gen Partridge, CG ARDC, Jul 53, in OSAF Files.

USAF roles and missions verged on paranoia, there were several strong justifications for that attitude. For example, after one GMIORG meeting in October 1951, an Air Force Special Weapons Team member inadvertently discovered a note passed from the Army to the Navy representative, both flag rank officers. The note read, "They [the Air Force] are fighting for their existence. If they lose that they will be another Transportation Corps in 15 or 20 years." [48]

Secretary Finletter, in May 1952, wrote to the Chairman of the RDB that the Army was attempting to seize Air Force roles and missions by gaining responsibility for all types of missiles. The Secretary underscored the Air Force position that guided missiles complemented aircraft in both air defensive and offensive operations; it, therefore, deserved to have dominant control in the missile field. Finletter added that the Army's attack on the Air Force coincided with a clamor in the press "promulgating the partition of the USAF." [49]

The Air Force strategy of retaining dominant control over guided missiles through the expedient of calling them "robot aircraft" and "pilotless aircraft" did not pass unchallenged. At a JCS meeting in July 1952, Gen. Omar N. Bradley (USA), the Chairman, and Gen. J. Lawton Collins, the Army Chief of Staff, demanded the removal of these designations before they would even discuss guided missiles. The Air Force Vice Chief of Staff, Gen. Nathan F. Twining, agreed to the demand temporarily, but only if the JCS would attempt to settle the missile issue. [50]

Meanwhile, the Army's Deputy Chief of Staff for Plans and Research and the Air Force's Deputy Chief of Staff for Operations—Lt. Gen. Charles L. Bolte and Lt. Gen. Thomas D. White respectively—agreed to attempt to resolve Army–Air Force differences peaceably. During June and July 1952 they adopted the following principles: [51]

- Neither service would seek to modify the other's roles and missions.
- The terms "tactical" and "strategic" would not connote any specific ranges or distances.
- Surface-to-air weapons which supported or extended either artillery or antiaircraft weapons were the Army's responsibility. Their employment, however, rested with the Air Force in conformity with established policies governing use of antiaircraft artillery.
- Missiles which supported or replaced fighter interceptors, that is aircraft, were Air Force responsibility.
- Battlefield isolation and interdiction of movement were Air Force functions.

In addition, the Air Force would not oppose Army development of missiles for low-altitude surface-to-air interception, and both services would consider withdrawing JCS Papers 1620/42 and 1620/44. Finally, the services appointed a four-member ad hoc committee, which comprised two Army and two Air Force officers, to continue the dialogue and to seek a solution to the interservice dispute. The members of the committee were all officers enrolled in advanced military schools. It was hoped that they would be more objective than staff officers and would be "guided by the fundamental principle of promoting the national interest" above parochial service concerns.[52]

The ad hoc committee submitted its report in August 1952. It began with a condemnation of JCS Memoranda 1620/42 and /44 as representing "basic differences and extreme divergencies of view."[53] The committee reasoned that these views could not be resolved; at best they could be compromised. After consulting with some 20 Defense Department agencies, the committee concluded that air-launched missiles, both air-to-air and air-to-surface types, clearly belonged to the Air Force. Thus, only the other two categories, surface-to-air and surface-to-surface, had "no clear line of demarcation."

The committee recommended that the Army hold primary responsibility for close support missiles. Although range would not be limited, these surface-to-surface missiles would include only those types that were coordinated with conventional antiaircraft artillery and integrated with the fire and movement of supported ground forces. Next, the Air Force was conceded to have primary responsibility for air defense. This decision would not preclude the Army from using surface-to-air missiles to protect its units from air attack. Finally, the committee acknowledged the Air Force's interest in, and responsibility for, interdiction and strategic operations.[54]

The Army General Staff, however, apparently displeased by the findings of the ad hoc committee, reneged on its promise to resolve Army–Air Force differences peaceably. Instead, the Army issued another proposal governing missile roles and missions. This version proposed to assign to the Army the air defense of the United States, as well as all surface-to-surface missiles for "general support required for defeat of enemy land forces." Predictably, the Air Staff rejected the latest Army proposal and insisted on applying the ad hoc committee report as the basis for resolving Army–Air Force differences.[55]

The notion that pilotless aircraft and guided rockets constituted merely other types of weapon systems that complemented aircraft was instituted as official Air Force policy in September 1952. Air Force Letter 136–3 viewed guided missiles as unproven weapons that would someday demonstrate their "effectiveness and reliability" and thereby become integrated with other aircraft into Air Force combat units. This official view was

John R. Sutherland. As a colonel, he argued against giving missiles any special status.

written and articulated by Col. John R. Sutherland, Deputy Assistant Chief of Staff for Operations, Guided Missiles. Sutherland pointed out that since 1946, when Operation Crossroads had demonstrated the utility of atomic weapons in tactical warfare, the Army had decided to combine atomic energy with guided missiles as a means of ensuring its continued role as the "mainstay of U.S. forces." Similarly, the Navy had sought to perpetuate its strategic role by developing guided missiles in the 2,000-mile range and by using the necessity for antisubmarine operations as its rationale.[56]

Sutherland argued that, at the end of World War II, missiles had been held in awe and regarded as something unique that required special handling. Since then, he said, the Air Force had come to recognize that guided missiles were simply another type of aircraft and designated them as such. "Push button war," Sutherland contended, would not be achieved for many more years. He believed that the time had come to break down the needless segregation between aircraft and missiles in the Air Force.[57]

Lt. Gen. Earle E. Partridge, ARDC's Commander, however, blasted Air Force Letter 136-3, especially the conclusion that missiles were not revolutionary weapons. He asked how anyone could not consider a weapon revolutionary that promised to transport hydrogen bombs over a distance of more than 5,000 miles. Partridge was convinced that the Air Force should recognize the fundamental changes that missiles were about to produce. Rather than integrating missiles within the Air Force organizational structure, Partridge called for entirely new assumptions requiring "a realignment of our thinking." Failure to recognize this truth, he warned, might produce two divergent schools of thought within the Air Force. "One of these schools will be small but vigorous and will insist that the job can be done by the guided missile. The other group, representing the old fogies, will continue to insist that we adhere to the tried and proven aircraft." Partridge cited as evidence past military splits that had separated flying and seaborne elements in the Navy and ground and air elements in the Army.[58] Lt. Gen. Thomas D. White, the Deputy Chief of Staff for Operations, did not revise Letter 136–3, possibly because he regarded as overriding the threats to Air Force roles and missions posed by the Army and Navy. White informed Partridge, "I tore up reply to you. You have some very cogent points."[59]

As of mid-1953 the roles and missions controversy still remained unresolved. The Army continued to claim that all missiles launched from the ground belonged in its province, as they were merely extensions of artillery. The Navy, intent on maintaining its roles and missions, pursued a large number of missile projects in various areas. For its part, the Air Force firmly believed that the Army and Navy were bent on capturing Air Force roles and missions. Everywhere, it seemed, there was evidence of a conspiracy.

For example, procurement of long lead-time equipment for the Matador apparently was delayed unnecessarily. Approval for the procure-

ARDC Commander Lt. Gen. Earle E. Partridge was convinced that missiles were revolutionary weapons.

ment of Matador equipment went from the Air Force to Keller at the Office of the Secretary of Defense. He forwarded the request to the Joint Chiefs, who would next send it to the GMIORG for comment and recommendation. In the case of the Matador, the process took about eight months and, even then, remained in abeyance until Keller was satisfied with development progress. The Air Force was extremely critical of Keller's appointment, particularly because of what it considered was his close association with the Army Ordnance Department. Also, because Keller devoted only part of his time to his position as Director of Guided Missiles, his deputy, Army Maj. Gen. K. D. Nichols, exerted undue influence. In fact General Nichols occupied a string of critical positions related to missiles. He was the Army's Director of Guided Missiles, a member of the RDB's Guided Missiles Committee, a member of the Military Liaison Committee, ex-officio member on the GMIORG, and served with the Armed Forces Special Weapons Program and the Atomic Energy Commission. Small wonder, then, that the Army and Navy outvoted the Air Force on most missile issues.[60]

With the inauguration of the Eisenhower Administration, guided missiles were about to undergo significant change. Keller, citing the "advanced state of missile development," recommended the dissolution of his Office of Director of Guided Missiles. (This was done in September 1953.) Earlier in June 1953, Secretary of Defense Charles E. Wilson appointed Air Force Secretary Harold E. Talbott to conduct a thorough review of the guided missile programs.[61]

Chapter IV

A Radical Reorganization

The mission of the von Neumann Committee was to assist the Air Force in weighing the difficulties presented by the ICBM, to invent scientific shortcuts and solutions, and to come up with a practical set of specifications designed to give us the weapon system we need in the shortest possible time.

* * *

What bothered the scientists was that in peacetime the cumbersome time-consuming machinery of government could not be streamlined to permit the swift mobilization of the necessary resources. As a result, the committee's most urgent recommendations were focused upon how to organize the effort.

Trevor Gardner, May 1956

As expected, the Eisenhower Administration conducted a thorough review of government organization, including the conduct of defense research and development. The Research and Development Board and the Munitions Board were replaced by assistant secretaries of defense. Because fiscal restraint would be one of the hallmarks of the new administration, all programs suspected of contributing to waste and duplication were carefully examined. The Air Force was directed to analyze and review missiles organization, and Trevor Gardner, Special Assistant for Research and Development, was assigned the task. Gardner set aside roles and missions controversies and concerned himself strictly with missile performance. His goals were to pursue promising technologies, eliminate waste, and standardize missile production. With regard to the long-range missiles, Gardner in October 1953 appointed a select committee of scientists and engineers, called the Teapot Committee, and chaired by the renowned Dr. John von Neumann. Among the eleven members of this committee were Simon Ramo

93

and Dean Wooldridge, who later became the systems engineers of the ICBM program. Brig. Gen. Bernard Schriever, the future program director, served as the military representative.

A year earlier, in November 1952, the United States had achieved a breakthrough in thermonuclear research which pointed the way to lighter, more powerful warheads. Nuclear weapons weighing between 1,500 and 3,000 pounds now seemed feasible. In practical terms, this breakthrough meant that Convair's Atlas ICBM, contemplated to weigh 440,000 pounds, could be reduced in weight by almost 50 percent, and the missile would not require extreme accuracy.

In its February 1954 report, the Teapot Committee noted that the Soviets had successfully tested a hydrogen bomb in August 1953 and were reported ahead in the development of long-range ballistic missiles. Consequently, the Teapot Committee recommended a "crash project" be undertaken, transcending Convair's capability. An operational ICBM could be built within eight years, provided that the project was assigned overriding priority, central authority, and adequate funding. Gardner strongly supported these findings with Air Force Secretary Harold Talbott. On March 1, 1954, nuclear tests under Operation Castle confirmed the feasibility of lighter, higher-yield weapons and helped Gardner persuade Secretary Talbott and Chief of Staff Nathan Twining to increase the ICBM budget for FY 1955 from $20 million to $50 million. The Air Force Council, under General White's leadership, supported assigning the Atlas top priority.

As an outgrowth of the Teapot Report, Brig. Gen. Bernard Schriever was selected to head the development of the Atlas. His field office, the Western Development Division, was near Los Angeles, California. To ensure his access to the top Air Force leadership, General Schriever also became an assistant to the Commander of ARDC. Early in his tenure, Schriever devised an arrangement with Air Materiel Command whereby it collocated a contracting office with WDD. The Ramo-Wooldridge Corporation was hired to provide systems engineering and technical direction of the entire program. This represented a departure from the "single prime" contractor approach practiced for aircraft development. As a further effort to centralize the program, Dr. von Neumann was appointed Chairman of the Atlas Scientific Advisory Committee, a body of scientific experts which would dispense advice on the ICBM to WDD, the Air Force, and the Department of Defense.

The new approach to developing the ICBM met with considerable resistance from Convair and the aeronautical industry, but Schriever and the Air Force were able to justify their management structure. WDD also explored the possibility of an alternate ICBM and initiated studies of a tactical ballistic missile that later emerged as an intermediate range ballistic missile. Meanwhile, Atomic Energy Commission laboratories confirmed the feasibility of developing a 1-megaton warhead weighing 1,500 pounds. This factor permitted WDD to discard the heavy Atlas design for a new 3-engine version, weighing 240,000 pounds. Thus, by the end of 1954 the Air Force was poised to proceed. The management team recommended by the Teapot Committee was in place, Convair was about to sign on as the airframe contractor for a new Atlas design, and an alternate ICBM and an IRBM were in the works. In 1955 these plans would be translated into hardware.

The New Look

The inauguration of Dwight D. Eisenhower on January 20, 1953—the first Republican President in twenty years—inevitably led to a thorough review of government organization. The Defense Department study committee, headed by Nelson A. Rockefeller and including Gen. Omar N. Bradley, Vannevar Bush, Milton S. Eisenhower, Arthur S. Flemming, Robert A. Lovett, and David Sarnoff, addressed the problem of strengthening research and development, as mandated by the National Security Act. In its April 11 report, the Rockefeller Committee recommended abolishing the Munitions Board and the Research and Development Board—because of the rigidity and complexity "inherent in the board-type structure"—and transferring their functions to the assistant secretaries of defense for research and development, applications engineering, and supply and logistics. President Eisenhower submitted these recommendations to Congress, and on June 30 they became effective as Department of Defense Reorganization Plan No. 6.[1]

Also in June 1953, shortly after the Air Force Scientific Advisory Board had reviewed the Atlas program, Charles E. Wilson—the economy-minded new Secretary of Defense—directed Air Force Secretary Harold E. Talbott to form a committee and conduct a comparative analysis of all military guided missiles. The objective of this study was to eliminate unwarranted duplication.* In turn, Talbott directed his Special Assistant for Research and Development, Trevor Gardner, to head the committee and undertake the study.[2]

Only 37 years old, Gardner nevertheless had broad experience in engineering and industrial management. During World War II he was head of development engineering on the Office of Scientific Research and Development's rocket and atomic bomb projects at the California Institute

---

* DOD obligations for IRBMs and ICBMs for FY 1954 rose to $14 million from $3 million the previous year, whereas other surface-to-surface missile budgets dropped from $403 to $336 million. All remaining missiles dropped from $760 to $717 million, and the total reduction equalled about $100 million.

Harold E. Talbott (left) is sworn in as Secretary of the Air Force in a White House ceremony in February 1943. President Eisenhower (center) looks on as the oath is administered by Frank K. Sanderson.

of Technology. After the war Gardner had joined the General Tire and Rubber Company* of California as General Manager and Executive Vice President. And in 1948 he formed and became President of Hycon Manufacturing Company, an electronics firm in Pasadena, California. According to General Doolittle, Trevor Gardner was a "sparkplug," an active individual who did "a tremendous job in expediting the development of the missile, in directing funds and brainpower into the missile program." Also described as "sharp, abrupt, irascible, cold, unpleasant, and a bastard," Gardner did not endear himself to senior Air Force officers, who were unaccustomed to taking orders from young, upstart civilians.[3]

The new Special Assistant immediately assembled a joint services committee to evaluate all military guided missile projects. In a departure from past practices, the Gardner Committee chose not to grapple with the difficult roles and missions issues but addressed only performance considerations. The committee met throughout the summer and fall of 1953 before

---

*General Tire and Rubber had bought out Aerojet General, the company that Dr. Theodore von Kármán and Frank Malina founded to build rocket engines.

96

drafting its report. Its recommendations were couched in broad terms, seemingly to avoid controversy: no promising missile project should be abandoned; unwarranted duplication should be eliminated; and, where practical, missiles should be standardized for production and use by all of the military services.[4]

Acting on the committee's advice, Secretary of Defense Wilson, in November, superseded all of the existing missile procurement procedures that had required approval by the OSD Director of Guided Missiles. (That office had become defunct with the departure of K. T. Keller in September.) Instead, Wilson authorized the service secretaries to approve their own missile programs after coordination with the newly established assistant secretaries of defense. Donald A. Quarles, Assistant Secretary of Defense for Research and Development, was impressed with the work of the Gardner Committee and incorporated the group under his office as the Coordinating Committee on Guided Missiles.[5]

While he fully supported Wilson's economy objectives, Trevor Gardner soon concluded that a growing communist threat overshadowed the need for fiscal restraint. That threat stemmed from several sources, including the Korean War; intelligence reports pointing to a Soviet lead in long-range missile development; and the announcement, in August 1953, that the Russians had tested a hydrogen device.[6]

Trevor Gardner, the young, energetic Special Assistant for Research and Development.

Earlier, on November 1, 1952, the United States had achieved a momentous breakthrough* when the first experimental hydrogen fusion device was detonated at Eniwetok.[7] Designated shot "Mike" of the Ivy nuclear weapon test series, the device was far too large for practical military application, but it overcame a major limitation to the development of intercontinental ballistic missiles. Before this achievement, a lighter warhead implied an unacceptably low yield. This limitation, in turn, imposed almost unattainable accuracy requirements on missile guidance. The promise of lighter—but more powerful—warheads meant that less accurate missiles could now be designed.

The thermonuclear breakthrough generated considerable excitement among a small group of Air Force personnel who shared the secret knowledge of the event. Retired Lt. Gen. James H. Doolittle, serving as a special assistant to Chief of Staff Hoyt S. Vandenberg, recommended the creation of a nuclear weapons panel on the Air Force Scientific Advisory Board. This panel was established in March 1953, with Dr. John von Neumann, a renowned mathematician and head of the Institute for Advanced Study at Princeton, New Jersey, as Chairman.[8]

Meeting in June at Los Alamos, New Mexico, the panel discussed the development of nuclear weapons for intercontinental ballistic missiles. The new bombs were expected to weigh approximately 3,000 pounds, measure 45 inches in diameter, and yield 0.5 megatons.[9] In September the Air Force Special Weapons Center confirmed the feasibility of producing nuclear warheads weighing as little as 1,500 pounds with no appreciable loss in explosive yield. As the gross weight of the missile was nearly in direct proportion to the warhead weight, missile design depended primarily on the warhead selected. In practical terms, these projections indicated that the weight of the Atlas ICBM might be cut almost in half—from 440,000 to 240,000 pounds—and that the missile would require considerably less thrust than previously anticipated.[10]

The new findings clearly pointed toward yet another review of the Atlas program. In October 1953, Trevor Gardner† established a second committee and directed that it study only strategic missiles—Snark, Navaho, and Atlas—all belonging to the Air Force. Gardner recruited eleven leading scientists and engineers to participate in the Strategic Missiles Evaluation Group, also known as the Teapot Committee. Dr. von Neumann served as Chairman, and the Ramo-Wooldridge Corporation was con-

---

*In 1950 President Truman ordered the development of large-yield thermonuclear weapons. The first positive sign came in May 1951 when the Atomic Energy Commission conducted a small-scale test (Greenhouse series, shot "George"). It indicated the possibility of fusion, or the joining of hydrogen atoms.

†Although called a special assistant, Gardner occupied a position comparable to an assistant secretary. In 1955 it became a statutory position. See page 133.

tracted to administer the work of the committee. The founders and chief officers of Ramo-Wooldridge, Simon Ramo and Dean Wooldridge, were also full members of the Teapot Committee.

A graduate of the California Institute of Technology, Simon Ramo had known Trevor Gardner since before World War II, when both had worked for General Electric at Schenectady, New York. After the war, Ramo joined Hughes Aircraft as head of electronics research. At Hughes, Ramo rose to the position of Director of Guided Missile Research and Development, and he and Dean Wooldridge gained acclaim for their work on the Falcon missile. Ramo had become Director of Operations and Executive Vice President when he and Wooldridge, in September 1953, left Hughes to form their own company.

Other members of the Teapot Committee were Clark B. Millikan, Charles C. Lauritsen, and Louis G. Dunn (all of Caltech); Hendrik W. Bode (Bell Telephone Laboratories); Allen E. Puckett (Hughes Aircraft); George B. Kistiakowski (Harvard); Jerome B. Wiesner (Massachusetts Institute of Technology); and Lawrence A. Hyland (Bendix Aviation). Col. Bernard A. Schriever, the Assistant for Development Planning, Office of the Deputy Chief of Staff for Development and a brigadier general selectee, served as the committee's military representative.[11]

Meeting first in November and twice more afterward, the Teapot Committee rendered its report on February 10, 1954. It initially had favored eliminating the Snark, but in its report the committee recommended only that Snark's guidance system be simplified and that development continue. Members contended that Snark's primary usefulness was as a decoy for the manned bomber force. Similarly, the Teapot Committee was not enthusiastic about the Navaho as a strategic weapon because of the inadequacies of ramjets. Nonetheless, the committee supported continued research in certain technological areas, especially propulsion systems, where the Navaho project would provide direct benefit for ICBM * development.[12]

The Teapot Committee centered its attention on the feasibility of developing the major subsystems for the Atlas—propulsion, guidance, airframe, and warhead. Given the reported Soviet lead in ICBMs and the advantage offered by the American nuclear breakthrough, the committee believed that it was essential to accelerate Atlas development. But early delivery of the Atlas could be accomplished only on a crash basis that would include modification of the missile's specifications and creation of a new management organization. In summary, the committee called for a "radical reorganization of the . . . project considerably transcending the Convair framework."[13]

---

* The original acronym IBMS (intercontinental ballistic missile system) conflicted with that of the International Business Machines (IBM) Corporation. At that time only Atlas qualified as an IBMS.

Retired Lt. Gen. James H. Doolittle. As General Vandenberg's Special Assistant, he recommended forming a nuclear weapons panel on the Air Force's Scientific Advisory Board.

Simon Ramo, member of the Teapot Committee and a chief officer of the Ramo-Wooldridge Corporation.

Head of the nuclear weapons panel and later Chairman of the Teapot Committee—Dr. John von Neumann.

Change of leadership. Gen. Hoyt S. Vandenberg (right) succeeded Gen. Carl A. Spaatz (left) as Air Force Chief of Staff in July 1948. Secretary of the Air Force W. Stuart Symington (center) congratulated both leaders.

Foremost among the committee's recommendations to accelerate the Atlas program was the call to revise requirements in conformity with the new realities created as a result of the thermonuclear achievements. The promise of lighter, higher-yield nuclear warheads was later confirmed during the test series Castle on March 1, 1954. As a result, the stringent 1,500-foot accuracy requirement for Atlas could be reduced to between 2 and 3 nautical miles. This revision would also permit slashing the missile's weight and diameter. As a further benefit, the lower accuracy requirement eased the guidance problem and thereby prompted the Teapot Committee to urge study of an on-board, all-inertial guidance system. Finally, technological progress with respect to the reentry problem led the committee to recommend discarding the Mach 6 speed over target requirement.[14]

The committee of missile experts also questioned Convair's ability to complete the Atlas work, based on its current development approach and the competence of its scientific and engineering talent. Teapot members further recommended that the Air Force undertake a thorough review of up to a year, if required, to determine how best to achieve the earliest possible operational capability. Pending such a review, the Air Force should curtail all production of full-scale flight test vehicles and detailed design of the guidance system. On the other hand, the committee members encouraged continuing basic research in guidance systems, North American's rocket propulsion work, and preparation of instrument flight test facilities.[15]

Acceleration of the Atlas program, according to the Teapot Committee, could succeed only if entrusted to "an unusually competent group of scientists and engineers capable of making systems analyses, supervising the research phases and completely controlling the experimental and hardware phases of the program." Unfortunately, no single industrial company currently employed persons of this caliber; they would have to be recruited from among several industry, university, and government organizations. Looking ahead, the committee also noted that this proposed new development-management group would have to be free "of excessive detailed regulation by existing government agencies."[16] The Teapot Committee concluded that, if given this crash basis priority, the Air Force could obtain an operational Atlas in six to eight years—that is, between 1960 and 1962.

The Teapot recommendations nearly duplicated those of a Rand Corporation study issued two days earlier, on February 8. The Rand study, headed by Dr. Bruno W. Augenstein, had begun in September 1953 for the purpose of finding ways to accelerate ICBM development. Not surprisingly, then, the Teapot Committee used and based much of its findings on Rand data. Rand also concluded that Atlas development could be accelerated further by designing a 1,500-pound warhead, enlarging the accuracy requirement to 3 miles, and easing the missile's skin cooling characteristics by lowering the speed over the target from Mach 6 to Mach 1. In connection with these studies, Trevor Gardner advised Assistant Secretary Quarles that an emergency operational capability could be attained as early as 1958 if enough money and priority were provided. Gardner meant that, in an emergency, contractor engineers would be able to launch the Atlas in lieu of trained Air Force personnel. This was facetiously called a "Ph.D. type capability." [17]

As an early alternative to Atlas, Rand proposed building a "psychological warfare type" weapon such as the three-engined X-12 flight test vehicle then undergoing study as part of the Atlas program. Still another alternative was to build a missile considerably smaller than the Atlas. But these alternatives held no attraction for the Air Research and Development Command, either in terms of cost or time. [18]

Earlier, in October 1952, in anticipation of the "Mike" thermonuclear test, ARDC had recommended* a 3,000-pound warhead weight requirement for the Atlas. [19] Ironically, in September 1953, when the feasibility of a 1,500-pound nuclear warhead emerged, the command opposed adapting it to the Atlas. The reasoning behind this position was that smaller warheads would result in scaling down the missile's size and, therefore, result in the development of smaller rocket engines with only 30,000 to 75,000 pounds of thrust. ARDC officials predicted that it would take as long to develop the smaller engines as those currently being built for the existing Atlas design. ARDC also considered unacceptable for the Atlas the 0.5 megaton yield of the projected 1,500-pound warheads. In February 1954, after the Teapot Committee issued its report, the research and development command stated a requirement for both the 3,000- and 1,500-pound bombs, but it was careful to obtain assurance from Air Force Headquarters "of the practicality of developing the desired warheads, so that the warhead-vehicle combination will be practicable and optimum." [20]

The Air Force Accelerates

Trevor Gardner had been instrumental in establishing radar listening posts in Turkey from which the United States gathered intelligence on Soviet missile launchings. (Subsequently, U-2 aircraft reconnaissance flights over the Soviet Union convinced Air Force leaders of the Russians' progress in

---

*Throughout 1952 and 1953 there were no definite nuclear warhead requirements for Atlas. In fairness to Convair, it must be noted that atomic energy information was tightly guarded. Thus, in December 1953 Trevor Gardner appealed to the Air Staff to provide contractors working on strategic missiles—North American, Northrop, and Convair—access to the SAB's June 1953 "Report of the Panel on Nuclear Weapons." [Memo, Gardner to Gens Cook and Craigie, no subj, Dec 9, 1953, in RG 340, 471.6, 557-50, Vol 6, NA.]

ICBMs.) Gardner believed that the acceleration of Atlas, like the World War II atomic bomb project, was critical. Even before the Teapot report was issued, Gardner wrote to Chief of Staff Gen. Nathan F. Twining * criticizing the existing specifications for Atlas as unnecessarily complex. He also labeled the Air Force's organization for missile development overly cumbersome. Gardner proposed to simplify the specifications and to remedy the organizational shortcomings by creating a central Air Staff † office for missiles headed by a general officer.[21]

On February 26, 1954, at a meeting of key officials from the Air Staff, ARDC, Convair, and the Teapot Committee, Gardner expanded on his ideas for managing missile development. The conferees agreed that, under its existing organizational arrangement, the Air Force could not produce an operational ICBM by 1960. The only way to achieve that goal, Gardner claimed, was for the Air Force to "dramatize the acceleration of the program and to simplify the normal controls and channels of coordination." Moreover, the proper effect could be obtained only if the Atlas won the approval of the Armed Forces Policy Council, the Joint Chiefs of Staff, the National Security Council, and the President. The organizational structure that Gardner envisioned called for a major general to serve both as an ARDC vice commander and as chief of missile development. A brigadier general would support him and be responsible for coordinating the program with industrial contractors. Gardner suggested Maj. Gen. James McCormack, currently ARDC's Vice Commander, and Brig. Gen. Bernard A. Schriever for the two positions. There was general agreement on all major points except the type of organization to perform the systems engineering. The conferees' opinions were divided among three options: a university, an industrial company, or a scientific group.[22]

In the midst of the reorientation deliberations came the most positive evidence of the feasibility of producing lighter, more powerful nuclear weapons: the March 1, 1954, "Bravo" test explosion in the Marshall Islands.‡ Although it is difficult to ascertain the direct influence of this event on Air Force decisions, it undoubtedly underscored the implication of losing to the Soviets in a race to deploy nuclear-tipped strategic missiles.§

On March 11, 1954, Gardner outlined his plan to accelerate Atlas

---

* Twining succeeded Vandenberg on June 30, 1953.

† General Putt recalled opposing Gardner's suggestion to separate the project completely from the rest of the Air Staff. [Interview, Lt Gen Donald L. Putt with James C. Hasdorff, Atherton, Calif., April 1–3, 1974, p 45.]

‡ This shot was part of the Castle nuclear weapons test series. Although "Bravo" technically was not a weapon, it could have been air dropped.

§ The Soviets reportedly had under development a rocket engine of 100 metric tons thrust (220,000 pounds), and its rockets were said to fly 1,600 nautical miles. [Air Technical Intelligence Center, "Soviet Capabilities in Guided Missiles," June 15, 1954.]

development to Secretary Talbott and General Twining. As a first step, he proposed to reallocate $20 million from other missile projects to Atlas, raising its Fiscal Year 1955 budget to $50 million. For the entire program—spread over 5 years—Gardner estimated the work to cost $1.5 billion:

Fiscal Year	Cost in $ millions
1955	50
1956	195
1957	700
1958	400
1959	200

If all went according to plan, the Air Force would possess "a preliminary capability by June 1958 consisting of 2 launching sites and 4 operational missiles" with 20 launch sites and 100 missiles operational by 1960.[23]

The Air Force Council, chaired by Vice Chief of Staff Gen. Thomas D. White, reviewed the Teapot Committee report and Gardner's five-year plan on March 11 and 15. Impressed by the projected weights and yields of nuclear weapons and what they could mean to Atlas development, the council readily endorsed Atlas acceleration and assignment of development responsibility to the ARDC Commander, with instructions to establish a competent military-civilian organization and to obtain the earliest possible operational capability "limited only by technical progress." Concern over "roles and missions" surfaced again, as the council emphasized that it wanted Atlas developed as an Air Force project and that it should continue to be called the B–65 pilotless bomber.[24]

Just as the Air Force Council was formally drafting these recommendations, Secretary Talbott directed General Twining to implement Atlas acceleration immediately. At the same time, Talbott designated Gardner as his "direct representative in all aspects of the program."[25]

General Twining accepted all of the Air Force Council recommendations except one: He vetoed the council's advice to discuss and coordinate Atlas plans with the Office of the Secretary of Defense. Twining thought it best to defer this step until "the Air Force [was] firmly established, organization wise, to fully exploit the Atlas weapon."[26]

Gardner agreed not to discuss the Atlas acceleration plan with his OSD counterparts prematurely, took steps to tighten security procedures, and went along with the Air Staff's desire to retain Atlas's designation as a bomber. And he expanded the term "acceleration" to mean "the maximum effort possible with no limitation as to funding." Only with respect to the Snark did Gardner and the Air Staff differ. Whereas the Air Staff wanted to continue Snark development as a weapon system, Gardner doubted that this could be done by the 1958 target date, and doubted that even if completed on time it would prove reliable. In September 1954 Gardner called for a comprehensive Snark review to resolve the issue.[27]

Presuming that the Atlas would remain under its control, rather than that of a superagency, the Air Force acted to ensure the program's success. A major supporter of the Atlas program was the Air Force Chief of Staff, General White, who one observer recalled "lectured the Air Staff on ballistic missiles—they were here to stay, he told them, and the Air Staff had better realize this fact and get on with it." On May 14, 1954, General White assigned Project Atlas the highest Air Force development priority—with the concurrence of the Secretary of Defense—and directed its acceleration "to the maximum extent that technology would allow." As earlier indicated, he vested development responsibility in a special ARDC field office, to be established on the west coast.[28]

The decision to speed Atlas development under special managerial and organizational arrangements forced the Air Staff to reexamine its missile doctrine, particularly its 1952 assessment that missiles represented "just another type of weapon"* that it could handle in normal functional fashion.

---

*See page 89.

**Gen. Nathan F. Twining,
Air Force Chief of Staff
(June 1953–June 1957).**

By February 1954 it was obvious that this was not the case, and Lt. Gen. Earle E. Partridge, the Deputy Chief of Staff/Operations, established an Assistant for Guided Missiles within his organization.[29] Earlier, as ARDC Commander, General Partridge had spoken out in favor of special treatment for missiles. In April, despite strong resistance from several Air Staff members,* the office was removed from DCS/Operations and elevated to the level of Assistant Chief of Staff for Guided Missiles. Maj. Gen. Samuel R. Brentnall, the first Assistant Chief, premised its establishment on interservice rivalry, claiming that "if we are to gain pace with the Army and Navy, we must place the office in a position where it can operate unfettered and on equal terms with the other services."[30]

Manned by ten officers and six civilians, the Assistant Chief of Staff's guided missile office initially consisted of tactical, air defense, strategic, and logistics divisions plus a special assistant for ballistic missiles.† Its responsibilities included formulating guided missile policy, providing coordination, and serving as the Air Staff focal point for contacts with the other services and outside agencies.[31]

A West Coast Facility

Despite the Air Force's resolve to accelerate Atlas development, implementation occurred more slowly than expected. Thus, not until June 21, 1954—three months after General Twining's approval—did ARDC receive official notification to reorient and accelerate Project Atlas. General Putt, the Deputy Chief of Staff for Development, instructed Lt. Gen. Thomas S. Power, the ARDC Commander, to speed Atlas "to the maximum extent that technological development will permit" and to "establish a field office on the west coast with a general officer in command having authority and control over all aspects of the program, including all engineering matters."[32]

On July 1 General Power ordered the establishment of an ARDC field office, designated the Western Development Division. Initially, WDD was located in a vacant former church building at 401 East Manchester Boulevard, Inglewood, California. Officers were instructed to wear civilian clothes to obscure the purpose of their organization. General Schriever,

---

*Maj. Gen. Osmond J. Ritland remembers that Air Force leaders opposed the missile program because it detracted from aircraft development. "I think the only people that supported the [missile] program," he said, "were those that were assigned to it." [Intv, General Ritland with Lt. Col. L. R. Officer, Mar 19-21, 1974, pp 148-49.]

†This organization lasted until 1957 when it was superseded on the Air Staff by the Ballistic Missiles Division. Also, in December 1954 the Deputy Chief of Staff for Development created an Assistant to the Director for R&D for Project Atlas.

earlier named as an assistant to General Power, was also appointed WDD Commander. (Gen. James McCormack, earlier tagged to serve as General Power's assistant, had suffered a heart attack and soon thereafter retired from the Air Force.) Thus, Schriever possessed the authority of an ARDC deputy commander which granted him direct access to all of the command's development centers and facilitated his contacts with Air Staff members.[33]

General Schriever was 43 years old when he assumed responsibility for Project Atlas. Born in Bremen, Germany, "Benny" Schriever and his family had emigrated to the United States during World War I. After his father died in an industrial accident, Schriever, his mother, and his younger brother worked hard to make ends meet. In 1931 he earned an engineering degree from Texas A & M College, after which he began a military career as a reservist with the Army Field Artillery. The next year he enrolled in the Army Air Corps's Flight School at Randolph Field, Texas, where he won his wings. There were several service breaks between 1932 and 1938, when Schriever worked as a commercial pilot and as a Civilian Conservation Corps camp director. During a duty tour at Albrook Field, Panama Canal Zone, he married Dora Brett, daughter of Brig. Gen. George H. Brett of the U.S. Army Air Corps. In 1938 Schriever received a regular commission and was posted to Wright Field, Ohio, as a test pilot. It was during this assignment that his interest in aeronautical research and development was aroused.

After earning a master's degree in mechanical engineering from Stanford University in 1942, Schriever went to the Pacific, where he flew sixty-three combat missions as a B–17 pilot. By war's end, Schriever had become a colonel and was serving as Chief of Staff of the Fifth Air Force. In January 1946 he was assigned to Army Air Forces Headquarters as Chief, Scientific Liaison Branch, Assistant Chief of Air Staff for Materiel. Following graduation from the National War College in June 1950, Schriever became the Deputy Assistant for Evaluation, Deputy Chief of Staff, Development, later renamed the Assistant for Development Planning.[34] A New York Times reporter described Schriever as:

> . . . a 6 foot 2 . . . general who goes about his awesome task with the relaxed precision of a champion golfer sinking a one-foot putt. . . . slim . . . a good looking man with alert but slightly bashful eyes, a straight nose and a chin that recedes without in the slightest suggesting weakness. . . . a model of informality and gives the suggestion that he has seen a lot of Jimmy Stewart films.[35]

On August 2, 1954, Schriever assumed command of WDD after personally choosing his top staff and most of the second echelon.[36]*

---

*Schriever's initial staff comprised a dozen hand-picked men, including Col. Charles H. Terhune, Deputy Commander for Technical Operations; Col. Harold W. Norton, Assistant for

Assistant Secretary Trevor Gardner and WDD Commander Maj. Gen. Bernard A. Schriever shared a devotion to building a strong missiles program.

Air Materiel Command had first obtained contracting authority in 1950 by delegation from the Secretary of the Air Force. Although AMC could redelegate this authority, it rarely did. Gen. Edwin W. Rawlings, its Commander, opposed this practice in principle because he believed that the previous creation of numerous small, special contracting entities had badly dissipated scarce Air Force resources. General Brentnall, the Assistant Chief of Staff for Guided Missiles, agreed with Rawlings's position and consequently approved the collocation of an independent AMC contracting office with WDD. He informed Schriever, however, that the arrangement would be scrapped if it proved unworkable.[37]

The newly created AMC field office was initially designated the

Technical Operations; Lt. Col. Benjamin P. Blasingame, Chief Guidance Project Officer; Lt. Col. Beryl L. Boatman, Executive Officer; Lt. Col. Philip C. Calhoun, Chief Program Status Officer; Lt. Col. Otto J. Glasser, Chief Warhead Officer; Lt. Col. Edward N. Hall, Propulsion Officer; Lt. Col. John P. Hudson, Security Officer; Maj. Roger R. Hebner, Materiel Officer; Maj. Paul L. Maret, Administrative Staff Officer; and Capt. Vernol L. Smith, Adjutant. [ARDC Personnel Action Memo No. 79, Sep 15, 1954, in BAS Papers.] Col. William A. Sheppard became Deputy Commander for Management. Three other names belong on the "Schoolhouse Plaque," according to WDD historian Dr. Alfred Rockefeller: MSgt. Wilford Burt, Maj. Roy Ferguson, and Lt. Col. Norman J. Keefer. [Intv, author with Dr. Rockefeller, Aug 16, 1977.]

Special Aircraft Projects Office (SAPO).* Its job was to prepare and issue purchase requests, work statements, and contract specifications; assist in procurement source selections; prepare and administer procurement instructions; and issue stop work orders and terminations. On the other hand, WDD was to exercise overall responsibility in initiating purchase requests; prepare work statements and specifications; evaluate contractor proposals; select procurement sources; and prepare, substantiate, and control budget requirements.

SAPO was officially established on August 15 with Col. Harold T. Morris as its chief. Colonel Morris, who also served as Special Assistant to AMC's Director of Procurement and Production, received extensive authority: to issue facility letter contracts of unlimited value without prior approval; to approve, award, and execute definitive contracts up to $350,000; to authorize sole source procurements; and to execute related actions to expedite missile development.[38]

Meanwhile, Trevor Gardner had acted to preserve the availability of the Teapot Committee expertise. In April 1954 he established the Atlas (later ICBM) Scientific Advisory Committee and persuaded Dr. von Neumann to continue as Chairman. (Hence, it was sometimes called the Second von Neumann Committee.) Seven of the original eleven Teapot Committee members agreed to serve along with nine new members.† The group's task was to monitor Atlas progress and seek to accelerate development. Gardner participated in the work of the committee as Secretary Talbott's executive agent, while General Schriever sat in as the military director.[39]

On July 20 and 21 the reconstituted Scientific Advisory Committee met for the first time to review Atlas's current technical status. Convair representatives recommended that it continue the development of the 440,000-pound, 5-motor missile while studying the feasibility of a smaller, 250,000-pound version. The Scientific Advisory Committee, however, was critical of this approach and sought a solution in a radically revised managerial and organizational arrangement. Under existing plans, WDD would oversee a prime contractor, with technical direction coming from a small, separate technical staff. This plan generally followed the Air Force's single prime weapon system development and acquisition approach, which

---

*It was redesignated the Ballistic Missile Office in March 1956 and the Ballistic Missile Center in September 1958.

†C. C. Lauritsen and A. E. Puckett resigned for personal reasons, whereas Ramo and Wooldridge felt that their membership might appear as a conflict of interest since they intended to participate in Atlas development. Among the new members were Brig. Gen. Charles A. Lindbergh (USAFR), Norris E. Bradbury (Los Alamos Laboratory), James W. McRae (Sandia Laboratory), Carroll L. Zimmermann (Strategic Air Command), Herbert York (Livermore Laboratory), Louis Dunn (Caltech), Franklin R. Collbohm (Rand), Jerrold R. Zacharias (Los Alamos), and Robert R. McMath (University of Michigan).

called for extensive testing of prototype vehicles before the gradual introduction of production models into the operational inventory. The "single prime" philosophy worked reasonably well where relatively minor technological advances were involved, as for example in the progression from the B-47 to the B-52 bombers. In the area of missile development, however, the concept had not proved successful because constant changes in configuration, components, performance specifications, and inventory planning had produced numerous slippages and large cost overruns. Thus, it was not surprising that a majority of the committee opposed the current organizational arrangement and reiterated the original Teapot Committee position: no aircraft company possessed the requisite scientific or managerial talent to meet the Atlas's objectives and, consequently, there was a need to establish both a new management philosophy and a new management organization with major "directive responsibility." [40]

Assistant Secretary of Defense for Research and Development Donald A. Quarles, an observer at the meeting, opined that the proposed management scheme would likely prove confusing because it obscured the division of responsibility and authority for systems engineering and technical direction. He suggested that the Air Force could do one of two things to clarify the matter. It could assign all the functions to its prime contractor, and Ramo-Wooldridge would provide technical support; or the Air Force could place Ramo-Wooldridge in a line position and assign it responsibility for systems engineering and technical direction. Accepting the latter alternative would require a greatly enlarged Ramo-Wooldridge staff. General Power, who had attended the meeting, then directed General Schriever to undertake a complete study to resolve the issue. [41]

WDD had its findings ready on August 18. First, it found that relying on an aircraft contractor for systems planning had many disadvantages. Contractors lacked the scientific competence for so complex an undertaking, were unable to attract top-flight scientific talent, and were heavily committed to other projects as evidenced by large backlogs of aircraft contracts. The second solution, employing a university laboratory, would attract the desired scientific personnel. It was unlikely, however, that any university could (or wanted to) control and manage so major an industrial undertaking. Under a third approach, the Air Force would retain systems responsibility and employ Ramo-Wooldridge in the role of a "deputy" (in a line rather than a staff position) to perform all systems engineering and technical direction.* To avoid charges of conflict of interest, Ramo-Wooldridge "would remain ineligible for development and production of the missiles and any components." [42] (See Chart 4-1.)

---

*Subsequently, Dr. Ramo attended General Schriever's staff meetings. [Airpower Hearings, Pt XIV, p 1159.]

Chart 4-1
WDD and R-W Arrangement

Pre-Gillette

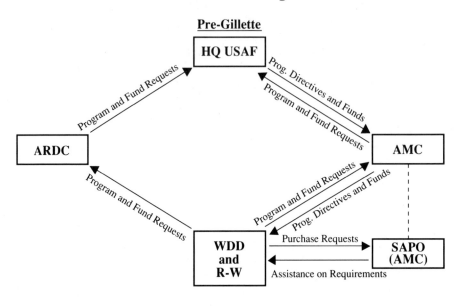

Gillette Procedures

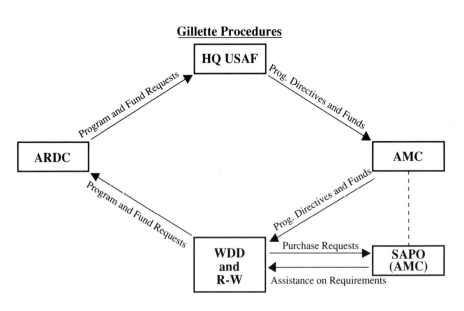

Schriever briefed Generals Power and Rawlings on the proposed Atlas reorganization on September 3 and secured their approval. On the same day, Ramo met with Roger Lewis, the Assistant Secretary of the Air Force for Materiel, to review company–Air Force relationships under the proposed arrangement. Of course, Lewis wanted Ramo-Wooldridge to abstain from development and production of missile hardware. Moreover, he wanted Thompson Products Company, a minority stockholder of Ramo-Wooldridge, which had made some components for Atlas, to adhere to specific restraints as pertained to that missile. On September 8, after securing agreement, Lewis approved Ramo-Wooldridge for the tasks of systems engineering and technical direction.[43]

At the October 15 meeting of the ICBM Scientific Advisory Committee, Dr. Ramo outlined his firm's plans for the ballistic missile. The company, he said, felt that it could attract highly competent scientists and engineers to increase the size of its guided missile division to about 400. Divided into 5 major subunits, the staff would oversee guidance and control, aerodynamics and structures, propulsion, flight testing and instrumentation, and weapon system analysis. Ramo also unveiled a detailed development plan listing various subsystem contractor selections, alternate sources, freezing of designs, and so on. He stressed that much of the plan depended upon the delivery of Atlas' rocket engines by North American in February 1956. To help avoid major delays, the subsystem contractors were required to prepare detailed plans and schedules which Ramo-Wooldridge and WDD would keep under constant scrutiny.[44]

Thus, by the fall of 1954, the program approach proposed by Schriever and Ramo had received approval at all levels—ARDC, AMC, the Air Staff, Gardner, and the ICBM Scientific Advisory Committee. There was, however, one dissenting voice—that of Franklin R. Collbohm, President of the Rand Corporation and a member of the advisory committee. Collbohm had opposed the separation of systems engineering from the airframe builder when that matter was originally discussed in July. He feared that this step would seriously disaffect aircraft manufacturers from taking on guided missile work. Now, in October, Collbohm was more convinced than before "that this approach will yield something less than the best results possible because it will fail to mobilize the best talents and the strongest resources available for the purpose." Collbohm believed so fervently in the worth and efficacy of industrial competition (he was a former Douglas engineer) that he offered to resign from the advisory committee.[45]

General Schriever believed that Collbohm's objections, if valid, could be blunted by immediately implementing the development plan. To that end he proposed and received General Power's approval to award Convair the airframe and assembly contract. (Power's approval was contingent on concurrence by Roger Lewis.) Although the advisory committee had been extremely critical of Convair's organization and its technical competence, it was undeniable that the company offered at least one major advantage: it agreed with the Air Force that the 5,500-nautical mile Atlas could be built in a relatively short time and without undergoing intermediate, lesser-range stages. Schriever also proposed to announce that the Air Force would sponsor "an alternate configuration and staging approach with a second source." [46]

If Schriever was unduly concerned about Collbohm's dissent, his worries were soon allayed. At an October 29 meeting, Assistant Secretary Lewis assured Schriever of his continued support for WDD's program approach; moreover, he wanted additional study of the Convair proposal before the Air Force committed itself to that company's designation as the Atlas airframe and assembly contractor. Specifically, Lewis wanted a thorough examination of Convair's proposed organization and manning for Atlas. Lewis also delayed approval of Convair's proposal to build additional facilities in southern California, in part because of current Air Force policy to place new production facilities in the central United States rather than on the east and west coasts. This policy subsequently developed into a major issue.[47]*

The Scientific Advisory Committee reacted by having a three-member panel—Charles A. Lindbergh, George B. Kistiakowsky, and Jerome B. Wiesner—consider Collbohm's objections. Noting Collbohm's claim that the Atlas was "within the capability of our technological and manufacturing knowhow . . . [and] ready to enter the engineering stage," Schriever insisted to the panel that, although Atlas was technologically feasible, it nonetheless represented an exceedingly difficult engineering task. Schriever also disputed Collbohm's assertion that the aircraft industry was fully competent to develop and produce missiles. For example, he observed that North American—considered the ablest of the aircraft companies—was now more than eight years behind in Navaho development, and that Douglas Aircraft and Bell Laboratories both asserted that the ICBM should first be developed in a short-range version before attempting the full-length operational vehicle.[48]

After an extended meeting with Collbohm and Ramo, the panel on December 3 reaffirmed the recommendations of its parent committee "that an unusual management structure" as represented by Ramo-Wooldridge was necessary to develop the ICBM at maximum speed. To Collbohm's proposal for a parallel ICBM development,† or the development of a

---

*See page 129.

†The concept of parallel development had already been discussed in part in August 1954, when Aerojet was mentioned as a second source for an alternate propulsion system.

medium-range ballistic missile, the panel supported the latter on condition that WDD oversee its development. Collbohm accepted the verdict and agreed to remain on the committee.[49]

Although the panel's conclusion served as a welcome vindication of the Air Force approach, it really only formalized a decision made three months earlier. Similarly, the medium-range ballistic missile proposal had been made earlier in 1954, and had been subordinated in importance to ICBM development; also, by June a proposal for a cooperative program with the British was under consideration. Moreover, the question of a medium-range or tactical ballistic missile* had become the subject of a roles and missions debate in the Joint Chiefs of Staff.

In August, when the Air Staff solicited comments on developing tactical ballistic missiles, General Schriever's response was decidedly negative. He believed that it would interfere with ICBM development and production; jeopardize the alternate ICBM development; place a premium on already-scarce scientific talent; invite in-house (USAF) competition for test facilities; and cause unnecessary duplication. And perhaps worst of all, it "could cause the transfer of responsibility to another service or, because of the high priority of ballistic weapons, the establishment of a separate management group for ballistic weapons directly under the DOD." † Schriever and Ramo believed that the best way to obtain a tactical ballistic missile was to let it evolve from the ICBM program, specifically from the two-stage alternate ICBM configuration that Collbohm and the aircraft industry had proposed.[50]

Although Headquarters USAF was not yet certain what to do with this shorter-range ballistic missile, it took several positive steps. On December 2, 1954, it issued a general operational requirement (GOR) for the tactical ballistic missile, and it authorized $500,000 to Martin, Douglas, Lockheed, and General Electric for design studies. Obviously, it expected to make no decisions before receiving the design proposals the following spring.[51]

In October 1954 Trevor Gardner recommended that the Air Staff put the Atlas in a separate, unidentified budget category for Fiscal Year 1956. Gardner's aim was to preserve program security and to protect the Atlas from competing with other, regular Air Force funding requirements. This

---

*The 1,000- to 2,000-mile range ballistic missile was variously called a medium range ballistic missile, a tactical ballistic missile, or an intermediate range ballistic missile.

†Curiously, Maj. Gen. Donald N. Yates, Commander of the Air Force Missile Test Center, suggested to General Power in November that the Air Force consider employing the Wernher von Braun group from the Army's Redstone missile program. Yates suggested that the group could contribute to either the tactical ballistic missile or to the Atlas. No one at ARDC, however, cared enough even to comment on the suggestion. [Ltr, Gen Yates to Power, no subj, Nov 22, 1954; memo, Maj. R. T. Franzel, ARDC to Gen Schriever, no subj, Dec 16, 1954, in BAS Papers.]

concept of a separate budget was part of the larger question under consideration, that of placing the program outside normal administrative and management channels and into a special "crash project" category.[52]

Schriever also believed that separate funding was critical to the success of the Atlas and urged Gardner to continue his efforts in that direction. Under normal procedures, there were numerous levels of approval, and although Schriever had received excellent cooperation to date, he feared that "the honeymoon cannot last forever." Thus, currently an OSD committee was seeking a detailed accounting of all rocket test facilities, including their relationship to all other U.S. rocket programs. Even a minor item, such as air conditioning for the Ramo-Wooldridge computer, required approval by another DOD agency. Schriever also foresaw increased funding competition within the Air Force between Atlas and forces-in-being advocates. He anticipated that this competition would lead to deferments that were certain to delay operational availability.[53] Gardner then urged Secretary Talbott to institute separate funding for the Atlas, suggesting that Lyle S. Garlock, the Assistant Secretary for Financial Management, prepare the requisite procedural machinery. Talbott, in turn, directed Garlock to organize a committee and to prepare the required arrangement, which he described as "extremely urgent."[54]

Although the Air Force in late 1954 still leaned toward Convair as the Atlas airframe and assembly contractor, there were several problems in need of resolution. In November General Schriever informed Joseph T. McNarney,* President of Convair, that the Air Force did not want additional missile production facilities in southern California, in line with its current policy of relocating research and development away from the east and west coasts. Schriever also asked McNarney for Convair's organizational and personnel plans for hiring qualified scientists and engineers in adequate numbers to perform the work. Finally, WDD's Commander wanted Convair to study the reconfiguration of the Atlas from a five- to a three-engined vehicle and the effects of an attendant weight reduction.[55]

Within a few days, McNarney assured Schriever that Convair's facilities at San Diego were adequate for the Atlas and that no additional space was needed. Should expansion become necessary, there was additional space at General Dynamics (Convair's parent company) plants in Fort Worth, Texas. In the matter of personnel, McNarney reported that he had appointed Thomas G. Lanphier, formerly an assistant to Air Force Secretary Symington, as Vice President for the Atlas, and James R. Dempsey, a former Air Force officer, as the Atlas Project Director to supervise the current 624-man workforce. Convair, he added, planned to employ as many

*General McNarney, USAF retired. See page 18. McNarney became President of Convair in 1952.

as 1,600 engineers in 1956 and more than 4,000 factory workers during 1958. Presuming that Atlas received continued high-level attention, McNarney anticipated the first Atlas flight test to occur in 1956 and the first operational ICBM flight test in March 1958.[56]

Although Schriever accepted Convair's facilities planning for San Diego and Fort Worth, he insisted that the company separate Atlas completely from its other work. Thus, Convair would have to disassociate Atlas from all other operations at San Diego and clearly define the interaction between Atlas and the other programs. Once these conditions were satisfied, Schriever informed McNarney, the Air Force would accept Convair as the Atlas airframe and assembly contractor.[57] During these same weeks, Trevor Gardner and Roger Lewis also harbored reservations about Convair. General Dynamics's Executive Vice President, Frank Pace, a former Secretary of the Army, personally assured them that Convair would meet its responsibilities.[58]

WDD made the Atlas nuclear warhead a matter of early concern. In September 1954, at General Schriever's request, the Air Force Special Weapons Center assigned a liaison officer to WDD specifically for Atlas. Schriever viewed this assignment as an endorsement of his command's responsibility to develop the warhead installation procedures. In addition, WDD organized a working group from the Atomic Energy Commission's Division of Military Applications, Los Alamos, Livermore, and Sandia contractors, the Armed Forces Special Weapons Project, Air Force Special Weapons Center, Ramo-Wooldridge, and the WDD to monitor progress on nuclear warheads. In October the AEC repeated its prediction that it could develop nuclear warheads that would weigh only 1,500 to 1,700 pounds but have a yield of 1 megaton.[59]

With the practicality of small, lightweight, high-yield warheads confirmed, the WDD was able to proceed toward a final Atlas design configuration. It subsequently discarded the 5-engine, 450,000-pound concept in favor of a 3-engine (1½- stage) vehicle weighing 240,000 pounds, with a diameter of 10 feet, and possessing a CEP of 5 nautical miles. To resolve the problem of the extremely high reentry temperatures, the Air Force abandoned the high Mach number terminal velocity requirement and substituted instead a blunt heat-sink nose cone * with a high subsonic speed over the target.[60]

Thus, as 1954 drew to a close, the Air Force stood poised to proceed with construction of the Atlas. WDD and Ramo-Wooldridge comprised the management development team that the Teapot Committee had envisioned in its call for a radical program reorganization. Convair was about to sign a contract based on new design requirements, and the Air Force was also

---

* See Chapter II.

considering other designs for an alternate ICBM and a medium range ballistic missile. The Atomic Energy Commission had provided optimistic assurances concerning nuclear warheads. The second von Neumann Committee, formally the ICBM Scientific Advisory Committee, would soon be chartered by the Air Force. In the coming year these plans would be translated into hardware.

Chapter V

A Family of Missiles

[The Western Development Division] created a
family of ballistic missiles that used every technology that we knew of at the time.

Maj. Gen. Osmond J. Ritland, 1974

The ICBM program resembled the Manhattan Project in scope and in
the challenge posed. To turn out the ICBM as quickly as possible, General
Schriever adopted a method of parallel development whereby separate
contractors were hired for every major subsystem. Although this method
was criticized as uneconomical, the Air Force insisted that it saved time
through competition, ensured that development would not be halted by the
failure of any one contractor, and permitted work on advanced designs
without jeopardizing the ICBM program. Another advantage of the paral-
lelism was that the subsystems could be made interchangeable. Further, the
more companies that became involved, the more expanded became the
industrial base for missile research and development.

In January 1955 the Air Force selected associate contractors for all of
the major missile subsystems—airframe and assembly, propulsion, guidance, computers, and nose cones. Potential contractors were rated as highly
qualified, satisfactory, or unsatisfactory, with the top firms invited to bid.
A complex contractual arrangement was devised with the Ramo-Wooldridge
Corporation. In return for higher service fees, considered essential to attract
the best scientists and engineers, R–W agreed to abide by a prohibition
against hardware production. The agreement did not sit well with the
aircraft industry, which had resented abandoning the "single prime"
approach and R–W's privileged status within the Air Force. The service
defended its arrangement with R–W as the only one promising to meet the
needs of the ICBM project and criticized the industry for its dismal record
in developing such missiles as the Matador, Snark, and Navaho.

A signal decision made during this period designated the Titan as an
alternate ICBM, rather than as a backup for the Atlas. The Air Force took

this action to maintain the support of the scientists. Gaining approval for the Titan was stymied by the so-called dispersal policy of the Eisenhower Administration. This policy sought to end a trend of aircraft firms concentrating along the east and west coasts by insisting that the government negotiate with companies in the nation's interior. The Air Force did not win a waiver of this policy until the fall of 1955, and the winning airframe and assembly contractor, the Martin Company, located its new plant at Denver, Colorado.

Trevor Gardner, the sparkplug behind the ICBM development, was convinced from the start that the missile program could succeed only if it gained top national priority. Gardner campaigned tirelessly until he had achieved his goal. In February 1955 the Killian Committee's report to the President noted a weapons disparity between the United States and the USSR and the growing vulnerability of North America to a surprise attack. After receiving a statutory appointment in March, Gardner testified in Congress that the Soviets could begin testing ICBMs by 1960. With the support of Senators Henry M. Jackson and Clinton P. Anderson, Special Assistant Gardner got the White House's attention. In July, Gardner, von Neumann, and Schriever briefed President Eisenhower. Although Secretary of Defense Wilson saw no need to single out the ICBM, Gardner was supported by the Joint Chiefs of Staff and the National Security Council, and in September his long-hoped-for "top national priority" was granted.

New organizational procedures were needed to ensure the ICBM's top priority. To that end, Gardner established a committee under Hyde Gillette, the Air Force Deputy for Budget. With Schriever's guidance, the committee devised a set of administrative procedures which made WDD solely responsible for planning, programming, and directing ICBM development. Approved in November 1955, the Gillette Procedures created a single level of approval within the Air Force. Called the Air Force Ballistic Missiles Committee (AF–BMC), this body was chaired by the Secretary of the Air Force and included his principal assistants and the Assistant Chief of Staff for Guided Missiles. After securing Air Force approval, WDD's plan was submitted to the new OSD–BMC (headed by the Deputy Secretary of Defense) for ultimate review and decision. The ICBM Scientific Advisory Committee, chaired by von Neumann, served as consultants to the Air Force and OSD. Overall, these Gillette Procedures cut the number of review levels from 42 to 10.

The two Ballistic Missiles Committees went to work soon after their establishment. On December 20, 1955, they approved the ICBM program for Fiscal Years 1956 and 1957 essentially as presented by WDD. For FY 1956 $336 million was approved, including $20 million for R&D, $233 million for procurement, $55 million for facilities, and about $28 million in associated costs. (See Chart 5–3).

The Gillette Procedures also addressed the question of the initial operational capability (IOC) date for the ICBM. ARDC was responsible for achieving the missiles' IOC but delegated its authority to General Schriever. Air Force leaders, however, would decide when the ICBM was combat ready and at that point would assign command and control to the Strategic Air Command (SAC). On November 18, Gen. Thomas D. White, the Vice Chief of Staff, directed that achieving IOC was the immediate objective of the ICBM program. Thus, the ICBM's top priority now included production as well as R&D.

Gen. Curtis E. LeMay, Commander in Chief of SAC, adopted a skeptical attitude toward missiles. He demanded that these weapons first demonstrate instantaneous launching and that they perform reliably and accurately. Until such time, LeMay insisted, missiles served only as "political and psychological weapons" and as "penetration aids" for manned bombers. Nevertheless, he assigned Brig. Gen. John P. McConnell, SAC's Director of Plans, to make operational plans.

Three operational sites were contemplated for the ICBM force, one each in the eastern, central, and western United States. Initially, the sites would not be hardened against nuclear attack. Ten missiles and launchers were expected to be in place by April 1959. The plan called for the number to rise to 120 missiles (80 Atlas and 40 Titan) at 60 sites by January 1960. Each base was required to be capable of launching 20 missiles within 2 hours, with a 15-minute reaction time. No date was specified for transferring the force to SAC.

The Thor intermediate range ballistic missile grew out of a meeting of the Scientific Advisory Committee in January 1955. The committee urged the Air Force to develop a tactical ballistic missile (TBM). Schriever initially opposed the recommendation, fearing that it would divert resources from the ICBM program. He suggested instead that the TBM grow out of the Atlas. Other developments, however, soon came into play. The United Kingdom expressed interest in a TBM in February, but ran into difficulties concerning U.S. policy on sharing atomic energy information. Also in February, the Killian Committee urgently recommended that the United States develop an IRBM before the Soviets. The U.S. Army, meanwhile, was developing a medium-range ballistic missile (later called the Jupiter) under the supervision of Dr. Wernher von Braun.

By May 1955 the Air Staff debated the issue and concluded that it was in the Air Force's and the nation's best interest to proceed. ARDC solicited industry bids for the tactical ballistic missile. In July Deputy Secretary of Defense Reuben B. Robertson, head of the OSD Ballistic Missiles Committee, ruled that the IRBM be carried out as a separate program and not as a derivative of the Atlas. The JCS were unable to resolve the interservice competition, thus leading to a compromise. Defense Secretary Wilson accepted the Joint Chiefs' position, and in November directed that the Air Force develop IRBM #1 (Thor) and that the Army and Navy would jointly undertake IRBM #2 (Jupiter). Moreover, Wilson assigned the IRBM a priority equal to the ICBM. This last decision shocked Trevor Gardner, for all his hard work on the ICBM was seemingly swept away; he felt betrayed.

By the end of 1955 the Air Force had selected associate firms for the IRBM, with Douglas Aircraft winning the airframe and assembly contract. WDD was now transformed from a special projects office to a virtual missiles complex. It had acquired responsibility for a family of missiles and reconnaissance satellites, and had begun working on solid propellant rockets. Moreover, WDD enjoyed top national priority, a separate budget, and an unusual degree of management freedom.

Parallel Development

Convinced of the urgent need for an operational ICBM, the Air Force borrowed a page from the Manhattan Project by adopting parallel development. This method stimulated competition to turn out a weapon in the shortest time. There was a separate associate contractor for each major subsystem for both the Atlas and Titan, a plan that provided insurance against failure of a single contractor.

General Schriever observed that one advantage of having second sources available was that the subsystems might be interchangeable between the missiles. The method also minimized risk by serving as a hedge against delay or failure in developing a critical component. Further, because the industrial base for missiles in the United States was extremely limited, the parallel approach would ensure an expansion of research and development firms and thus raise production capacity later on. (After the Thor IRBM was approved for development, it too used subsystems produced for the ICBM program.) Finally, the Air Force created "a family of ballistic missiles that used every technology that we knew of at the time."[1]

The Air Force first considered parallel development for the ICBM in August 1954, with an analysis of the Aerojet General Corporation as a second source contractor for the Atlas rocket engine.* At the same time, Ramo-Wooldridge engaged the Lockheed and Martin companies to study two-stage ballistic missile configurations. Initial results, in October, indicated that two-stage rockets were especially well suited for missile testing. This finding encouraged General Schriever to recommend additional studies. General Power approved.[2]

---

*See page 114n. This notion was instigated by the Scientific Advisory Committee, which was displeased with North American's work on rocket engines. On January 12, 1955, Aerojet was awarded the second source propulsion contract.

On January 3 and 4, 1955, Schriever included the study results as part of an overall ICBM program review before the Scientific Advisory Committee.* The Lockheed-Martin studies confirmed the advantage of the two-stage approach for testing and also suggested that this approach might serve as a source for the development of an intermediate range ballistic missile. The Air Force was still convinced that Atlas represented the best choice for an early operational ICBM, and envisioned the two-stage rocket as a test vehicle and a backup to the Atlas. The committee, however, remained skeptical of Convair's capabilities and insisted that the two-stage configuration be designed from the start as an alternate ICBM. Several scientists felt that an alternate two-stage ICBM—although starting development later—might reach operational status earlier if the Atlas program was delayed. Believing they could not afford to lose the support of the scientists, Gardner and Schriever endorsed the need for an alternate ICBM.[3]

From the standpoint of a complete weapon system, the alternate ICBM (the two-stage version) represented the fullest application of parallel development. Another program objective—interchangeability of subsystems—would provide replacements if any of the primary subsystems encountered trouble, or for transfer in case of a major technological breakthrough by an alternate contractor. Also, parallel development afforded a convenient means of working on advanced designs without jeopardizing the entire ICBM program. Designated the XSM-68 (Weapon System 107A-2), subsequently the Titan, the alternate ICBM was to use the same components under development for the Atlas. As a result, the funding impact was expected to be minimal. Moreover, because the Titan might serve as a substitute for other test vehicles, it would engender a relatively small funding increase of about $40 million in Fiscal Year 1956.[4]

Beginning in January 1955, the Air Force selected associate contractors for the major ICBM subsystems of the Atlas and Titan, including airframe and assembly, propulsion, guidance, computers, and nose cones (reentry vehicles). The contract selection procedure was instituted in two phases. First, an Air Materiel Command–Air Research Development Command board at Wright-Patterson AFB, Ohio, prepared a listing of potential contractors for each component, subsystem, or service required for the ICBM and then rated them as highly qualified, satisfactory, or unsatisfactory. The ratings were based on seven factors: managerial performance, manufacturing capacity, financial condition, development capability, cost and delivery record, security, and vulnerability. For the second phase, a Western Development Division–Special Aircraft Projects Office board

---

*On January 3, 1955, Air Force Secretary Talbott chartered the committee as an Air Force entity. Gardner was designated Executive Agent, Schriever became the Military Director and an ex officio member, and von Neumann continued as Chairman.

A successful test launch of a Titan I from the Air Force Missile Test Center at Patrick AFB, Florida, 1960.

evaluated in greater detail the potential contractors ranked highly qualified and satisfactory, and selected those to approach with requests for contract proposals.[5]

During the first quarter of 1955 the Air Force signed several of the most important ICBM contracts. As noted previously, in January it contracted with Convair to reconfigure the Atlas design and terminated all requirements for the 1-, 3-, and 5-engine versions. The new Atlas, designated the XSM-65 (Weapon System 107A-1), would be a 240,000-pound vehicle powered by 2 North American rocket engines[*] delivering 135,000 pounds of thrust each and a third, or sustainer, engine of 60,000 pounds thrust.[6]

The reconfigured Atlas required an entirely new testing philosophy. Because missiles did not depend on pilots' reports, the new approach held that primary reliance on flight testing for ballistic missiles would be both inadequate and expensive. In its place, General Schriever devised a comprehensive ground, or captive, test program as a prerequisite for flight testing. The strategy was to add systems progressively to the basic propulsion unit until a complete, integrated system had been tested. Schriever hoped that this approach would "eliminate many possible causes of potential failure for later flight tests." Another important aspect of this test philosophy was that the Air Force—not the contractors—would control the missile tests.[7]

Under the revised missile flight testing, all vehicles, from the beginning, would be configured as nearly identical to the final operational ICBM as possible. The first missile in the test series, the Atlas A, would fly under the power of only the two main engines. This configuration would provide additional time for North American to complete development of the sustainer engine. The Atlas B would be flown with all three rocket engines, and as the flight test program continued, subsystem components would be added to subsequent vehicles in the series. The new contract with Convair also restricted the company's responsibility to the airframe and control systems, although it was permitted to compete for other missile components.[8]

One of the most complicated contract negotiations was with the Ramo-Wooldridge Corporation. Settlement fees and general research and development clauses proved particularly troublesome. The original one-year contract with R–W[†] was renewed monthly while negotiations proceeded. At first the Air Force proposed to award the company a standard six to eight

---

[*] The propulsion system was developed under the Navaho project.

[†] On October 15, 1953, ARDC issued letter contract AF 18 (600)–1002 to R–W to provide support to the Teapot Committee and awarded $25,000 for "Long Range Analytical Studies of Weapon Systems." This basic contract was increased in stages to $250,000 by April 1954, and in May a new letter contract (AF 18 (600)–1190) was drawn up for $500,000. [Chronology of Events, "Participation of R–W in AFGMP," Dec 31, 1954.]

percent service fee (worth about $460,000), a common government grant for engineering contracts. But this was no ordinary contract, and the standard amount was not expected to attract the high-caliber people sought for the work. Consequently, contracting officials devised a scheme involving extra rental for facilities.

The contract contained a clause that required the Air Force to lease buildings from R–W, both for itself and for R–W.* The fees would amortize the buildings over a five-year period, and they would then belong to R–W. In November 1954, however, Assistant Secretary of the Air Force Roger Lewis and the Air Materiel Command had rejected this plan. Lewis wanted to ensure that the Air Force received R–W's complete attention and believed that the best way to accomplish that aim was through a contract provision which restricted R–W from undertaking general research without Air Force approval. As this clause and an earlier prohibition on hardware production † deprived the company of income, Lewis justified raising the compensation to a 14 percent rate, equivalent to $668,000.[9]

In January 1955, the Air Force also signed an agreement with Aerojet General for a second-source propulsion system and with Lockheed for the X–17 test vehicle. The latter was a three-stage, solid-propellant rocket used to gather reentry data. Quarter-scale model test flights of the X–17 were scheduled to begin in mid-summer 1955. These tests would be followed a year later by instrumented full-scale vehicles to be launched from the Air Force Missile Test Center at Patrick AFB, Florida. During February 1955 the Air Force contracted with General Electric to develop a ground-based, radio-inertial guidance system to back up an all-inertial system for the Atlas which the Massachusetts Institute of Technology and the AC Spark Plug Company would build.‡ In March the Air Force signed separate agreements for computers with Remington Rand and Burroughs.[10]

Even as the Air Force implemented parallel development, the practice came under attack from the Office of the Secretary of Defense. In August 1955 John B. Macauley, the Acting Assistant Secretary of Defense for Research and Development,§ charged that parallel development was not

---

* In October 1955 WDD and SAPO began to relocate to R–W's Arbor Vitae complex near Los Angeles International Airport.

† R–W and its holding company, Thompson Products, were barred from developing and producing components for the ICBM program. In addition, the aircraft industry—particularly Hughes Aircraft, where Simon Ramo and Dean Wooldridge had previously worked—extracted a pledge that R–W would not try to recruit Hughes' scientists and engineers. [Msg, Power to Schriever, no subj, 27/1900Z Aug 1954; memo, Schriever to Ramo, subj: Hughes Aircraft Company, Oct 25, 1954, in BAS Papers.]

‡ On April 12, 1955, the Arma Division of American Bosch Arma Corporation received a contract to develop a competing all-inertial guidance system.

§ On August 15, 1955, Donald A. Quarles succeeded Harold E. Talbott as Secretary of the Air Force. Macauley acted in place of Quarles at OSD.

economical. Trevor Gardner successfully rebutted this claim on the grounds that parallel development insured against failure and provided a means of buying time through competition.[11]

The Air Force's decision to establish the Western Development Division and to hire Ramo-Wooldridge to help manage the ICBM program caused much resentment throughout the aircraft industry. The industry had not accepted the Air Force's rejection of the single prime contractor approach in ICBM development and had exerted heavy pressure to reverse the decision. General Schriever and his staff repeatedly refuted industry allegations that ICBM development was being delayed because the Air Force had injected competition in selecting contractors. The WDD Commander also countered a rash of industry propaganda "extolling the virtues" of Convair and General Dynamics while denigrating WDD and R–W.[12]

In February 1955 Schriever delivered a stinging ten-page rebuttal of these allegations, in a memo to Gen. Thomas S. Power, ARDC Commander, which justified his actions and defended the Air Force's management technique. He noted that the aircraft industry's primary goals were "avoidance of strong Air Force system management control" and the elimination of R–W as a competitor. Reviewing the aircraft industry's

Air Force Secretary Talbott (left) swears in Roger Lewis (right) as Assistant Secretary for Materiel.

127

performance in missile development, Schriever catalogued its unimpressive record in developing the Navaho, Snark, and Matador missiles. He strongly defended the selection of R–W and denied that the Air Force was attempting to build up that company, as was alleged in trade journals. "The airframe industry owes its existence and present affluence to Government support in contracts and Government facilities," Schriever said. As examples, he cited $100 million worth of government-owned facilities used by Douglas, $80 million used by North American, and $22 million used by Lockheed. Thus, Schriever characterized charges of unethical conduct by R–W as "in the category of the 'pot calling the kettle black.'" The Air Force and the scientific community, Schriever said, wanted to reverse the expansionist trend of the airframe industry into component fields, such as electronics, guidance, and metallurgy. A great competence already existed in these fields, and it was feared that intrusion by the airframe companies might dilute the available scientific talent.[13]

Although Schriever had supported the selection of Convair as the airframe and assembly contractor for the Atlas, relations between that company and the Air Force were strained. Writing later, Simon Ramo indicted Convair for its "dismal" role in the ICBM program. He criticized Convair's insistence on performing the entire Atlas development program and particularly its work on the guidance system. Ramo accused Convair of having failed to anticipate the need for a large number of engineers as the ICBM program spilled into numerous subsystems—including metallurgy, heat transfer, instrumentation, and attitude control—and thus did not recruit the necessary personnel. When Convair insisted on competing against contractors in those component fields, it clearly lost every time. As late as April 1955, Assistant Secretary of the Air Force Roger Lewis encouraged General Schriever to meet with Convair's President, Joseph McNarney, to "air your problems completely . . . and arrive at a satisfactory working relationship." Schriever agreed and in May, accompanied by Simon Ramo, "candidly discussed all matters concerning a harmonious working relationship" with Convair. While the Air Force published written procedures for carrying out the technical direction of the Atlas program, Convair hired a number of highly qualified scientists and engineers.[14]

Meanwhile, the recommendation for development of an alternate ICBM advanced by the Scientific Advisory Committee in January 1955, progressed from the ARDC, through the Air Staff, and on to Air Force Secretary Talbott. In April, Gardner urged Talbott to approve the alternate ICBM based on the results of a two-month competition among the Martin, Bell, Douglas, Lockheed, and General Electric companies. To underscore the importance of quick action, Gardner cited General Twining's opinion that, unless the ICBM program demonstrated results and soon, the Air Force risked losing responsibility for its development to some outside agency. One major impediment to an acceleration of the ICBM program was known as the "dispersal policy." * This Eisenhower Administration policy required that future missile development be conducted away from the seacoasts—where the airframe and electronics companies were concentrated—so as to effect a wider national distribution of missile development and production. The dispersal was also intended to lessen the vulnerability of these industries to enemy attack. Gardner asked Talbott to exempt development of the alternate ICBM from the dispersal policy restrictions, adding that General Rawlings, the AMC Commander, had agreed to attempt to locate that missile's production facilities in the central United States.[15]

Talbott, however, acting on a conflicting directive from President Eisenhower not to erect new facilities in California, rejected in unmistakable terms Gardner's recommendation to waive the dispersal policy:

> Do not place any more contracts for production and development with West Coast contractors unless you have written approval of this office. My feeling is very definite that we must develop strength in the the engineering and technical ability of the Middle West and the Eastern manufacturers. I do not believe that continued concentration in the California area to be [sic] constructive.[16]

---

* Also called the California policy.

Edwin W. Rawlings. As a four-star general, he commanded Air Materiel Command and managed missile procurement.

Another difficulty arose regarding Atlas test facilities. Because studies and analyses on the reconfigured Atlas were not completed in time, facility requirements were presented for approval in piecemeal fashion rather than according to a master plan. In early 1955 WDD, Convair, and North American finally devised a plan to speed facility construction. Unfortunately, it was at this point that Secretary Talbott injected the dispersal policy criteria.

General Schriever alerted General Power to certain urgently needed facilities, including the North American and Aerojet rocket engine test stands; launch stands and assembly buildings at the Air Force Missile Test Center, Holloman AFB, New Mexico; missile system static test stands at Camp Elliott, California; and the 1-A test stands at the Air Force Flight Test Center, Edwards AFB, California. General Power brought these matters to the attention of the Chief of Staff.[17] On April 27, 1955, a comprehensive review of the ICBM program was presented to Air Staff and Secretariat officials. The briefing projected its estimates of cost and number of missiles. (See Table 5-1.)[18]

Secretary Talbott finally relented on April 28, approving the development of an alternate ICBM. But he stipulated that missile construction must be conducted in areas away from seacoasts. Similarly, he designated as undesirable the missile test stands at Edwards AFB, California, which had already been approved at a cost of $5.5 million. Talbott also asked the Air Staff to review the long-range plan for missile testing and to recommend sites that were removed from the coasts.[19]

The Atlas development plan, submitted in April, was approved on July 27, 1955. General Putt, the DCS for Development, confirmed that the ICBM held the highest development priority in the Air Force. He called for acceleration of the program to operational status as rapidly as possible, "restricted only by technological considerations."[20]

In August Trevor Gardner reopened the dispersal policy matter with the new Secretary of the Air Force, Donald A. Quarles. Gardner noted that, while companies bidding on the alternate ICBM continued to present proposals that conformed with the dispersal policy, it was essential to relax this policy in order to speed deliveries. On October 8 Quarles exempted the ICBM program from the dispersal policy* wherever it interfered with achieving the earliest operational capability.[21]

Alternate ICBM (subsequently Titan) development again raised the question of whether to use competitive bidding and contracting procedures, or to award a "sole source" contract. General Schriever doubted that any

---

*The Martin Company had already purchased 4,500 acres of land near Denver, Colorado, and proposed to build the Titan there, rather than at its plant in Baltimore. [Ltr, Schriever to Ch SAPO (AMC), subj: Glenn L. Martin Site Location, Dec 14, 1955, in Basic Documents.]

Table 5-1

ICBM Development Budget Estimate ($ millions)

Fiscal Year	1955	1956	1957	1958
Research and Development (accounting code 600)	20.0	20.0	20.0	20.0
Procurement (150)	87.7	233.0	450.0	500.0
Facilities (131)	46.2	50.0	13.0	—
Public Works (300)	7.1	26.3	8.5	—
Total	161.0	329.3	491.5	520.0

Four-year cost = $1,501.8 million

Missiles Procured	13	80	116	140

Four-year procurement = 349 missiles

contractor was "uniquely qualified at this time to provide an outstanding advantage to the Air Force over all other contractors." Consequently, on May 6, 1955, the Air Force invited bids on the Titan ICBM. A source selection board composed of WDD and SAPO officials, with Col. Charles H. Terhune as chairman, evaluated the proposals of the three finalists: the Martin, Douglas, and Lockheed companies. The board chose Martin because of the company's superiority in several engineering and management categories. On September 15 Schriever submitted the board's recommendation to Generals Edwin W. Rawlings and Thomas S. Power. They approved, and on October 27 Martin signed a contract to design, develop, and test the Titan.[22]

The Martin Company proposal was for a two-stage ICBM, in tandem configuration, and having a gross weight of approximately 225,000 pounds. Titan's development plan showed that completion was scheduled about 18 months after the Atlas was developed. At this time the WDD grouped the associate contractors into two teams under Atlas and Titan. (See Chart 5-2.)[23]

Chart 5-2

Atlas and Titan Contractors

	Atlas	Titan
Airframe	Convair	Martin
Guidance Radio-inertial	General Electric	Bell Telephone
All-inertial	A.C. Spark Plug	American Bosch and MIT
Propulsion	North American	Aerojet General
Nose Cone	General Electric	AVCO
Computer	Burroughs	Remington Rand

A National Priority

The Air Force's sense of urgency concerning ICBM development was not generally shared within the Eisenhower Administration, which assumed that American strategic power was superior to that of the Soviets. On February 14, 1955, however, the Technological Capabilties Panel * of the President's Scientific Advisory Committee (Office of Defense Mobilization) issued distressing news. Called the Killian Report after its Chairman, Massachusetts Institute of Technology President James R. Killian, Jr., the report warned of an alarming potential disparity in weapons between the United States and the Soviet Union and drew attention to the vulnerability of North America to a surprise attack. Noting Soviet progress in rocket technology, the Killian Report recommended that the U.S. ICBM should become "a nationally supported effort of the highest priority." [24]

---

* In March 1954 President Eisenhower had asked the panel to consider the vulnerability of the United States to surprise attack. Rather than confine itself to a strictly technological approach, the forty-two-member panel conducted a broad investigation that considered almost the entire spectrum of offensive and defensive weapons.

This was exactly the opening Trevor Gardner had sought. Also, on March 1, he gained greater personal influence when the Senate Armed Services Committee confirmed his nomination as the first Assistant Secretary of the Air Force for Research and Development.* At a Congressional hearing on May 25 before the Military Applications Subcommittee of the Joint Atomic Energy Committee, Gardner predicted that the Soviet Union would test full-scale ICBMs sometime between 1960 and 1963. But, Gardner believed, the United States could have a rudimentary ICBM design ready for use in an emergency by mid-1958, provided the program was conducted on a crash basis. Senator Henry M. Jackson, the committee chairman, was encouraged by Gardner's prediction because it improved upon earlier estimates of a 1960 availability.[25]

Gardner devoted the entire summer of 1955 to advocating the ICBM program as the highest national priority. He and Schriever emphasized to Secretary Talbott that the program was being hampered by undesirable competition from other government agencies for the use of key scientists and engineers. Gardner warned that the situation would only worsen as the ICBM program progressed; he had already discerned a lack of support from certain elements within the aircraft industry. Some kind of policy machinery—from outside the Air Force—was required to focus national attention on the ICBM. In June, Gardner urged Talbott to ask that a high-level policy committee responsible to the President and the National Security Council be established. As precedent, Gardner cited President Franklin D. Roosevelt's creation of a policy committee to manage the Manhattan District Project during World War II.[26]

Seeing the Air Force program as a "race to achieve an operational ICBM ahead of the Soviets," Gardner worked hard to convince the President and Congress of its importance. He sought a Presidential directive that would assign the ICBM the highest national priority. The directive would also grant the Air Force complete authority and responsibility for directing the program, including procurement and funding; instruct the Bureau of the Budget on separate funding for the ICBM; and order the Atomic Energy Commission, National Advisory Committee for Aeronautics, and Commerce Department to assist the Air Force in achieving the earliest possible initial operational capability.[27]

Gardner's campaign gained significant support on June 30 when Senators Henry M. Jackson and Clinton P. Anderson† wrote to President

---

*Gardner was nominated to the statutory position in August 1954, but the committee tabled the nomination. Although the record of the hearing remains closed, associates surmise that Gardner was initially not confirmed because of his support of Dr. J. Robert Oppenheimer against allegations of disloyalty to the United States.

†Senator Anderson chaired the Joint Committee on Atomic Energy, and Senator Jackson was Chairman of the Atomic Energy Subcommittee on Military Applications.

Eisenhower, urging him to establish a crash program for the ICBM. The Senators deplored the "peacetime footing" under which the ICBM was proceeding. They also recommended that Secretary Talbott reexamine the ICBM program to ensure that it was receiving sufficient authority; that he soften procurement regulations wherever they hampered progress; and that he relax the "dispersal policy" with respect to all research and development work. Jackson and Anderson proposed that the President appoint an assistant to make certain that all government resources and facilities were at the disposal of the ICBM program.[28]

In response, President Eisenhower* immediately ordered Arthur S. Flemming, Director of the Office of Defense Mobilization, to arrange a personal briefing on the ICBM and referred the Senators' recommendations to Secretary of Defense Wilson for comment.[29]

Gardner agreed with all of the points made by Senators Jackson and Anderson except for the need to appoint a special presidential assistant on the ICBM. Gardner believed that the Air Force itself could perform that role, provided that the program had overriding national priority and a separate budget. On August 1, Gardner outlined his ideas on separate budgeting to USAF Chief of Staff Twining. Gardner asserted that if the Secretary of the Air Force exercised control over ICBM funds, the program would be safe from reprogramming actions taken by the Air Staff. To accelerate the program and provide greater security, he proposed to eliminate Air Staff reviews. ICBM funds would come under the control of the Secretary through a high-level committee, which would include the four assistant secretaries, the Chief of Staff, and the Special Assistant for Installations.[30]

On July 28, 1955, the long-awaited briefing to the President and the National Security Council concerning the urgency of the ICBM program was finally conducted. Gardner, von Neumann, and Schriever made the presentation. As a result of this briefing and recommendations by Secretary Wilson, the National Security Council, on August 11, directed its staff to draft a course of action.[31]

Arthur Flemming, of the Defense Mobilization Office, proposed that the President accord the ICBM the "highest priority as a research and development objective" and direct the Secretary of Defense to take whatever organizational action was necessary to accelerate the program. Secretary Wilson noted, however, that the ICBM already possessed the highest priority within the Department of Defense,† including the objective of achieving an operational

---

*On June 8 President Eisenhower was hospitalized following an attack of ileitis. He completed convalescence by July 20 and then embarked on a trip to Panama. There is no evidence that the illness distracted his attention from the ICBM matter. [See Herbert E. Parmet, *Eisenhower and the American Crusades,* New York: The Macmillan Co., 1972, p 449.]

†It was implicit in Wilson's approval of top Air Force priority for the ICBM in May 1954. See page 106.

capability as soon as possible. Nonetheless, Wilson asserted that national security policy (NSC 5501 and NSC 5408) recognized a varied and continued threat posed by the Soviet Union, a threat that required the military to be capable of performing a variety of missions. Therefore, "the assignment of an absolute overriding priority for one specific weapon system, such as the ICBM, . . . [was] not necessarily the most effective way to utilize national resources, particularly since no one form of weapon can be considered sufficient to meet the varied needs of national security." Wilson's stand was unambiguous. While the Air Force focused on the ICBM, it was not the ultimate weapon; and Wilson rejected the idea that it was in the national interest to concentrate exclusively on the ICBM.[32]

On August 30 the NSC staff recommended that the ICBM be designated "a research program of the highest national priority, second to no others unless modified by future decision of the President." The staff also recommended that the Secretary of Defense prosecute the program with "maximum urgency." The Joint Chiefs of Staff endorsed these points, and the National Security Council also agreed with its staff that the ICBM deserved top national priority. On September 13, 1955, the President approved. He also supported the Air Force's handling of the program and rejected transferring the ICBM to another agency.

That same day, Eisenhower wrote to Senators Jackson and Anderson: "I am convinced that in order to achieve maximum acceleration of this project, [we] should continue to build on the solid foundation that has been laid." He added, "any method involving lifting this program out of the context in which it has been established" would dissipate momentum and postpone operational readiness. Finally, the President pledged to use all available resources "to the end that nothing surmountable shall stand in the way of the most rapid progress of this program . . . no other development program is now the subject of so urgent and emphatic a directive."[33]

Acting "with maximum urgency," the Defense Department passed the President's directive to Air Force Secretary Quarles and authorized him to recommend whatever organizational procedures he thought necessary to accelerate ICBM development. Trevor Gardner had been concerned for some time with the proliferation of DOD committees which subjected the ICBM program to time-consuming reviews.* On September 13 he assigned Hyde Gillette, Deputy for Budget and Program Management, to evaluate management controls for the ICBM and to devise means to reduce delays—especially with regard to facilities—due to financial procedures, procurement policies, and other administrative aspects.[34]

---

* Earlier, in June, an Air Staff ad hoc group considered establishing the use of a "management fund" for the ballistic missile program. Brig. Gen. Bruce K. Holloway, Acting Deputy Director for R&D, asserted that the Atlas held the highest development priority and that its funding requirements would be met at all costs—even at the expense of all other Air Force projects.

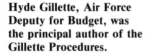

Hyde Gillette, Air Force Deputy for Budget, was the principal author of the Gillette Procedures.

Members of the Gillette Committee included General Schriever, Gen. Charles M. McCorkle, Dr. H. Guyford Stever, Richard Horner, Joseph Hoover, Col. Ray E. Soper, Col. William Rogers, Col. E. N. Ljunggren, Col. William Leonhard, Col. Harold T. Morris, Lt. Col. Vincent J. Ford, Lt. Col. Charles Waldecker, and Maj. E. C. Saltzman. In October the committee submitted what was officially called the Air Force Plan for Simplifying Administrative Procedures, or simply the Gillette Procedures.

This document proposed to confirm that WDD alone would be responsible for planning, programming, and directing ballistic missile development in the Air Force. It also recommended establishing a single level of formal approval in the Air Force, to be known as the Ballistic Missiles Committee. Similarly, it called for the creation of a single committee at the OSD level to exercise ultimate review and decision authority. Overall, the Gillette Procedures streamlined the review process by cutting the number of reviewing authorities from forty-two to ten.[35] (See Chart 5-3.)

On October 15 Quarles submitted the Gillette Procedures to Deputy Defense Secretary Reuben B. Robertson, Jr. for approval. Quarles requested that the Air Force be granted expediting authority until the ICBM attained an emergency, or initial operational capability. (It was expected that beginning with the production phase, the ICBM would revert to regular DOD procurement procedures.)[36]

OSD approved the Gillette Procedures on November 8 and announced the creation of an OSD Ballistic Missiles Committee (Chart 5-4). Chaired by

Deputy Secretary Robertson,* this committee was charged with reviewing and approving the annual ICBM development plan. Additionally, OSD established a special ICBM funding category, separate from other Air Force programs. The Air Force's ICBM Scientific Advisory Committee, chaired by von Neumann, was transformed into an advisory body of the Department of Defense. It was provided with complete access to all technological developments and made subject to call by all of the military services and OSD for technical program review and advice. This action provided that "the Air Force ballistic missile programs [would] be subject to no other outside scientific consultant review." [37]

Quarles chaired the Air Force Ballistic Missiles Committee which included Assistant Secretaries Gardner, Lyle S. Garlock, and Dudley C. Sharp,† and Maj. Gen. Samuel R. Brentnall, the Assistant Chief of Staff for Guided Missiles. The Air Force committee could approve facility requirements; establish completion dates; designate construction agencies; and approve construction criteria and standards. The Bureau of the Budget was expected to provide the Air Force with a separate ICBM budget, as justified by the development and financial plan and approved by the OSD Ballistic Missiles Committee. Western Development Division was required to submit a comprehensive plan which, when approved, provided the basis for all programming, planning, budgeting, testing, and production for the ICBM program. This plan would be submitted annually to OSD on October 1, except for the first plan due on December 1, 1955. [38]

Subsequently, General White established a secretariat for the Air Force Ballistic Missiles Committee and designated General Brentnall as the single point of contact between the Air Staff and all other Air Force agencies on ballistic missile matters. White directed that "only insurmountable causes would be accepted for failure to meet a deadline" in the program. [39]

On December 20 Secretary Robertson advised Quarles that the OSD Ballistic Missiles Committee had approved the Air Force ICBM program for Fiscal Years 1956 and 1957 essentially as presented and reserved the accounts within the 1956 budget as shown in Table 5-5. [40]

Initial Operational Capability

In July 1955 Col. William A. Sheppard, Schriever's Deputy for Plans, proposed to concentrate his efforts on accelerating Atlas's operational

---

*Other committee members were the Assistant Secretaries of Defense for R&D, Applications Engineering, Properties and Installations, the Comptroller, and an executive secretary. It also included an Assistant Director of the Bureau of the Budget.

†Sharp succeeded Lewis on October 30, 1955.

Chart 5-3

Major Offices and Agencies
Having Independent or Separate
Review Responsibility in the ICBM Program

Present System	Proposed System

Present System

Congress

Bureau of the Budget

National Security Council

Office Secretary of Defense
  Secretary of Defense
  Deputy Secretary
    of Defense
  Armed Forces Policy Council
  Assistant Secretary,
    Comptroller
  Assistant Secretary, R&D
  R&D Policy Council
  Joint Coordinating Committee
    on Guided Missiles
  Technical Advisory Panel
    on Aeronautics
  Committee for Aeronautical
    R&D Facilities
  Assistant Secretary,
    Applications Engineering
  Assistant Secretary, Properties
    and Installations
  Assistant Secretary,
    Atomic Energy

Office Secretary of the Air Force
  Secretary of the Air Force
  Assistant Secretary, Materiel
  Assistant Secretary, Financial
    Management
  Assistant Secretary,
    Manpower & Personnel
  Assistant Secretary, R&D

Proposed System

Congress

Bureau of the Budget

National Security Council

Scientific
Advisory
Committee*

Secretary of Defense
OSD Ballistic
  Missiles Committee

Scientific
Advisory
Committee*

Secretary of the Air Force

Air Force Ballistic
  Missiles Committee

Headquarters USAF
  Chief of Staff
  Air Council
  Deputy Chief of Staff,
    Operations
  Deputy Chief of Staff,
    Materiel
  Deputy Chief of Staff,
    Development
  Deputy Chief of Staff,
    Comptroller
  Deputy Chief of Staff,
    Personnel
  Assistant C/S, Installations
  Assistant C/S, Guided
    Missiles
  Program Status Committee
  Budget Advisory Committee
  Aircraft & Weapons Board
  Installations Board
  Scientific Advisory Board
  Weapon Systems Committee

Chief of Staff

Air Research and
  Development Command

Air Research and
  Development Command

Air Materiel Command

Industrial Facilities Review
  Board

Western Development Division

| Scientific Advisory Committee* |

Western Development Division

*OSD's Scientific Advisory Committee could be consulted by all of the services and OSD.

Chart 5-4

Ballistic Missile Organization Structure

As of October 1955

Scientific Advisory Committee

Prof von Neumann, Chairman
Dr H. Bode
Dr N. E. Bradbury
Mr F. R. Collbohm
Mr L. A. Hyland
Prof G. Kistiakowsky
Brig Gen Lindbergh
Dr J. McRae
Dr I. R. McMath
Dr C. B. Millikan
Prof J. B. Wiesner
Dr H. F. York
Dr J. R. Zacharias
Dr C. L. Zimmerman

OSD

Ballistic Missiles Committee
Dep Sec Robertson, Chairman*
Asst Sec Newbury
Asst Sec McNeil
Asst Sec Floete
Asst Sec Macauley
Exec Sec A. G. Waggoner

Air Force

Ballistic Missiles Committee
Sec Quarles, Chairman
Asst Sec Gardner, Vice Chairman
Asst Sec Garlock
Asst Sec Sharp
Maj Gen Brentnall
Secy Col R. E. Soper

HQ USAF

Asst Chief of Staff for Guided
  Missiles
Maj Gen Brentnall
Brig Gen McCorkle
Col R. E. Soper

ARDC

Lt Gen Power, Commander
Gen Schriever, Dep Cmdr for
Ballistic Missile Programs

AMC

Maj Gen Rawlings, Commander
Col H. T. Morris, Dep Cmdr for
Ballistic Missile Programs

WDD

Maj Gen Schriever,
  Commander
Col C. H. Terhune,
  Dep Cmdr, Tech Opns
Col W. A. Sheppard,
  Dep Cmdr, Plans
Lt Col J. B. Hudson,
  Dir Support Opns

Ramo-Woolridge Corp

(Serves as WDD technical staff;
provides systems engineering and
technical direction to contractors)
Dr Simon Ramo, Exec VP
Dr Ralph Johnson, VP Research
Dr Louis Dunn, Dir Guided
  Missiles Research Division
Dr R. F. Mettler, Asst Dir GMRD
Dr M. H. Nichols, Asst Dir GMRD

Special Aircraft Projects Office (AMC)

Col H. T. Morris, Commander

* Beginning in April 1956 the Special Assistant for Guided Missiles served as chairman.

Table 5-5

FY 1956 Budget ($ million)

Research and Development (accounting category 600)	20.036
Missiles Procurement (150)	233.426
Facilities (131)	55.000
Public Works (300)	26.300
Maintenance and Operations (400)	.935
Other Procurement (200)	.250
Total	335.947

readiness date. Sheppard noted that the Air Force was not well organized to accomplish the task: "The major operating commands are strongly oriented toward near-term programs and have a distinct reluctance for undertaking strong and specific action in connection with a program for 1960 and beyond." He recommended that an executive agent with broad authority be named to accelerate the Atlas. Sheppard suggested that General Power, the ARDC Commander, would be an ideal candidate for the job.[41]

The concept of an initial operational capability, however, was not broached in detail until the preparation of the Gillette Committee report in October. The committee recommended that the Chief of Staff extend ARDC's responsibility to include the Atlas IOC. Air Force leaders would decide at what point the ICBM was combat ready; command and control would then pass to the Strategic Air Command.[42]

On November 18 General White directed that the immediate objective of the ICBM was "the earliest possible attainment of an initial operational capability." * The term IOC was defined as the ability to launch prototype

---

* The significance of adding IOC responsibility meant that top priority now also included production. [Summary of JCS 1620/116, Nov 16, 1955, WDGH (WDD), May 18, 1956, in Basic Documents.]

weapons that were still under development and included activating one or two operational bases. General White understood the limitations of this "capability" and fully accepted that "initially, the ICBM will probably incorporate certain marginal technical features." He assigned the IOC to the Air Research and Development Command and directed the Strategic Air Command to "establish the closest possible working relations" with ARDC. This close relationship was meant to facilitate the later transfer of the ICBM force to SAC.[43]

Gen. Curtis E. LeMay, the Commander in Chief of SAC, acknowledged the long-term value of ICBMs in qualified terms: "I consider an ICBM with capability of instantaneous launch and with acceptable reliability, accuracy and yield to be the ultimate weapon in the strategic inventory." For the interim, however, LeMay viewed missiles principally as aids to the penetration of manned bombers. This view conflicted with official Air Force policy, which called for the speediest possible integration of missiles and aircraft. LeMay believed that the military worth of ICBMs lay in their "political and psychological value," but in no case would ICBMs alone "be capable of destroying the target system."[44]

SAC's position notwithstanding, Generals LeMay and Power met on September 27 to discuss the ICBM initial operational capability. As a result of the talks LeMay agreed to assist ARDC by formulating the ICBM operational concepts and establishing prototype bases. Brig. Gen. John P.

Gen. Curtis E. LeMay commanded Strategic Air Command, which would gain operational control over the new missiles.

McConnell, SAC's Director of Plans, was assigned to carry out the project.[45]

On December 14, 1955, based on General White's directive, ARDC delegated to General Schriever its responsibility for the IOC. Ten missiles and launchers were expected to be in place by April 1959. It was initially contemplated that the missile/launcher sites would not be hardened, that is, they would be unprotected and above ground, and located on government land. The force would increase to 120 missiles (80 Atlas and 40 Titan) at 60 launch sites by January 1960. Three missile bases were required to be operational, one each in the eastern, central, and western parts of the country. At each missile base, crews were required to be capable of launching 20 missiles within 2 hours and with a 15-minute reaction time. No date was specified, however, for transferring control of the missile force to SAC.[46]

Thor

Among the recommendations made by the Scientific Advisory Committee at its January 1955 meeting was that the Air Force consider developing a tactical ballistic missile.* General Schriever opposed the separate development of this weapon because he felt that it would divert scarce resources and talent from the ICBM program. He noted, for example, that Douglas Aircraft and Bell Telephone Laboratories were delaying bids on the ICBM in the expectation of winning the tactical ballistic missile contract. Similarly, Reaction Motors, the propulsion subcontractor to Aerojet General, seemed more interested in bidding on the tactical ballistic missile than in putting forth its best efforts on the ICBM. Schriever, therefore, suggested that the tactical missile emerge as an outgrowth of the Atlas development. The Scientific Advisory Committee agreed that the smaller missile could "fall out" from components of the ICBM program. But the committee preferred that it emerge from the alternate ICBM—the Titan—rather than from the Atlas. Trevor Gardner accepted the scientists' recommendation and asked the Air Staff to withhold separate development of the tactical ballistic missile and to cancel the ongoing design competition.[47]

---

* Variously known as the Tactical Ballistic Missile (TBM), Medium Range Ballistic Missile (MRBM), and lastly the Intermediate Range Ballistic Missile (IRBM). All of these designations referred to a missile varying in range between 1,000 and 2,000 nautical miles. The TBM was originally meant to replace the Matador tactical missile. The Air Force, however, decided that the TBM more properly belonged in the strategic category. It eventually became the Thor. This meeting was held at Walter Reed Army Hospital, as von Neumann was about to undergo cancer surgery. [Hartt, Juliam, *The Mighty Thor: Missile in Readiness* (New York: Duell, Sloan and Pearce, 1961), p 64.]

The British government was interested in the Air Force tactical ballistic missile and first inquired about it in February 1955, but the issue concerning disclosure of atomic energy information hampered American and British cooperation. During the spring of 1955 Trevor Gardner recommended modifying U.S. policy so as to allow for an exchange of atomic data. By the end of the year an agreement had been drafted but remained unsigned.[48]

The report of the Killian Committee, in February 1955, had also urged development of an intermediate range ballistic missile. The report considered the IRBM vital to the Soviet military because with this weapon the Soviets could target virtually all of Europe and Asia. Moreover, the Killian Committee believed that an American IRBM could be made available earlier than an American ICBM because the former was technologically easier to develop. The committee also recommended the high-priority development of nuclear propulsion for aircraft and artificial satellites for intelligence gathering. Both the Air Force and the Department of Defense readily endorsed these recommendations. The only differences between the military and the Killian group concerned the availability of funds to carry out the recommendations.[49]

In March Schriever informed General Power that the Army was not about to phase out its ballistic missile group—the team headed by Wernher von Braun—at the Redstone Arsenal in Alabama. Moreover, he reported that the Army intended to build a medium range ballistic missile and proposed that it be used as the first stage for a non-military scientific satellite. When the Army offered to serve as contractor and develop a medium range ballistic missile for the Air Force, Schriever ridiculed the idea:

> It would be naive to think that the Army would develop a weapon and then turn it over to the Air Force to operate. Therefore, I strongly recommend that our relationship with Redstone remain on an exchange of information basis.[50]

Schriever noted that the ICBM program enjoyed solid support at the highest levels and favored the Air Force pursuing its own development. He counselled against becoming involved with the scientific satellite, viewing the military satellite project as the more important one.[51]

On March 16 the Air Force issued a general operational requirement for a "strategic reconnaissance satellite weapon system" that was expected to become available within ten years. That fall it transferred management of the military satellite, designated Weapon System 117L, from the Wright Air Development Center to WDD.[52]*

---

*The transfer became official in February 1956.

144

In May a general officer board, chaired by Maj. Gen. Donald Yates, recommended that the Air Force establish a missile development center. The board's report noted that the ICBM required separate facilities because of technical and applied engineering differences between manned aircraft and missiles, which operated outside the atmosphere. Although facility needs could be projected only in the most general terms, the Administration was clearly under pressure from Congress and the press to take on and defeat the Russians in a missile and space "race." General Yates noted that the Air Force was locked in intense interservice rivalry and, with the Defense Department's predilection to compromise such issues, the result would lead inevitably to an uncontrolled competition for scientists, engineers, and facilities. Therefore, he reasoned that it was only "natural" for the Air Force to move ahead into the space environment, as it was related to the functions that the ICBM, IRBM, and military satellites would perform. The Air Force enjoyed an advantage over the other services in terms of having available a development-management organization, scientific support, facilities, and an industrial base. In this context, it made sense to establish a missiles and space development center; Holloman Air Development Center, New Mexico, seemed the ideal site.[53]

Only one week after it had approved proceeding with the alternate ICBM, on May 9, 1955, the Air Staff encouraged ARDC to solicit industry proposals for studying the tactical ballistic missile. Among the contractors formally considered were Douglas, Lockheed, Martin, General Electric, North American, McDonnell, and the Army's Redstone Arsenal. In forwarding the Air Staff action, General Power instructed Schriever to "avoid the appearance of solicitation of a competition, and it should be clearly understood that the Air Force is making no commitment for follow on contractual action." But pressure for a medium range ballistic missile intensified.[54]

The DOD established a Technical Advisory Committee, under Deputy Secretary of Defense Robertson, to consider the best approach to develop the intermediate range ballistic missile. In July the committee concluded that the IRBM was not a natural derivative of the ICBM and that it should, therefore, be carried out as a separate development. The Robertson Committee conclusions stemmed from earlier studies by Ramo-Wooldridge which showed that the IRBM could not emerge from a second stage of the Titan. The most serious limitation was that the longest range expected of this type of IRBM was approximately 700 nautical miles.[55]

Asked to recommend another IRBM development approach, General Schriever instructed R–W in August to evaluate contractor studies that had been performed in connection with the IRBM operational requirement. Commander Robert C. Truax, a Navy officer serving with WDD, was put in charge of the project.[56]

National Security Council deliberations regarding the ICBM had also considered the status and priority of the IRBM program. These discussions led to a roles and missions issue among the military services, each proposing to develop the IRBM and prepared to justify its interest in operating the weapon. After an initial "split paper"—a report indicating lack of unanimity—the Joint Chiefs of Staff tried to resolve the issue in October by recommending the development of two IRBMs. IRBM Number 1 (XSM-75), subsequently the Thor, would be an Air Force project; IRBM Number 2 (XSM-68), subsequently the Jupiter, would be a joint Army and Navy undertaking. The OSD organized an Army–Navy Ballistic Missiles Committee with the Secretary of the Army as Chairman and the Navy Secretary as Vice Chairman. The Redstone Arsenal was assigned systems responsibility for IRBM Number 2. On November 8, Defense Secretary Wilson* accepted the JCS compromise and placed the IRBM under the direction of the OSD Ballistic Missiles Committee.[57]

In addition to establishing the machinery for managing the IRBM programs, Wilson assigned to the IRBM "a priority equal to the ICBM but with no interference to the valid requirements of the ICBM program." He sought to carry out both programs "at the maximum rate technology will permit." IRBMs 1 and 2 would have equal priority. But the unique status of the ICBM program—which Trevor Gardner and the Air Force had obtained through much labor—was rudely swept away. On December 1, 1955, President Eisenhower approved a National Security Council (NSC 1484)† recommendation to assign the ICBM and IRBM "joint" highest national priority.

This peculiar status was subject to various interpretations. Thus, Secretary Wilson understood the directive to mean that, in the event of a conflict between the ICBM and IRBM that might "harm the national interest," the issue would be resolved by the President himself.[58] Trevor Gardner, by contrast, believed that, if a conflict arose between the ICBM and other programs, the others would have to give way. In December Gardner drafted a reply to Atomic Energy Commissioner Lewis Strauss, who had tried to reconcile priorities for atomic warheads between the ICBM and IRBM. Curiously, Gardner's reply did not consider NSC 1484; instead it adverted to the President's September 13 decision to place the ICBM "on

---

*Trevor Gardner was especially bitter about Wilson's approval of parallel IRBM development by the Army and Navy. Gardner decried the wastefulness of this action and noted that it was Wilson who considered "competition in missiles . . . as desirable and necessary as it was in the automotive industry." [Gardner, "How We Fell Behind in Guided Missiles," *Air Power Historian,* Jan 1958, p 11.]

†Deputy Secretary Robertson intended to enforce NSC 1484. On December 23 he directed his assistant, Clifford C. Furnas, to prepare monthly progress reports on all ballistic missile programs.

a priority by itself and above other development programs." Gardner, Power, and Brentnall drafted an agreement with the Army and Navy, stipulating that the IRBM would not interfere with ICBM development. The draft memorandum was to have been signed by Gardner, William H. Martin, the Army's Director of R&D, and James H. Smith, the Navy's Assistant Secretary for Air. Apparently, however, it was never executed.[59]

The decision to assign the ICBM and IRBM equal priority was probably influenced by a State Department study. The study considered the implications of the ballistic missile race and concluded that, should the Soviets be the first to develop a long range ballistic missile, this achievement would greatly reduce Free World confidence in American technological superiority and might lead several nations toward a "third world orientation." But, if the United States managed to develop an IRBM at the same time that the Soviets demonstrated an ICBM, that feat would mitigate the problem.[60]

On December 14 ARDC assigned the IRBM development and IOC missions to WDD. Only Douglas, Lockheed, and North American were to be considered in this competition; the other study contractors were eliminated for various reasons. Ramo-Wooldridge was disqualified because it did not possess a production capability. WDD assumed that the Redstone Arsenal would be busy developing IRBM Number 2. Northrop had not submitted a proposal for a ballistic missile, and the Martin Company had been awarded the alternate ICBM contract. Finally, WDD rejected McDonnell Aircraft's proposal for a glide missile because it raised too many problems that were not considered solvable within the imposed time constraints. The Air Force source selection board chose Douglas to develop the IRBM, subsequently Thor (WS-315A) XSM-75. Following Air Force approval, a contract was signed on December 27.[61]

The addition of the IRBM to WDD's responsibilities resulted in a rearrangement of several associate subcontractors during December, as shown in Chart 5-6.[62]

By the end of 1955, WDD had been transformed from a special project office to a major weapons development center. It acquired responsibility for building a "family of missiles," including the Atlas and Titan ICBMs, the Thor IRBM, and as the WS-117L reconnaissance satellite. It also undertook experimentation in solid-propellant rockets. The division was granted the highest national priorities and an unusual degree of management freedom to produce, as soon as possible, several vitally needed weapon systems.

Chart 5–6

Thor Contractors

Airframe	Douglas
Guidance	
Radio-inertial	Bell Telephone Laboratories
All-inertial	A.C. Spark Plug
Propulsion	North American
Nose Cone	General Electric

Chapter VI

The Poor Man's Approach

> With every tick of the clock, the Soviet Union is moving closer to . . . knocking this country out. Intercontinental air power and missiles are the new double-edged sword of destruction, hanging by a hair over us all.
>
> Trevor Gardner, 1956

Even as it wrestled with the philosophic problems of equal or unequal treatment of ICBMs and IRBMs, the Air Force had to resolve the question of how fast to deploy missiles. Agreement on this issue was as difficult as it was in the matter of which kind of missiles to produce. In attempting to establish initial operational capability dates for the ICBMs, General White favored an early schedule. General Schriever, by contrast, worried about deploying the missiles prematurely. He wanted more systematic testing and incorporation of modifications. In May 1956, Schriever, with the support of Generals Power and LeMay, persuaded General White to delay the initial IOC to January 1960 and the final IOC to March 1961.

When the plan supporting this schedule came before the Air Force Ballistic Missiles Committee in July 1956, it received a cool reception from Air Force Secretary Donald Quarles. Undoubtedly influenced by the Congressional hearings on airpower, he found little to his liking in the plan. In particular, he disapproved of the Fiscal Year 1957 budget. Quarles favored applying a "poor man's approach," whereby the final IOC was extended from March to December 1961, and he wanted to delete either the Atlas or the Titan. A revised plan, presented in September, resulted in the elimination of one group of Atlas missiles. The AF–BMC also rejected the new cost estimates and ordered further cuts.

The Western Development Division reduced the Fiscal Year 1958 budget by 20 percent, cautioning that the resulting document represented the lowest prudent level. The AF–BMC approved in November and the

OSD–BMC in December 1956. The plan then went forward to the National Security Council. President Eisenhower, however, postponed his approval until March 1957; he did not specify the number of missiles to be deployed and ordered that no changes were to be made without his express consent. Also, in a significant policy shift, the Administration called for the earliest practical operational readiness instead of the previously announced earliest possible date. Thus, despite reported Soviet advances in missilery, economic concerns prevailed over military ones. The approved missile force was one-third smaller than originally specified. The Air Force ICBM force was to consist of two groups containing forty Atlas and forty Titan missiles respectively. The initial IOC date was moved up to March 1959, although only three operational launchers were now required. The final IOC date was extended to July 1961.

In March 1956 WDD (ARDC) was also made responsible for achieving the IRBM initial operational capability. The original plan called for eight Thor squadrons at three bases in the United Kingdom. The initial IOC called for ten missiles by October 1958, with the final IOC scheduled for July 1959. Responsibility for the IRBM IOC was then split between ARDC and SAC. The IRBM involved bilateral negotiations between the United States and the United Kingdom and included an emergency plan. As with the ICBM, General Schriever worried that the IRBM IOC date was too optimistic, especially because of the high production rates required. He persuaded General LeMay to delay the final IOC date from July 1959 to July 1960.

The IRBM plan also came under the close scrutiny of Air Force Secretary Quarles. In September 1956 Quarles directed revisions to the plan, but WDD insisted that only minor changes were possible. The Air Force Secretary then directed that only the IOC dates had to be met, not the number of Thor IRBMs. As a result, WDD was obliged to cut the IRBM force in half, from eight to four squadrons. By the end of 1956, this plan had been approved by both the Air Force and OSD Ballistic Missiles Committees and then went to the White House. As he had done with the ICBM program, the President withheld IRBM approval until March 1957.

A major decision made in November 1956 assigned to the Air Force operational responsibility for the IRBM. In effect, this meant that the Army's Jupiter would come under Air Force control.

The reductions in the numbers of missiles scheduled for operational deployment served as a harbinger of more budgetary cuts. In May 1957 the missile program's Fiscal Year 1958 budget was reduced by $200 million. Two months later the Administration wielded a heavy economic axe by reducing missile deliveries, lowering overtime, and delaying payments to contractors. Schriever warned that these steps would delay the deployment of ballistic missiles by three years.

When the Administration failed to heed this warning, it received an unexpected jolt. On October 4, 1957, the Soviet Union launched the world's first artificial satellite into orbit. The event caused a national furor and obliged the Administration to reverse itself.* In February 1958, after considering a series of alternate missile deployment plans, the President approved the deployment of four Thor, four Jupiter, nine Atlas, and four Titan squadrons.

The Air Force disapproved of President Eisenhower's granting the IRBM coequal priority with the ICBM. In February 1956 General Twining protested to Secretary Quarles, noting that the IRBM would be more difficult and time-consuming to deploy than the ICBM. Also, the IRBM was more vulnerable to enemy attack and more difficult to support. Nonetheless, the Air Force met with the Army and Navy to resolve any conflicts at the working level concerning ballistic missiles. The services exchanged liaison officers, established a schedule for delivery of common components, and discussed reimbursement for use of facilities.[1]

Quarles forwarded the Chief of Staff's protest to Defense Secretary Wilson, but Wilson closed the issue on February 7 without responding. The next day, Trevor Gardner informed Quarles that he intended to resign. Officially, Gardner explained that he had become disenchanted with Wilson's policy of reduced spending for research and development. At the core, however, was the missiles issue. Gardner was convinced that the United States could not afford to dissipate its limited technological resources by pursuing duplicative and competing missile programs in all of the military departments. An emergency meeting between Gardner and Wilson aboard the latter's yacht in Miami failed to avert Gardner's resignation on February 10. The press speculated that Gardner resigned because of disappointment at not being named the OSD Special Assistant for Guided Missiles. The post of "Missile Czar" was filled in March by Dr. Eger V. Murphree, an Esso Oil Company executive. There were also rumors of a possible conflict of interest and that Gardner was under Congressional investigation. None of the allegations was substantiated.[2]

Gardner's resignation cost the Air Force its most effective missile advocate. Although often abrasive and outspoken, Trevor Gardner was instrumental in establishing the Air Force ICBM program and permitting the United States to compete with the Russians in the missile field. Gardner returned to the presidency of his small electronics firm, Hycon Manufacturing, in Pasadena, California, and wrote several magazine articles intended to alert the public and President Eisenhower to the risk of not

---

*See page 169 and following for the effect of the Sputnik crisis.

proceeding at full speed with the missile program.* The administration ignored Gardner's warning and embarked on a policy that retarded missile development.[3]

ICBM Initial Operational Capability

About eighteen months after the Air Force accelerated ICBM development, the Eisenhower Administration assigned the highest national priority to building the IOC force and approved the deployment schedule. In the process of gaining the top priority, the Air Force missile proponents ran the gauntlet of officials from their own department, OSD, and the Administration.

In his November 18, 1955, directive to ARDC,† General White specified neither the size of the ICBM force nor the schedule for attaining the IOC. General Schriever's command, the Western Development Division, had studied operational concepts from the beginning. On December 20 WDD had briefed representatives of ARDC, AMC, SAC, and Air Training Command (ATC) concerning ICBM operations, logistics, personnel, and installations. At that time WDD offered recommendations on the force structure as well as operational readiness dates.[4]

Based on these recommendations, enemy target requirements, and other strategic considerations, on December 28 General White outlined the expected size of the ICBM force and specified dates for its availability. The IOC would consist of 1 wing with 3 support bases, each having 40 missiles and 20 launching positions. The schedule called for 10 operational missiles to be in place by April 1, 1959, and the entire force of 120 missiles and 60 launchers to be ready by January 1, 1960. Because of this hurried schedule, the 3 bases—1 each in the eastern, central, and western United States—were to be located on government land. Headquarters USAF was to approve ARDC's site selection and facilities designs; ARDC would coordinate its efforts with SAC.[5]

The short schedule also dictated designing "soft" bases, that is, facilities unprotected from nuclear explosive effects. Survival and retaliation depended on the dispersion of the launchers, a rudimentary air defense, and rapid reaction time. White defined the last as the capability for each base to launch 10 missiles (25 percent of the force) within 15 minutes after an alert warning and another 10 missiles within the next 2 hours.[6]

WDD had completed a ballistic missile development plan shortly after Secretary Wilson's November 8, 1955, directive to accelerate the program,

---

*On February 1, Senator Henry M. Jackson also stated that the United States must accelerate its ICBM program or risk losing the race.

†See page 140.

A model of Sputnik I on display at the Academy of Sciences Pavillion Agricultural and Industrial Exhibition, Moscow.

but before White's two directives on the IOC. Consequently, the plan that the Air Force Ballistic Missiles Committee reviewed on November 23, 1955, contained no reference to the IOC; the committee then asked for a detailed IOC plan.[7]

On March 19, 1956, WDD presented its detailed plan, but it differed sharply from the guidance set down by General White in November and December 1955. In the plan, WDD proposed a slight delay in the operational date for the first missiles, but more than one year's slippage in completion of the IOC. Schriever feared that, if the missiles were built according to existing IOC specifications, they would not fly. He reasoned that the delay would be beneficial because it would enable the contractors to build up production more slowly and permit them to incorporate essential modifications during assembly. The Air Force Ballistic Missiles Committee, however, rejected WDD's plan and instructed Schriever to submit a revised plan by mid-June 1956.[8]

General White was disturbed by WDD's failure to follow his earlier guidance. He had previously heard the rationale for delaying the IOC and dismissed it. Accordingly, White ordered that a new IOC plan—based on the original requirements—be prepared as soon as possible.[9]

Nonetheless, Schriever was confident of his correct approach. On May 7 Schriever briefed Generals Power and LeMay on WDD's plan and obtained the backing of both men. Power challenged White's guidance as impractical on technical as well as operational grounds. He contended that the Vice Chief's directives would produce unsuitable and untested developmental missiles. Moreover, White's hurried schedule would not allow procurement of proper training equipment and, therefore, would slow the personnel buildup. Conversely, a slower initial production rate would allow the timely introduction of essential modifications before too many developmental missiles rolled off the production line. By using expedited but realistic lead times, Power argued, the 120-missile IOC force would be achieved, at the earliest, by March 1961—more than one year later than White had directed.[10]

General LeMay also supported Schriever and considered it foolish to freeze designs and commit the ICBM to production before the contractor was able to flight test the missile adequately. To meet the IOC in this way would negate the entire purpose of the flight test program and would preclude the application of essential modifications from early operational missiles. LeMay said that it was more realistic to establish IOC dates based on the already-compressed developmental schedules, rather than the other way around.[11]

On May 22, following a comprehensive briefing by an ARDC–WDD team, General White reversed his position. He informed Power, LeMay, and Schriever of his agreement to the following ICBM IOC changes: 25

operational missiles to be in place by January 1, 1960, and 120 missiles by March 1961. The complete force would comprise 2 Atlas groups and 1 Titan group employing a total of 120 missiles, 72 launching pads, and 24 guidance stations. White directed WDD to prepare a detailed plan for his approval by June 15.[12]

On June 14 Schriever submitted the IOC plan. Containing essentially what had been briefed in May, the plan won quick approval. Four days later the Air Force Council and the Aircraft and Weapons Board, meeting in joint session, endorsed the plan and passed it on to the Air Force Ballistic Missiles Committee.[13]

The committee, meeting on July 3, 1956, found little to its liking in the plan other than the final inventory of 120 missiles. Secretary Quarles, the committee chairman, was most distressed over the $187.3 million Fiscal Year 1957 IOC budget and favored stretching out certain actions to allow for funding in subsequent years. He also considered postponing the IOC completion from March to December 1961 and deleting either the Atlas or the Titan program, and he favored concentrating on the construction of only the projected training-operational base (Camp Cooke). Quarles criticized the dual development of missile subsystems as "over insurance," opposed building production facilities beyond those needed for the development program, and demanded more austerity in planning base facilities. At the close of the marathon meeting—which lasted 6 hours and 20 minutes—Quarles refused to approve the IOC plan and directed that it be reorientated using a "Poor Man's" approach, to incorporate the many suggestions made during the meeting. He directed that a revised plan be submitted in September.[14]

The cost-cutting approach was no doubt influenced by the airpower hearings in Congress, which also examined the missile program. These hearings, conducted by Senator Stuart Symington's Subcommittee on the Air Force (of the Senate Committee on Armed Services), ran from April through July 1956.* The committee questioned Defense Department officials as to the rationale for having applied deep cuts in Fiscal Year 1957 research and development funding. Secretary Quarles testified on June 26 and 28, just prior to the crucial July 3 meeting of the Air Force Ballistic Missiles Committee. He defended his concurrence with the Administration's R&D reductions thusly:

> I believe it both necessary and feasible to provide adequate military defenses and, at the same time, to preserve the sound, economic foundations of the Nation . . . I consider it part of my duty to seek and to urge the most economical methods of providing adequate air power for the country.

---

*The record of the hearings was not made public until January 1957.

* * *

This [FY 1957 budget] is a huge research and development effort. It does not provide for doing all things the mind can conceive . . . as a practical matter some restraint must be placed on the otherwise runaway tendency research and development projects.[15]

During July Maj. Gen. Samuel R. Brentnall, the Assistant Chief of Staff for Guided Missiles, advised General White to oppose Secretary Quarles's position. In August General Brentnall's successor, Brig. Gen. Charles M. McCorkle, did the same. The generals cited the September 1955 National Security Council action, which called for an ICBM operational capability "at the earliest possible date." Quarles's "Poor Man's" approach, they contended, would not satisfy the military requirements. Worse, it threatened to create an imbalance in ICBMs between the United States and the Soviet Union by 1960. But General White declined to engage in a dispute with the Secretary of the Air Force. Instead, he awaited the findings of a WDD cost-saving study aimed at retaining the major objectives outlined in the disapproved IOC plan.[16]

Undersecretary of the Air Force James H. Douglas (second left) congratulates Donald A. Quarles (extreme right) on his appointment as Secretary of the Air Force. Secretary of Defense Charles E. Wilson (second right) and Air Force Chief of Staff Gen. Nathan F. Twining (extreme left) look on.

Gen. Thomas D. White served as USAF Vice Chief of Staff until he became Chief of Staff in July 1957.

On September 19, WDD presented its eagerly anticipated study to the Air Force Ballistic Missiles Committee. Much to the committee's consternation, however, WDD's program estimate of $1.672 billion for Fiscal Year 1958 represented an increase despite Quarles's clear demands to reduce costs. And, while WDD had recommended several cost-saving features, it favored keeping the original objective of fielding 120 operational missiles by March 1961.[17]

Although the Air Staff sympathized with Schriever's program, it also appreciated the necessity of meeting the cost reductions demanded by Secretary Quarles. Noting that the National Security Council had not specified the size of the ICBM IOC force, the Air Force Council recommended deleting from the plan one of the three programmed ICBM groups and one of the three missile support bases. The council favored thereby eliminating the Titan program. But General Schriever argued that canceling or deleting the Titan threatened to delay Atlas development because of the close interrelationship in subsystems testing between the missiles. The council, therefore, agreed to recommend one of the Atlas groups for elimination while keeping the scheduled end date and the quick reaction features. On September 26 General White approved the council's recommendations.[18]

The next day the Air Force Ballistic Missiles Committee was briefed on the development plan. It accepted the Air Force Council's proposals to reduce the ICBM force and to maintain the unit activation dates. But "because of the indicated magnitude of the resources required," the committee rejected the plan's cost estimates and once again returned the development plan to WDD for revision.[19]

WDD's second revision, submitted in November 1956, reduced the Fiscal Year 1958 budget estimate to $1.335 billion, about twenty percent less than the previous submission. Besides eliminating one group of Atlas (forty) missiles, Schriever canceled North American's sustainer engine program for the Titan. He also curtailed Titan nose cone tests and spread out the missile's operational dates and costs over a span of several years. The Air Force Council and General White endorsed the new plan and warned that program costs and objectives were "as low as we dare go." The plan was next approved by the Air Force Ballistic Missiles Committee and signed by Quarles on November 19.[20]

Although now approved by the Air Force, the program still had to clear other hurdles before it could be implemented. On December 5, General Schriever presented his plan to the OSD Ballistic Missiles Committee, which approved, but only "in principle." The revised plan advanced to the National Security Council on January 11, 1957, as part of the annual DOD

**Eger V. Murphree,
Wilson's Special Assistant
for Guided Missiles.**

briefing. The council generally accepted the program, but President Eisenhower cautioned that he was not prepared to approve a specific number of either missiles or units. Moreover, the President emphasized that no major changes could be made to the ballistic missile program without both his and the council's concurrence.[21]

Over the next several weeks Quarles appealed to Wilson for a firm decision on the ICBM force structure and schedule. But Wilson did nothing until Eger V. Murphree, his Special Assistant for Guided Missiles, reopened the subject by pointing out the necessity to determine first the rates of production, training requirements, and logistics for the ICBM. Wilson then arranged for a special presentation on March 28 before the NSC and the President. Following this briefing, the President at last approved aiming for an IOC "at the earliest practicable date." * This qualification represented a significant shift from the NSC guidance, provided eighteen months earlier, to achieve the objective "at the earliest possible date." † Indeed, the Air Force had formulated its plans on the earlier premise, assuming that the Administration would provide whatever financial support was needed. Apparently, however, economic considerations prevailed over military ones, as the Administration held down costs and willingly reduced its programmed ICBM force by one-third despite reports of rapid Russian advances in the missile field.[22]

While awaiting a final decision from the White House, Air Force Headquarters issued a directive on March 5, 1957, that superseded the earlier and long obsolete guidance of December 1955 and May 25, 1956. The new directive redefined the IOC as one wing, with one group of Atlas and one group of Titan missiles. Each group would have four squadrons, each squadron possessing ten missiles, six launchers, and two guidance stations: [23]

ICBM Wing

Atlas Group
4 Squadrons

Titan Group
4 Squadrons

ICBM Squadron

10 Missiles
6 Launchers
2 Guidance Stations

---

*Eisenhower had just returned from the Bermuda Conference with British Prime Minister Harold Macmillan, during which the two had agreed to base the Thor IRBM in the United Kingdom.

†See page 135.

One and one-half Atlas squadrons were to be located at Camp Cooke,* California, planned as a combined training and operational base. The two other operational bases, to be located "in the interior of the North American Continent," would accommodate the remaining Atlas and Titan squadrons. Again, the bases were to be "soft" and were expected to survive an enemy attack through a combination of dispersion, air defense, and quick launch reaction. These bases, however, other than Camp Cooke, would be hardened if this action did not require postponement of their scheduled operational dates.[24]

The March 5 directive also spelled out the transition from development to operational readiness. Thus, ARDC would command the missile units until the entire IOC was reached. Operational control would pass to SAC as each missile acquired the requisite crew, support equipment, and launch capability. The IOC schedule specified that an initial increment—one complex of three launchers,† six missiles,and one guidance station—was to be operational in March 1959 at Camp Cooke. The remainder of the force would be operational by March 1961. However, the eighth squadron was not scheduled to receive its full complement of Titans until July 1961.[25]

The "Poor Man's" approach reduced the projected missile force by one-third, from 120 to 80 missiles, and the number of bases from 3 to 2. The planned stretchout sought to relieve financial pressure without impairing the overall schedule, which involved personnel, training, construction, and ground support. It actually improved upon the original timetable by planning to field a token operational capability in March 1959.

IRBM Initial Operational Capability

On March 24, 1956, WDD was assigned the task of implementing an initial operational capability for the intermediate range ballistic missile. The plan called for establishing 1 IRBM wing with 8 squadrons to be supported from 3 bases in the United Kingdom. Each base would have 4 complexes containing 5 launchers each, or a total of 20 launchers. The overall IRBM force would consist of 120 missiles and 60 launchers.

The initial schedule called for ten IRBMs to be operationally ready by October 1958 and the entire force to be ready by July 1, 1959.[26] The IRBM IOC planning and approval paralleled that of the ICBM. Although action on both programs ran concurrently and with considerable interplay, there were several notable differences. These included the split responsibility

---

*Renamed Vandenberg AFB on October 4, 1958, in memory of the late Chief of Staff, Gen. Hoyt S. Vandenberg.

†A reduction from the initial requirement for ten launchers by April 1959.

assignment to ARDC and SAC; negotiations with the British government for bases in the United Kingdom; and a short-lived emergency capability plan.

On May 7, 1956, Generals Power and LeMay signed a detailed agreement of responsibility for the IOC for their respective commands. Under the agreement, ARDC was responsible for carrying out all actions pertaining to the IRBM in the United States. ARDC would develop, man, train, and equip the force. SAC was responsible for all actions outside the country, including selecting and building the IRBM bases, deploying the force overseas, and achieving operational status.[27]

But even as Power and LeMay inked the IRBM agreement, WDD officials cautioned that chances for meeting the prescribed schedule were not good. A major problem was the requirement for a very high IRBM production rate early on, long before there was enough opportunity for flight testing. As with the ICBM, Schriever feared that missile designs would have to be frozen too early and thereby cause inordinate modifications during production and deployment. Additionally, the diplomatic problems involved in negotiating for the oversea bases, coupled with technical problems in constructing launch and support facilities, had been grossly underestimated. The only chance for attaining operational readiness in the prescribed time was to begin base construction immediately, even for the most austere "soft" facilities. Schriever and LeMay urged General White to postpone the IOC completion by one year, from July 1959 to July 1960. They proposed, however, to have thirty IRBMs combat ready by July 1959, approximately nine months behind the original schedule for the initial ten missiles. Headquarters USAF approved the plan for a more gradual buildup and additional time for base facilities construction.[28]

On June 14, 1956, WDD submitted its first detailed IRBM IOC plan, calling for eight Thor squadrons, each equipped with fifteen missiles. SAC was to begin deployment in March 1959, and have two squadrons operational by July 1959 and the remainder by July 1960. To alleviate some long-lead construction and equipment time, SAC planned to convert some existing British bases for the Thor. As with the ICBM, the Thor quick reaction time specified launching twenty-five percent of the force within fifteen minutes of a strategic alert, another twenty-five percent within two hours, and the remainder within four hours. The task of training the missile crews devolved upon WDD, to be conducted at an unspecified base in the United States.[29]

Although the Thor development plan gained quick approval from the Air Staff, it encountered opposition at the July 3, 1956 meeting of the Air Force Ballistic Missiles Committee, especially from Secretary Quarles. As he had done to the ICBM, Quarles imposed the "Poor Man's" approach on the Thor, with the objective of conserving Fiscal Year 1957 and 1958 funds by stretching out the end dates and buildups into succeeding years. Again, Quarles directed that a revised plan be submitted in September.[30]

As the Thor derived most of its major subsystems from the ICBM development program, there was little left to cut except for the airframe. Secondly, because of the stringent deadline, base construction costs were already set at a minimum level, with existing SAC bases in Britain designated for the missiles and "soft" rather than "hard" launch sites contemplated. It was not surprising, therefore, that the plan submitted by WDD in September hardly differed in its essentials from the original one.[31]

Nonetheless, on September 27, 1956, the Air Force Ballistic Missiles Committee rejected the Thor plan along with the ICBM development plan and directed WDD to revise its cost proposals. Secretary Quarles added that the only portion of the Thor plan that he considered "sacred" was the time schedule. Subsequently, ARDC, AMC, and Air Staff officials devised a new arrangement that retained the planned Thor IOC schedule but sliced the force in half. After review and approval by the Air Force Council and the Ballistic Missiles Committee, Quarles signed the revised plan on November 16.[32]

General Schriever next presented the Thor plan to the OSD Ballistic Missiles Committee on December 5. The OSD committee approved "in principle." The plan also passed through the NSC on January 11, 1957. As with the ICBM plan,* President Eisenhower withheld full approval of the IRBM until the end of March. At that time, he endorsed the requirement for four Thor squadrons but changed the emphasis for completing deployment from the earliest "possible" date to the earliest "practicable." [33]

On March 5, 1957, anticipating approval of its revised plan, the Air Force issued a new missile program directive that essentially reaffirmed the November 1956 plan. The March directive called for one Thor wing in the United Kingdom to comprise four squadrons, each possessing fifteen missiles and five launch positions, with three launchers at each position. Again, because of the deadline, the bases had to be "soft." Transfer of missile units between ARDC and SAC would take place according to the agreement between the two commands signed on May 7, 1956. That agreement specified that, once a unit passed an operational readiness test at the training base, SAC would assume responsibility for its overseas deployment and operational readiness. The first Thor squadron was scheduled to be shipped in March and to become operational in July 1959; the last squadron was to be operational in July 1960.[34]

After more than a year, the Thor IOC plan finally gained approval, although it provided for only half of the original force. Most important, however, the time schedule had survived intact. As with the ICBM plan, the

---

*See page 159.

net result was a program cutback that did not affect the beginning or end dates. Production rates remained low, with existing facilities producing the requisite number of missiles on schedule. As fewer missiles would be produced, it was expected that the unit cost per missile would be higher but the overall cost would be considerably lower. The lower total cost helped the Administration meet its objective of controlling the national debt. As with the ICBM, economic considerations proved decisive in shaping both the Thor force size and schedule.

The question as to which service would operate the IRBM remained unresolved until 1956. In October 1955 Secretary Wilson had submitted the matter to the Joint Chiefs of Staff. The Chiefs, however, produced a "split" decision—meaning that they could not agree. Wilson then decided to leave the question open and to concentrate instead on developing the IRBM under a dual program. Thus, the Air Force Thor was designated IRBM Number 1, whereas the Army and Navy jointly developed the Jupiter, or IRBM Number 2.* Finally, on November 26, 1956, Wilson issued a new roles and missions directive that assigned the "operational employment" of land-based IRBMs as "the sole responsibility of the U.S. Air Force" and prescribed a 200-mile range limit on any missiles used by the Army. (Schriever's successor, Maj. Gen. Osmond J. Ritland, later acknowledged that the Thor won out over Jupiter, "but not because of any technical capability, because the Jupiter was performing equally as well.") The Army continued to develop the Jupiter, however, perhaps hoping for vindication if the Jupiter was chosen over the Thor as the land-based IRBM.[35]

Besides the basic Thor operational plan, the Air Force Ballistic Missiles Committee also studied an alternate approach. On November 10, 1956, after approving the latest version of the Thor plan, the committee considered the feasibility of an "IRBM Emergency Capability" consisting of three to six Thors on alert. General Power pointed out that a force of that size could have only political value:

> It should be noted that the emergency capability will not represent a true military capability. Also, this fact, in all probability, will be known to Soviet intelligence. This is considered pertinent in evaluating the political and psychological value of the emergency capability in relationship to our NATO allies.[36]

On December 24, 1956, WDD provided a detailed plan for achieving the contemplated emergency capability. Schriever concluded that it was technically

---

*In December 1956 the Navy received OSD approval to develop its own IRBM—the Polaris. Several factors led to the Navy decision, including news from the AEC in July that smaller nuclear warheads would be available. Also, the Navy much preferred solid-fuel rockets for shipboard use. Finally, it determined that a smaller, wider submarine would be more suitable for underwater launch.

feasible to launch between three and five Thor missiles from the United Kingdom as early as July 1958—one year ahead of the existing schedule—provided that a go-ahead was granted by February 1957. But the Thors would be developmental missiles, rather than production types, and could be launched only with the help of contractor personnel. Also, a concerted effort was required to resolve, at an early date, differences between the United States and Great Britain regarding base selection and construction.[37]

Some Air Staff officials opposed this emergency plan on the basis of its military worth versus the high cost. They doubted if any real "weapon-on-target" capability would result because of the low reliability and the reaction of the missile at such an early stage of development. Others, however, viewed the contemplated small Thor force positively in terms of its propaganda value and the possibility that it might help speed negotiations with the British. Also, the experience to be gained from this deployment would be useful in the overall siting of the Thor force.[38]

On January 9, 1957, General White decided to proceed with the emergency capability. Before the end of January the plan had gained the approval of Quarles and Wilson.[39]

Subsequently, the emergency plan became part of the overall Anglo-American negotiations during the first quarter of 1957. But the thorny siting and base construction problems dragged on unresolved. By mid-March the approval deadline had passed, and Air Force officials told OSD that the emergency plan was growing less attractive each day. Without agreement on the bases issue, the plan's desirability was greatly diminished.[40]

On April 18 the United States submitted a draft bases agreement to Britain, including the particulars about the emergency Thor capability. But by this time the Air Force had already given up on the plan. At the end of March, General White advised Secretary Quarles and the Air Force Ballistic Missiles Committee that no additional funding was warranted for the emergency capability effort. Quarles agreed, and during April Headquarters USAF notified its major commands and agencies of the plan's demise. Nonetheless, the plan survived in diplomatic channels through October, when a new basing agreement was drafted.[41]

The Air Force had recognized the urgency of resolving the basing problem from the start of Thor planning in early 1956. The original plan envisioned deploying American-manned Thor squadrons to several bases in the United Kingdom. In April, Secretary Quarles asked Wilson to inform the State Department of the Air Force's Thor plan. Apparently, however, not much was done to secure base rights until Quarles raised the matter informally with his British counterparts in July. The British were prepared to negotiate, and discussions proceeded through the end of the year. It became obvious during the negotiations that the British wanted an active role in the program, including the right to man some of the Thor squadrons.[42]

164

At the November 10 meeting of the Air Force Ballistic Missiles Committee, when it first endorsed the Thor plan, Quarles suggested that the British might operate the Thor either in cooperation with American crews or alone. Accordingly, the committee directed the preparation of an alternate plan under which British personnel manned the first or subsequent Thor units. At any rate, Quarles emphasized that the Air Force would maintain the IOC schedule.[43]

By year's end WDD submitted a plan that proposed to deploy two American-manned squadrons first, followed by two British-manned squadrons. The Americans would then be replaced by British missile crews. SAC, however, wanted to retain command and control over all Thor squadrons—regardless of their nationality—and fought against the plan. At the very least, SAC insisted on permanent control of two American squadrons.[44]

Negotiations between Secretary Wilson and British Defence Minister Duncan Sandys in January 1957 produced a draft agreement on basing Thor missiles in the United Kingdom according to the IOC schedule. The agreement proposed to delineate responsibility between the two governments regarding Thor deployment and operation. In March, President Eisenhower and British Prime Minister Harold Macmillan met in Bermuda, where they discussed Thor deployment and ratified the Wilson–Sandys agreement. Ostensibly, the Thor plan seemed to be resolved. But the Bermuda Conference had not addressed the selection of specific bases and had ignored the myriad details involved in deploying the missiles overseas. These problems later caused months of deliberation and delay. Finally, operating the missiles became a political issue, as public pressure mounted in Britain to prevent the Americans from operating the Thor.[45]

The Economy Axe

The Air Force had budgeted $1.335 billion for ballistic missiles in Fiscal Year 1958. In May 1957, however, the Air Force Ballistic Missiles Committee reduced this figure by $200 million (to $1.135 billion) and warned that it intended to monitor the program closely to avoid alternate developments.[46]

This reduction proved a harbinger of things to come as Secretary Wilson pressed for further cuts. Behind the cuts lay the national debt, which threatened to surpass its authorized ceiling. Wilson began by directing the military departments to slow the rates of deliveries by contractors, minimize overtime costs, and delay payments. The Secretary of Defense specifically instructed the OSD Ballistic Missiles Committee to examine overtime costs for the ballistic missile program. Even while this study was under way, the Air Force Ballistic Missiles Committee acted to reduce overtime costs from its 13.8 percent rate (a ratio of overtime to total hours) to 8 percent by the end of the year. The OSD committee approved the action in July 1957.[47]

At a July 3 briefing on the missile programs, the National Security Council admonished Secretary Wilson that program costs were too high in light of other national requirements. Wilson subsequently announced his intention to reduce strategic missile * costs to $1 billion annually. As the Air Force's program alone exceeded that figure, the decision spelled trouble.[48]

At the end of July, Wilson submitted a list of proposed changes to the ballistic missile program, including some rather drastic measures. Atlas retained its high priority, but Titan's rating dropped; contractor overtime was curtailed further; Thor and Jupiter production plans were suspended pending the results of an ad hoc study for a single land-based IRBM. On August 1, President Eisenhower and the National Security Council readily

---

* In addition to the Atlas, Titan, and Thor, other strategic missiles included Jupiter, Polaris, Goose, Hound Dog, Quail, Snark, and the recently terminated Navaho. OSD imposed an expenditure ceiling on the Air Force of $17.9 billion for FY 1958. [Ltr, Brig Gen O. J. Ritland to AF–BMD Staff, subj: Economy in Operation, Aug 30, 1957, in Basic Documents.]

Maj. Gen. Bernard A. Schriever (left), Commander of the Ballistic Missile Division, with his Army counterpart, Maj. Gen. John B. Medaris, head of the Army Ballistic Missile Agency.

accepted Wilson's proposals, including the inherent delay in the IRBM program.[49]

The Air Force, meanwhile, had prepared to defend its missile program. On July 19 General White succeeded Twining as Chief of Staff when the latter became Chairman of the JCS. White directed General Schriever to draft a plan anticipating additional financial reductions and to determine the impact that these cuts would have on meeting the IOC schedule.[50]

The Air Force Ballistic Missile Division (BMD)—the new designation for WDD since June 1, 1957—submitted the requested plan. On August 6, apparently without knowledge of the NSC action of August 1, General White appealed to Secretary of the Air Force James H. Douglas* to intercede with Defense Secretary Wilson. White argued against any further reductions to the missile program, but if they were unavoidable, he wanted the Air Force—rather than OSD—to apply the cuts.[51]

One major issue involved the rate of missile production, as that rate had a direct bearing on the IOC. The existing program specified a monthly production rate of 6 Atlas, 7 Titan, and 6 Thor missiles. At this 6-7-6 rate, the last of 8 ICBM squadrons would become operational in March 1961 and the fourth Thor squadron in July 1960. OSD considered lowering production to 4 missiles per month, that is, to a 4-4-4 rate. But General White noted that the reduced production would delay completing the IOC on time as required by the NSC's March 28, 1957, action. That document called for a force of 12 ICBM/IRBM squadrons "at the earliest practicable date." Any change in objectives required the council's approval. Congressional ratification was also mandated, in line with a directive from the House Committee on Appropriations recommending against any cuts in the ballistic missile program. White also cited intelligence reports indicating that the Soviets had an extensive ballistic missile program underway, with frequent test launchings and an expected start of quantity production by the early 1960s. Again, if the reductions were unavoidable, White offered the 4-4-4 production rate as the lowest acceptable.[52]

As a result of the NSC's August 1 action, Wilson made several far-reaching decisions. On August 16 he ordered that Thor be reduced to a research and development program with a monthly production rate of only 2 missiles—a number sufficient only to permit flight testing. This restriction was expected to remain in effect until OSD decided between the Thor and the Army's Jupiter as the nation's land-based IRBM. Wilson also imposed a temporary 2 missiles per month production on the Titan and directed the Air Force to consider the effects of a 2-2-2 rate on the IOC schedules. Moreover, he directed the Air Force to suspend or cancel ground support

---

*Secretary since May 1957. Douglas served as Undersecretary of the Air Force from March 3, 1953 to April 30, 1957.

and training equipment contracts and slashed the authorized overtime figure from 8 to 3 percent. Finally, Wilson appointed William Holaday,* Schriever, and Maj. Gen. John P. Medaris, manager of the Jupiter, to review the Thor–Jupiter issue and to make a recommendation.[53]

Wanting to keep the bad news from the missile industry, Schriever instructed his staff to stress to the contractors "that there had been no change in national priority for achieving an operational capability at the earliest practicable date. . . . [T]he R&D program must proceed at the maximum rate that technology will permit." He wanted contractors told that program changes were due to the necessity for making "certain adjustments of key milestone dates" and that "budgetary considerations" dictated that the Air Force "consider a logical stretch-out" of the missile program.[54]

Schriever was candid in writing to the ARDC Commander: "I consider that we do not at this time have an approved FY 58 program as represented in our development plan." Schriever predicted that the reductions would adversely affect management and morale, both at BMD and among its contractors. In September BMD staffers briefed General LeMay, the Vice Chief of Staff since July, and the Air Force Ballistic Missiles Committee concerning the effects of the reduced production on the IOC. As shown in Chart 6–1, changing from the 4–4–4 to 2–2–2 resulted in an average delay of three years.[55]

The differences between the August and September 1957 4–4–4 plans related to considerations for building hardened facilities for the Titan and relegating Thor to research-and-development-only status. Also, with respect to Thor, the September plan assumed that OSD's choice between Thor and Jupiter would not be made before January 1958, whereas the August plan had been predicated on an immediate go-ahead.[56]

On September 12 the BMD team briefed Secretary Wilson and Deputy Secretary Quarles. The OSD officials emphasized funding as the main determinant in the missile program. Although he made no decision at this time, Wilson acknowledged that he favored the 4–4–4 plan over the 2–2–2.[57]

Air Force Secretary Douglas then asked OSD to approve the 4–4–4 production for Atlas and Titan and to release funds to permit meeting the new IOC dates. The Thor program was not mentioned because the Thor–Jupiter issue remained unresolved. (Douglas himself was not enthusiastic about the Thor and favored a delay.) Wilson's reply to Douglas, on September 19, was still noncommittal.[58]

---

*Holaday succeeded Murphree as OSD Director of Guided Missiles. The position of Special Assistant to the Secretary of Defense for Guided Missiles was abolished on November 15, 1957, by DOD Directive No. 5105. [In Basic Documents.]

Chart 6–1

Effect of Monthly Production Rates
on IOC for Atlas, Titan, and Thor

	Mar 1957 6-7-6	Aug 1957 4-4-4	Sep 1957 4-4-4	Sep 1957 2-2-2
ATLAS				
First Capability	Mar 1959	Jun 1959	Jul 1959	Oct 1960
Complete IOC	Mar 1961	Oct 1961	Oct 1961	Sep 1964
TITAN				
First Capability	Oct 1960	Aug 1961	Nov 1961	Dec 1962
Complete IOC	Jul 1961	Oct 1962	Oct 1962	Sep 1965
THOR				
First Capability	Jun 1959	Dec 1959	Jul 1960	Oct 1961
Complete IOC	Jun 1960	Jun 1961	Jan 1962	Mar 1966

The Furor Over Sputnik

Russia's announcement, in late August 1957, that it had successfully flight-tested an ICBM made no apparent impression on American leaders. Then came a rude jolt on October 4 with the launching of Sputnik—the world's first artificial satellite—followed on November 3 by Sputnik II. Despite U.S. disclaimers to the contrary, the Soviet feats that ushered in the "space age" served as concrete evidence that Russia possessed an extremely advanced technology. Lt. Gen. Donald L. Putt, Air Force Deputy Chief of Staff for Development, wrote at the time, "As you would expect, the Russian launching of an earth satellite has caused considerable alarm not only in the Air Force but also in the Department of Defense." Just as the outbreak of the Korean War in June 1950 had spurred the United States into action, so did Sputnik stimulate American defense spending. Sputnik came just after another round of reductions in the ballistic missile program; it reversed this trend.*

---

*See "The Economy Axe," page 165 ff. Ironically, on the eve of the Sputnik launch, the restrictions on contractor overtime were reinforced. [Msg, Gen Anderson to Schriever, RDGP-10-2-E, 04/2101Z Oct 1957.]

Lt. Gen. Donald L. Putt, Deputy Chief of Staff for Development.

The first reversal occurred on October 5, when Wilson approved the 4-4-4 production plan. This plan, it will be recalled, contemplated having a three-launcher complex of Atlas operational by July 1959 and the complete four-squadron force by October 1961. The first Titan element was to be ready by November 1961 and the complete four squadrons by October 1962.* Wilson was soon succeeded as Secretary of Defense by Neil McElroy, who advised the President that existing ballistic missile plans were "of historical interest" only.[59]

In the fall of 1957, syndicated columnists Joseph and Stewart Alsop first broke the news disclosing the existence of U.S. radars in Turkey. Through a secret agreement with Wilson, the Alsops promised to withhold the story of Russian long-range missiles, if the Administration did not deny the existence of the Turkish radars. The agreement held until Wilson made a disparaging remark about the Alsops and freed the brothers to disclose the missile activity. The episode suggests that Defense officials were not as surprised by Sputnik as many have contended.[60]

In the wake of Sputnik, various plans were advanced to accelerate the U.S. ballistic missile program. Carried out against the backdrop of a Congressional inquiry† and under a tremendous wave of public pressure,

---

*See Chart 7-5, page 236. The Air Force's ballistic missile budget for FY 1958 had been reduced to $991 million from the original $1.671 billion.

†The Preparedness Subcommittee of the Armed Services Committee hearings ran from November 1957 to January 1958. See Chapter VII.

the acceleration moved ahead rather chaotically. At first only tentative steps were taken to buoy up the program. The JCS, NSC, Armed Forces Policy Council, and others deliberated long and hard over the available alternatives. Indeed, several months elapsed before a reorientation was implemented. On October 8 General White sensed a "new climate" and directed the drafting of a new plan to accelerate the missile program by six months or more. BMD had anticipated the request and the next day forwarded a proposal. Meanwhile, the furor created by Sputnik inspired several "crash" program proposals. Armed with instructions that "money would be no object," Air Staff planners hurried to refine myriad proposals into a comprehensive plan to speed and increase the missile program. The Air Force proposals wended their way up the chain of approval through the JCS, OSD, Bureau of the Budget,* NSC, and on to Congress for the necessary funding appropriations.[61]

Initially the Air Force and the Department of Defense tried to accelerate the missile program under the existing budgetary appropriations and concentrated on the IRBM. Although Thor and Jupiter were the farthest along in development of the ballistic missiles, the difficult problem remained of choosing between them for operational deployment. The special review committee proved unable to choose one missile over the other, and William M. Holaday saw "little doubt as to the producibility of either weapon system. The significant differences which exist between the two programs are primarily the result of differences in basic Army–Air Force philosophies of approach." Holaday recommended that both programs continue until one missile emerged clearly superior. On October 10—in response to the political and psychological advantages accruing from both missiles' potential early operational capability—the President and NSC relaxed IRBM requirements by calling only for "reasonable accuracy" and allowing for slower reaction capability.[62]

On October 31, Secretary of Defense McElroy withdrew the mid-August directive that had reduced the Thor to research and development status, but he kept in effect the missile overtime and production restrictions (two missiles per month). McElroy also issued similar directives on the Jupiter, elevating that IRBM to the status of a complete weapon system— meaning that it would be mass-produced and deployed. The Jupiter gained a great advantage over the Thor because the former was not hampered by restrictions on long-lead items, overtime, or production tooling.[63]

General Schriever charged that McElroy's directive helped "to tie the hands of the Air Force, to delay the achievement of an operational IRBM capability and to permit the JUPITER program to close the gap in the vital production and operational areas in which the THOR program is now clearly ahead of the JUPITER." Brig. Gen. Charles M. McCorkle, USAF

---

*Predecessor to the Office of Management and Budget (OMB).

Assistant Chief of Staff for Guided Missiles, noted that the Thor program had begun as a complete weapon system development aimed at producing an operational IRBM. Accordingly, production, training, and operational activities proceeded concurrently with technical development. McElroy's directive penalized the Air Force in those areas where it was ahead, while accelerating and expanding the less advanced Jupiter. In McCorkle's opinion, OSD wanted to postpone a decision because of the extreme political sensitivity of the Thor–Jupiter issue. He predicted that in the end OSD would declare that its intent was to treat the Army and Air Force fairly, to hurt neither one.[64]

On November 8 Air Force Secretary Douglas informed McElroy that, unless Thor's restrictions on overtime and ground support equipment—that is, long lead-time items—were lifted, the missile would not meet its assigned objectives. McElroy acceded only to the overtime.[65]

A week later the Air Force submitted to OSD an expanded plan for 16 Thor squadrons. The plan proposed to advance the operational date of the first squadron, as defined in the September 4-4-4 plan, from July 1960 to August 1959, and the four-squadron force from January 1962 to May 1960. The additional 12 Thor squadrons would be deployed by June 1962. This new plan was predicated on a production rate of 8 missiles per month, starting in July 1959, and 10 missiles per month after June 1961.[66]

Even as OSD's Ballistic Missiles Committee studied this latest proposal, Schriever's staff examined alternatives. It produced the startling finding that existing Thor facilities were capable of producing up to twenty missiles per month. If OSD approved the twenty-missile rate, one Thor squadron could be fielded by July 1958, and four squadrons could become operational by January 1959.[67]

In November Secretary Douglas proposed immediate approval of an eight-missiles-per-month production. He claimed that this plan would yield one operational Thor squadron by June 1958, the fourth by June 1959, and one additional squadron every three months thereafter. Douglas's plan required that contractor personnel augment military crews for the first two Thor squadrons.[68]

McElroy contemplated both Air Force proposals, but did not act immediately on either. Meanwhile, Headquarters USAF instructed its field agencies to be ready to accommodate a six-missiles-per-month production, but to stay within the two-missile rate for the time being. Schriever provided Vice Chief of Staff General LeMay with data supporting the twenty-missile per month rate; LeMay endorsed the plan.[69]

At last, on November 25, Secretary McElroy decided to place both Thor and Jupiter into production. The next day President Eisenhower approved, and McElroy announced the decision during his testimony before the Preparedness Subcommittee of the Senate Armed Services Committee.[70]

William M. Holaday informed the Army and Air Force that they should plan on production and deployment of four squadrons each. The first Thor squadron was scheduled to have a limited capability in June 1958 and to become operational before the end of December. The second squadron was to be ready by July 1959, the third by October 1959, and the fourth by March 1960. (Jupiter was assigned an identical deployment schedule.) The Thor production was set at six missiles per month, whereas five Jupiter missiles would be built each month. There was one more thing: the Air Force would operationally deploy both IRBMs.[71]

The decision did not please Air Force leaders, and they protested this "dual approach" as inherently wasteful in terms of time, money, and effort. The total of eight IRBM squadrons authorized represented about half the number required.* On December 3 General White persuaded Secretary Douglas to press OSD for a reversal of the decision, to terminate the Jupiter program, and to increase Thor squadrons. The political considerations here proved overwhelming, however, and McElroy reaffirmed his decision on

---

*Prospects for more IRBMs in the future seemed bleak with many defense officials regarding the liquid-fueled missile as an interim weapon. [Minutes, ICBM Ballistic Missile Scientific Advisory Committee to SAF, mtg, Dec 16–17, 1957, in Basic Documents.]

William M. Holaday had a key role in production and deployment decisions as Director of Guided Missiles in the Office of the Assistant Secretary of Defense.

173

December 20. Resignedly, Douglas directed full cooperation with the Army in the Jupiter buildup.[72]

The accelerated Thor plans raised to the forefront the critical matter of bases in the United Kingdom. In June 1957, the U.S. Air Force and the RAF were near agreement on technical arrangements when the talks stalled at the governmental level. Negotiations remained closed until October, when Sputnik provided an impetus to continue. By late December Deputy Secretary of Defense Quarles told Douglas that agreement was imminent. In January 1958 USAF and RAF representatives discussed squadron manning, base selection, dispersion of launch sites, personnel training, construction, logistics, and maintenance. Once again, no agreement was reached because internal British politics—including public demonstrations against the deployment—intervened. As a result, the RAF was obliged to modify some positions, and the final bases agreement was not signed until June 26, 1958.[73]

In contrast with the hurried measures taken with the Thor, post-Sputnik planning for the ICBMs proceeded at a slower, more orderly pace. The pressure did not seem as great on the ICBMs because their operational deployment was farther off. Also, unlike the Thor, the Atlas possessed an approved operational plan. Attention turned to the ICBM on October 8, when Holaday informed Douglas that OSD was considering lifting the overtime restrictions; on November 22, OSD did remove the restrictions. At about the same time, it also authorized construction of a Titan launch facility that had been deleted previously for economy reasons.[74]

In the interim, BMD worked feverishly on alternative plans to expand and accelerate the ICBM program. These plans formed the basis for the Air Force's recommendation to OSD on November 14. Essentially, BMD had concluded that only minor improvements in the first phases of the ICBM operational deployment were possible. Construction of base facilities, production of ground support equipment, and personnel training constituted the primary limitations. These factors forestalled any significant advancement of the operational date for the first Atlas squadron. It was possible, however, to speed up operational readiness of subsequent units and even to deploy the missiles into hardened facilities. With respect to the Titan, as the Air Force had planned from the start to place this ICBM into hardened facilities, it was not possible to advance Titan's operational readiness appreciably due to the lack of design criteria for construction of crew training and operational facilities.[75]

The Air Force's ICBM acceleration plans submitted to OSD on November 14, proposed to field nine Atlas squadrons.* Based on a

---

*This plan represented an increase of only four squadrons, as the original plan included a composite training-operational squadron at Cooke AFB (Vandenberg) possessing an emergency launch capability.

six-per-month production rate (in lieu of the current four), the first Atlas complex was to become operational in July 1959—a plan that represented no advance over the existing schedule. The fourth squadron, however, was to become operational in June 1961, three months earlier than expected. The remaining Atlas squadrons, all in hardened facilities, were to become operational between March 1962 and March 1963.[76]

Under the same plan, the Air Force asked for eight Titan squadrons instead of the four that had been planned. Again, based on the six-missile production rate, the first Titan squadron was expected to be operational in May rather than November 1961. The increased production was to speed the readiness of the fourth Titan squadron by nine months, from October 1962 to January 1962. The last four Titan squadrons were to be in place between April 1962 and January 1963. Chart 6–2 summarizes this information.[77]

OSD considered the Air Force's latest proposal for about a month and then on December 12 approved only the Atlas portion, thereby keeping that missile at its planned four squadrons. While Air Force leaders had requested seventeen ICBM squadrons, they envisioned a much larger force—up to sixty

Chart 6–2

Effect of Revised Monthly Production Rates on IOC for Atlas, Titan, and Thor

	Sep 1957 4-4-4	Sep 1957 2-2-2	Nov 1957 6-6-8	
ATLAS				
First Capability	Jul 1959	Oct 1960	Jul 1959	
Complete IOC	Oct 1961	Sep 1964	Jun 1961	(4 sqdn)
			Mar 1963	(9 sqdn)
TITAN				
First Capability	Nov 1961	Dec 1962	May 1961	
Complete IOC	Oct 1962	Sep 1965	Jan 1962	(4 sqdn)
			Jan 1963	(8 sqdn)
THOR				
First Capability	Jul 1960	Oct 1961	Aug 1959	
Complete IOC	Jan 1962	Mar 1966	May 1960	(4 sqdn)
			Jun 1962	(12 sqdn)

squadrons—by Fiscal Year 1964. Late in December 1957, BMD submitted a proposal for twenty-one squadrons—thirteen Atlas and eight Titan—to be operational by the spring of 1963. Secretary Douglas approved and authorized its presentation to the Air Force and OSD Ballistic Missiles Committees.[78]

On January 30, 1958, Holaday presented the third annual ballistic missile briefing to the NSC and the President. Holaday reported that the IRBM IOC, consisting of four Thor and four Jupiter squadrons, would be achieved much earlier than had been scheduled. The Atlas force consisted of five squadrons under an accelerated schedule and four additional squadrons that were to be deployed into hardened facilities later. A four-squadron Titan force was planned, but with no change to the original schedule. The President approved the program as briefed.[79]

Despite the continuing military requirement for ballistic missiles since 1954, the program was marked by frequent and extensive reprogramming actions, especially during the three months between the launch of Sputnik and the end of 1957. Taking notice of the constant changes, BMD concluded that the original plan would have been more productive and less expensive:

> Included in these [reprogramming] directives were "stretch-out" of the program; acceleration of the "stretch-out"; limitations in production rates; budget restrictions; overtime restrictions; lifting of restrictions; changes in operational force structures; and changes in operational concepts of "soft-base" versus "hard-base". The net result . . . was the difficulty in making long-lead procurement and planning, generally affecting the ability to build up a sizeable operational force as early as originally possible. Inevitably, the time consumed by the Air Force and contractors in frequently redeveloping the program schedules diverted from the primary effort.[80]

Final Plans

When the Western Development Division was created, it assumed broad responsibilities for the ICBM, including "the development of recommended operational, logistic, and personnel concepts." Although unusual, this assignment acknowledged the Air Force's lack of experience with ballistic missiles. In September 1954, planners reasoned that flexible concepts were necessary to adapt to changes in the weapon system development. Close liaison was established with ARDC, SAC, AMC, and ATC, through representatives assigned to Los Angeles. In March 1955 WDD adopted some basic operational concepts for the Atlas: the missile would be sited inside fixed, underground facilities; it was to have a quick launch reaction; it was to be stored in a launching position; the launch site would require minimal support; and the launch units were to be self-supporting for two weeks.[81]

A similar lack of experience existed with respect to training. Because of the complexity of the task and the long lead time required, WDD decided to send Air Force personnel to the contractors to train on the equipment as it was being developed; unit training followed individual training. Also, Patrick AFB, Florida, emerged as a likely operational training site.[82]

To some extent manning and training requirements were determined by technical and logistic considerations. Wherever possible, launch complexes and control centers were located so as to permit using a centralized support facility. A "quick reaction" capability of about two hours was initially assigned, but the time was expected to be reduced eventually to fifteen minutes. The quick reaction assumed the availability of highly skilled crews and implied that a series of operational tests would be accomplished prior to the completion of missile development.[83]

Numerous studies were undertaken to recommend solutions for anticipated operational problems, including the quick reaction capability, missile checkout procedures, and handling equipment, as well as problems associated with installation requirements. Studies were also initiated to determine optimal missile base designs, site selection criteria, cost requirements, and alternative techniques of missile employment. The latter included fixed, underground facilities that posed such complex problems as methods for exhausting rocket engine flames, missile and fuel storage, and the degree of hardness or overpressure protection needed. Separate investigations were also needed in the more mundane areas of maintenance, transportation, spares, communications, and general support.[84]

On December 20, 1955, Generals Power and LeMay settled on site criteria for the ICBM force, including a single combined operational and training site. At first the sites would be above ground, but ultimately the ICBMs would be sited in hardened, underground silos and stored vertically—poised for launching. A combined site screening group was established to consider likely bases.[85]

In June 1956 a special site selection board recommended Camp Cooke, California—an inactive Army post on the Pacific coast—as the most desirable location for the first ICBM training and operational base. Air Force Secretary Quarles scrutinized the Camp Cooke proposal, but preferred Patrick AFB. The estimated costs for Camp Cooke were $42 million in Fiscal Year 1957 and $400 million in Fiscal Year 1958. Quarles also worried about the risks of training launches from the California site because they involved overflying populated areas. But the Air Staff unanimously favored Cooke, and Quarles approved in September 1956. OSD approved in November after several interservice matters were settled. Redesignated as Cooke AFB,* the facility would serve as a training center for Atlas, Titan, and Thor and as an emergency operational base for the

---

*On October 4, 1958, the base was renamed Vandenberg AFB in honor of the late Chief of Staff, Hoyt S. Vandenberg.

Atlas. In May 1957 work began on Atlas facilities, and in June construction of Thor launchers started.[86]

While deliberating on Cooke, BMD formed another panel to investigate suitable Atlas and Titan base sites. In August 1957 the Air Force selected Warren AFB, Wyoming as the first Atlas operational base and Lowry AFB, Colorado as the first Titan site. By October, work was completed at Cooke for siting two Atlas launchers and a contract was let for design and construction of a Titan launch and support facility. The Titan silo was to be hardened to withstand nuclear explosive overpressures of up to 100 pounds per square inch.[87]

Convair had started Atlas fabrication in February 1955 and delivered the first missile to the Air Force on August 29, 1956. By that time the various subsystems had undergone static testing, intended to build confidence in the success of the actual flights. Ground test facilities included stands at Edwards AFB, Sycamore Canyon, and Point Loma—all in California. Missile 4A—the first Atlas flight vehicle—arrived at the Air Force Missile Test Center, Patrick AFB, Florida, in December 1956. After passing a series of rigorous static tests, Atlas 4A was launched on June 11, 1957. Ten seconds after ignition the missile lifted off its pad at Complex 14,

A Convair Atlas ICBM on the launch pad at the Air Force Missile Test Center, May 20, 1957.

but had risen only a few thousand feet when one of its two engines failed. As the experimental missile spun into a series of violent maneuvers, the range safety officer pressed a button detonating an on-board explosive charge that destroyed the missile after a flight of less than one minute. Despite the flight test failure, the Atlas demonstrated its structural integrity and the ability to gimbal its engines. Most important of all, it flew.[88]

On September 25 a second launch, Atlas 6A, behaved the same way as the first missile and was also destroyed after experiencing engine failure. Following the Russian spectaculars with Sputnik I and II in October and November, the United States attempted to launch its International Geophysical Year satellite aboard the Navy's Vanguard rocket. The Navy space vehicle exploded on its launching pad.[89]

The United States did not record its first launch triumph until December 17, 1957, while President Eisenhower was attending a NATO summit meeting in Paris. On the 54th anniversary of the Wright Brothers' historic flight, Atlas 12A was launched. Its engines burned for 2 full minutes, as programmed, propelling the "bird" some 600 miles down the Atlantic Missile Range. The flight was declared a complete success with all systems performing as designed.[90]

In June 1956, 18 months earlier, ARDC had prepared plans for organizing and manning operational missile units. The command presented these plans to the Air Force Council and won general acceptance. On November 21, 1956, after the Air Force Ballistic Missiles Committee had approved the IOC force and schedule, ARDC submitted its first request for personnel allotments to support the growing activity at Cooke AFB and to begin missile training. Headquarters USAF approved the request for 26 officers and 133 airmen.[91]

In January 1957 ARDC requested that an air division be created to supervise missile training and operations, and asked for an air group to run Cooke AFB. Also included was a requirement to establish a missile wing by June 15 and a Thor training squadron by December.[92]

Headquarters USAF authorized activation of the 1st Missile Division and the 392d Air Base Group, both effective April 15, 1957.* In July it authorized establishment of the 704th Strategic Missile Wing and approved creation of the 392d Missile Training Squadron (THOR) in September. Also in July, BMD activated the 6952d Support Squadron (Missile Technical) to compute target trajectories and provide guidance settings for operational units. Once fully trained, the 6952d was to be transferred to SAC.[93]

Thus, by the fall of 1957 BMD had built the nucleus of a missile force, but consisting of support rather than operational units. Soon after Sputnik, the Air Force sped through its plans to establish operational missile units.

---

*The 1st Missile Division was relocated from Los Angeles to Cooke AFB on July 15, 1957.

BALLISTIC MISSILES

On January 1, 1958, the 672d Strategic Missile Squadron (THOR) and the 706th Strategic Missile Squadron (ATLAS) were activated.[94]

Since its creation as a specialized agency assigned to manage the ballistic missile program, Schriever's Western Development Division (later BMD) had caused resentment within the Air Force establishment. Its privileged position was reinforced when the ICBM achieved top national priority and by Schriever's direct access to Air Force leaders, which enabled WDD to bypass regular channels. Moreover, the aircraft industry resented the hiring of Ramo-Wooldridge to perform systems engineering and technical direction for the missile program. Initially, Ramo-Wooldridge established its Guided Missile Research Division, which for three years was occupied exclusively with providing systems engineering and technical direction for the ballistic missile program. During the latter part of 1957 the company reorganized[*] and established the Space Technology Laboratories. The laboratories continued to provide services to BMD; however, STL was now grouped by separate divisions, including electronics, aeronautics, and systems engineering. Through Fiscal Year 1958, Ramo-Wooldridge had earned approximately $70 million for its services on a cost-plus-fee contract.[95]

Because of the dynamic nature of the missile program, the Air Force made provisions early on to adapt to frequent changes. The situation demanded a continuous review of plans, schedules, progress, funding, and problem areas. Among the internal management controls employed was the program control room, where up-to-date information on all program elements was maintained. Schriever instituted a monthly conference to enable project officers to make reports and to discuss any difficulties encountered. Monthly meetings were also held with the missile contractors to monitor progress in all technical areas.[96]

Initially, Schriever's organization had separated responsibility according to technical areas, with each office accountable for the technical adequacy and complete integration of a particular system. But later, as parallel development was instituted and the IRBM and other programs were added, it became necessary to create a weapon system project office organization. Under a February 1956 reorganization, WDD established weapon system assistants for Atlas, Titan, Thor, and WS–117L.[†] General Schriever also collocated his personnel with the Ballistic Missile Office (the Air Materiel Command field unit at Inglewood) and with Ramo-Wooldridge. With the assignment of the IOC, manpower requirements rose markedly (Table 6–3) and more changes were made in the support and planning areas at the missile complex.[97]

---

[*] It also created the General Electronics Group to manufacture control and communications equipment.

[†] See page 144.

Table 6–3

Personnel Authorized

	1954	1955	1956	1957
Ballistic Missile Division (ARDC)				
Military	40	70	319	485
Civilian	41	85	224	222
Ballistic Missile Office (AMC)				
Military	3	7	47	55
Civilian	9	56	102	155
Ramo-Wooldridge	170	760	1557	1961
	263	978	2249	2878

Source: U.S. Congress 86/1 House Subcommittee on Governmental Operations, "Organization and Management of Missile Programs," Feb–Mar 1959, p 676.

As the missile complex acquired additional responsibilities and programs, General Schriever sought to establish a more permanent role for his organization to develop all Air Force strategic ballistic missiles and space systems. This objective proved elusive, but did result in the redesignation of the Western Development Division as the Ballistic Missile Division, effective June 1, 1957.[98]

In the space area, BMD had acquired responsibility to develop an artificial satellite, called the Advanced Reconnaissance System or Weapon System 117L. The satellite program office was relocated from Wright Air Development Center to Los Angeles in February 1956. At first the satellite was accorded a low priority, as compared with the missile program. Schriever recalled that the Eisenhower Administration did not consider space to be militarily significant. In a February 1957 speech, Schriever had suggested that the United States possessed the means to explore space. Shortly thereafter Schriever was directed not to use the word "space" in future public utterances. Priorities changed markedly after the launch of Sputnik, as evidenced at a planning conference in December 1957:

BALLISTIC MISSILES

> The recent Soviet successes with earth satellites lend substance to claimed achievements in missile developments of ICBM range and the stated Soviet intention [of] placing satellites in orbit. . . . We must agressively [sic] pursue courses of action in our R&D planning and management that will yield maximum results in developing Space Technology as an instrument of military power.[99]

BMD also had taken an active interest in the field of solid propellant rocketry. But although it had initiated work in this area, the project was transferred to Wright Field. In February 1956, Schriever had outlined the feasibility of solid propellants to the Scientific Advisory Committee, a body that served both the Air Force and OSD. He was joined at this briefing by Navy representatives, who also supported the case for solid fuels. Sufficiently impressed by both presentations, the committee approved development of solid rocket technology. In particular, it permitted the Navy to break off its involvement with the Army's Jupiter program and to proceed on its own. The Navy effort, which later evolved into the Polaris, received top priority for development, on a par with the Air Force and Army IRBMs. Moreover, the committee observed that the Air Force program might possibly lead to "the design of a solid fuel ICBM." [100]*

Despite the strong possibility of designing a solid-fuel ICBM, the Air Force continued to regard solids as best suited for the IRBM role. On March 20, 1957, General Putt wrote to General Power of "the many significant advantages offered by the solid propellant rocket . . . and the early indications of success." In July, Headquarters USAF established a general operational requirement for a 700–nautical mile–range ballistic missile. Envisioned as a replacement for the limited-range Matador, the solid fuel missile also represented a potential improvement over the Thor. Although BMD had transferred solid rocket research to the Wright Air Development Center, it continued to experiment with the X–17 solid rocket reentry test vehicle—from April 1956 to August 1957—to establish the design for an Atlas reentry vehicle. Technical advances seemed to indicate the feasibility of developing a 3-stage solid-propellant ICBM. General Schriever proposed to investigate the idea by developing a solid rocket as a second stage for the Titan. By October—on the eve of the Sputnik launch—it was apparent that the Air Force was about to make large solid rockets a high priority research program. In December 1957 General Schriever requested that the solids be transferred back to BMD.[101]

In an effort to accelerate the IOC for the ballistic missiles program, General White ordered a review of the Air Force's management structure. Meeting at Wright-Patterson AFB, Ohio, on November 27, 1957, Generals

---

*In fact, this decision marked the beginning of the Minuteman program. On a technical level there were numerous military advantages favoring solid rockets, including operational simplicity, quick reaction, and greater survivability.

Samuel E. Anderson.
As a lieutenant general,
he commanded the Air
Research and Development
Command (August 1957 to
March 1959).

Rawlings, Power, Anderson, and Schriever, together with Brig. Gen. Ben I. Funk,* agreed to recommend abolishing the IOC concept for missiles and reverting to normal procedures used in fielding aircraft. Consequently, all missile training, units, and bases were to be transferred to SAC. In announcing these changes before the National Press Club, General White emphasized the imperative to augment air power with ballistic missiles to meet the challenges of the future.[102]

General Schriever and SAC's Chief of Staff, Maj. Gen. Charles B. Westover, ironed out the details of the transfer in the course of several meetings and formalized the change through a memorandum of understanding signed at the end of December. Effective January 1, 1958, SAC assumed responsibility for the training and deployment of all ballistic missile units, including the 704th and 706th Strategic Missile Wings and the several subordinate groups and squadrons. BMD's Office of Deputy Commander for Plans and Operations was also transferred and redesignated as the Office

---

*Funk headed AMC's Ballistic Missile Office, which had replaced the Special Aircraft Program Office and was responsible for ICBM/IRBM procurement and production matters.

of the Assistant Commander-in-Chief, Strategic Air Command for Missiles, known by its acronym as SAC–MIKE. SAC also took control of Cooke and Warren AFBs, whereas BMD retained responsibility for research and development, programming, and the installation of equipment and launch facilities.[103] *

The IOC transfer acknowledged SAC's accumulation of experience and growing enthusiasm for ballistic missiles. Heretofore, missile planning was based entirely on theoretical studies. But with the creation of operational units, the importance of combat experience emerged. SAC, with its global command structure and worldwide command and control facilities, seemed better suited for the task of integrating ballistic missile units and bases into strategic war plans and operations. It was also deemed important that the missile units be "SAC oriented," that is, adapted to the peculiarities of the SAC system of operation. And the transfer permitted SAC to deal directly with the Air Force Ballistic Missiles Committee, rather than through the BMD.[104]

On January 30, 1958, William Holaday told the President and the NSC that the transfer of the IOC to SAC was "a step that had been planned from the beginning" and that it would "accelerate the planning, training, and strategic-operational capabilities." General Power stated that the transfer was "in line with General White's desire to get SAC into the picture as soon as possible without 'rocking the boat'" and upsetting the overall program.[105]

Regardless of the true motivation, while the Air Force had altered the IOC management structure and returned responsibility along formal channels, it retained its primary objective: to deploy missiles ready for launching "in anger" at the earliest practicable date.

---

*Warren AFB was scheduled for transfer on July 1, 1958, but the move was postponed until February 1959. SAC and ARDC agreed to define the IOC as "that capability which must be achieved coincident with the research and development of the ballistic missile program to attain the earliest operational capability with *prototype* vehicles, associated equipment and facilities." [MOU, SAC and BMD, subj: Ballistic Missiles IOC Responsibilities, Dec 31, 1957, in Basic Documents; SAC GO 1, Jan 2, 1958; emphasis added.]

Chapter VII

The Operational Force

It is hard to believe that any one weapon, no
matter how powerful, can by itself enforce peace
in this uneasy world. But we are confident that
weapons like the ICBM and IRBM will help the
Air Force to enable the free world to maintain
deterrent forces which no aggressor in his right
mind would dare to challenge.

Maj. Gen. Bernard A. Schriever, 1958

Plans for the number of ICBM squadrons to be deployed fluctuated
wildly throughout 1958 and 1959. One reason for the uncertainty concerned
the so-called "missile gap," a controversy that had grown in the wake of the
Sputnik launch. The Democrats, charging that the United States had fallen
behind the Soviets in missile development, used the controversy as a political
weapon against the Administration. Although President Eisenhower denied
that a "gap" existed, two studies commissioned by the President himself—
the Gaither Report (1957) and the Killian Report (1958)—seemed to
contradict the Administration's stance and fueled debate. Another factor
influencing the numbers and mix of ICBMs to deploy was the variety of
configurations that had evolved, each offering different capabilities and
potential. Technical problems, including some highly publicized, spectacular flight test failures on the launch pad, complicated matters further. They
gave pause to decision makers and science advisors.

Congressional scrutiny of the missiles program considered both the
technical problems that affected deployment and its exorbitant costs.
Building, testing, and installing the missiles was not only an enormous
engineering enterprise but also a considerable management challenge.
Moreover, a sense of urgency to catch up with the Russians underscored the
project. Thus, the concurrency concept, justified as indispensable for
speeding missile development, proved very costly.

With the advent of the Kennedy Administration, the missile program was reevaluated. Thirteen ICBM squadrons of Atlas and six of Titan became operational. The Atlas D and E models went on alert over a fifteen-month period from August 1960 to November 1961. Titan I and Atlas F ICBMs became operational between April and December 1962. Meanwhile, the "missile gap" had faded and emphasis shifted from concern over the numbers of missiles to their reliability and flexibility. Increased attention was also given to space programs. Consequently, the Air Force underwent major reorganization, including the establishment of Air Force Systems Command and Air Force Logistics Command in April 1961. Corresponding changes were applied to subordinate units, notably the creation of a Space Systems Division.

The Thor and Jupiter IRBMs had also entered the inventory. Thor became operational in Great Britain between June 1959 and April 1960, whereas Jupiter missiles were installed in Italy between April and July 1961 and in Turkey from August 1961 to March 1962. Deployed more for psychological and political reasons than for military ones, the IRBMs did not serve for long. Thus, the Thors were removed between November 1962 and August 1963, the Jupiters in Italy during April 1963, and the Jupiters in Turkey in July 1963.

Even as the first-generation, liquid-fueled missiles were being installed, important decisions were being made with respect to their successors. Beginning in 1955, solid-fueled missiles were initially considered for tactical roles, but by 1957 technical progress showed that they might be feasible for longer ranges. Scientists increasingly recommended their development, and by 1958 the promise of these missiles had gained widespread support. Although the Office of Secretary of Defense and the Army and Navy departments resisted adding yet another ICBM crash program, the Air Force persisted. In March 1961, Defense Secretary McNamara visited the Ballistic Missiles Division and came away convinced of the necessity for the Minuteman ICBM. The development of Minuteman was so rapid and so successful that it accelerated the phase-out of the liquid missiles by several years. By the end of December 1964 the Atlas D missiles had been removed; the Atlas E, Atlas F, and Titan I came off alert by June 1965. Meanwhile, the first Minuteman flight became operational during the Cuban Crisis in October 1962. Eventually its force grew to 1,000 ICBMs. Joining Minuteman in 1963 were 6 squadrons of the advanced Titan II ICBM.

ICBM Squadrons

In January 1958, the National Security Council solicited the military's views on the Gaither Report* to quiet demands from Congress and the public for an accelerated ICBM program.[1]

---

*The Gaither Report predicted that by the early 1960s the Soviets would have enough ICBMs to destroy America's retaliatory power.

Air Force Secretary James H. Douglas proposed a force ranging from nine to thirteen Atlas squadrons and eight Titan squadrons to be deployed by June 1963. As a hedge against failure, the Air Force provided for an additional four Atlas squadrons. Related to this proposal were plans to deploy a force of solid-fueled Minuteman missiles which were undergoing development at that time.* ICBM force proposals fluctuated up to thirteen Atlas and seventeen Titan squadrons, ostensibly in response to the Gaither Report.[2]

Defense Secretary McElroy sought guidance from the Joint Chiefs of Staff on the subject but received conflicting recommendations. General White favored enlarging the ICBM force, but the Chief of Naval Operations, Admiral Arleigh A. Burke, wanted to enlarge the projected Polaris force at the expense of the Air Force ICBMs. Gen. Maxwell D. Taylor, the Army Chief, believed that the United States already possessed enough "overkill" capability and argued for enhancing conventional war forces instead. In March a study by the Weapon Systems Evaluation Group recommended against the Air Force proposals. Subsequently, McElroy decided not to increase the Atlas force but supported speeding the Titan program. Air Force plans remained predicated on deploying a force of nine Atlas squadrons by June 1962 and eleven Titan squadrons by June 1963.[3]

On May 20, 1958, the Ballistic Missile Division submitted a major revision of its ICBM development plan. It proposed that the first two Atlas squadrons to be deployed at Vandenberg and Warren remain "soft" and undispersed, as had been planned, because of the base construction progress to date. The third and fourth Atlas squadrons (Warren II and Offutt) also would remain soft but dispersed in a 3 × 3 configuration—that is, three complexes of three launchers each, which would constitute three targets for the enemy. The last five of the planned nine Atlas squadrons (Warren III, Forbes, Fairchild, Schilling and Lincoln) would be dispersed in the 3 × 3 configuration, would employ all-inertial guidance, and would be placed in "semi-hardened" silos capable of withstanding overpressures of twenty-five pounds per square inch. These changes would require a FY 1958 budget of $1.231 billion and a FY 1959 budget of $1.908 billion, but they promised to advance the completion date from June to April 1962 and to improve greatly both the Atlas squadrons' survivability and reaction time.[4]

The "semi-hardened" Atlas missiles would be stored horizontally, then raised to the vertical position for launch. The first 2 of the 9 squadrons would deploy 6 Atlas missiles, and 9 missiles were to be emplaced in the remaining squadrons. Adjacent complexes were to be dispersed 18 miles apart. Although various alternatives were offered to provide Atlas with more dispersion and hardness, this basic plan remained in effect throughout 1959. During 1959, approval was given to disperse the 5 all-inertial Atlas E

---

*See discussion of Minuteman, pages 227-230.

The erector is lowered away from a Titan ICBM prior to a test launching at Cape Canaveral, Florida, April 3, 1959.

squadrons. This plan provided for a 1 × 9 or unitary configuration,* meaning that each missile was individually controlled. Approval was also granted to design a 100–pounds per square inch hardened Atlas system, beginning with the eighth Atlas squadron. According to the February 1958 proposals for Titan squadrons, all sites would be in the concentrated 9 × 1 configuration, hardened to 100 psi, and operational by June 1963. Under BMD's May 20 plan, Titan completion was accelerated to March 1963.[5]

After approval by the Air Force Ballistic Missile Committee, the Ballistic Missiles Division plan was submitted to the OSD Ballistic Missiles Committee. The OSD committee took no action until July 3 and then only to approve the 3 × 3 configuration for the third and fourth Atlas squadrons. Finally, on August 19, the OSD–BMC approved the nine-squadron Atlas force but held the Titan portion of the plan to only four squadrons. In fact, William Holaday proposed that the Air Force eliminate the Titan altogether and substitute four or more Atlas squadrons, thus creating a total of thirteen or even twenty Atlas squadrons.[6]

Begun in 1955 as a hedge against the failure of the Atlas, Titan emerged with many improvements over the Atlas in terms of range, speed, warhead, and other performance characteristics. But Titan development lagged behind Atlas by about two years, and this delay worked against the Titan—especially since the Atlas development was on schedule. The high cost of pursuing a dual approach on the ICBM was a further complication. These factors influenced the downgrading of the Titan during the fall of 1957 and the subsequent hesitation to expand the Titan program after Sputnik.[7]

The Air Staff split over the Titan issue. Some wanted to abandon the missile and stop funding 2 systems instead of 1.† Ironically, this faction also argued that the eventual growth of the Atlas would suffice for both the military and space applications for which the Titan had been deemed better suited initially. Air Staffers favoring Titan cited its broader production base, which would permit a more rapid ICBM buildup if necessary; the benefits of competition at a time when neither system was as yet fully proven; Titan's superior performance characteristics and growth potential; the greater confidence stemming from dual production sources; and, finally, the relatively simpler task of obtaining hardened missile facilities (100 pounds per square inch) for Titan as compared with Atlas.[8]

---

*Originally Atlas and Titan were designed for deployment in squadrons of nine missiles and launchers, the so-called 9 × 1 configuration. Consequently, these missiles presented a single target, subject to destruction by one enemy nuclear bomb. To make the new 1 × 9 concept economically feasible, BMD and SAC proposed to institute a mobile maintenance philosophy. This plan entailed changes in facilities and equipment which, in turn, affected missile site construction.

†The Air Force also opposed the Army's Jupiter IRBM on the grounds that it duplicated the Air Force's Thor IRBM.

BALLISTIC MISSILES

On November 13, 1958, the AF–BMC reaffirmed its support of an operational ICBM force of nine Atlas and eleven Titan squadrons by June 1963. The OSD committee supported the Air Force recommendation on November 18 and submitted it to the National Security Council. At last, on December 6, the NSC endorsed and President Eisenhower approved the ICBM expansion.[9]

Meanwhile, a long-smoldering controversy, the so-called "missile gap," was renewed. An outgrowth of the Soviets' Sputnik space spectacular, the controversy involved relative missile strength. In November 1958 the Russians boasted of having started "serial production" of ICBMs. American military intelligence estimates announced at that time seemed to confirm public fears by predicting a widening missiles disparity favoring Russia over the next five years.[10]

Administration officials denied that a missile gap existed, insisting that, even if the United States lagged behind in numbers of ICBMs, there was no "deterrent gap." With neither side possessing a clear superiority, the strategy of deterrence was working. Finally, they believed that any attempt to match the Soviets in numbers of weapons through a crash missile project would threaten to wreck the national budget.[11]

During the Mahon and Chavez Congressional hearings on the Fiscal Year 1960 budget, Democratic congressmen—joined by a segment of the press and some military commanders—challenged the Administration's view. The critics claimed that America's strategic forces were deteriorating steadily and were neither being improved nor augmented fast enough to match the enemy. They claimed that, over the next five years, the United States would possess only marginal detection and warning systems and no defense at all against ICBMs. In their view, these weaknesses would tempt the Soviet Union to action.[12]

Air Force intelligence depicted an even wider gap than did the other intelligence agencies. This assessment prompted Air Force leaders to establish stricter operational readiness schedules and to emphasize ICBM survival through hardening, dispersal, and mobility. Moreover, the missile gap controversy focused national attention on the enemy threat and thereby helped the Air Force present its case for missile funding and programming. During the first half of 1959, in anticipation of Congressional calls for an expanded program, BMD and the Air Staff prepared several missile plans. The most ambitious plan called for increasing the ICBM force to twenty-nine squadrons (seventeen Atlas and twelve Titan).* Fiscal Year 1960 funding required for this expansion was $365 million, with an increase of $3.7 billion from 1961 through 1963.[13]

---

* It also included provisions for 3 Minuteman squadrons (i.e., 150 missiles) and 6 Thoric squadrons (90 missiles). The Thoric was a Thor–Able rocket combination used to test nose cones (reentry vehicles).

190

The twenty-nine-squadron plan won the backing of the Strategic Air Command, a proponent of the largest possible strategic arsenal. The plan quickly gained momentum within the Air Staff and was subsequently endorsed by both Air Force Secretary Douglas and General White. On April 14, 1959, Douglas presented the proposal to Secretary of Defense McElroy.[14]

OSD took no immediate action on the Air Force recommendation and apparently contemplated none. In May, Congress asked to see the Air Force proposals. The proposals were subsequently approved as part of the Air Force's 1959–1970 objective force structure, and Convair was authorized to increase its monthly Atlas production capability from eight to twelve missiles. In June 1959 the House of Representatives added $85 million to the Atlas budget request and an additional $77 million for the Minuteman. Secretary McElroy indicated, however, that although the Fiscal Year 1960* supplemental funds for Minuteman would probably be used, he did not intend to spend the Atlas money.[15]

The Eisenhower Administration continued to resist adopting the larger, twenty-nine-squadron missile force advocated by the Air Force. A proponent of the "counterforce" strategy,† the Air Force sought to install enough missiles to absorb a first-strike enemy attack and then be able to retaliate against the enemy's force. On the other hand, as supporters of the "countervalue" or city target strategy, the Army and Navy considered Air Force goals excessive and considered adequate the projected twenty-ICBM squadron force of nine Atlas and eleven Titan. The Navy went further, favoring canceling the Titan altogether and deploying mobile Minuteman missiles instead.[16]

While the Atlas and Titan plans underwent policy examination, the Air Force concentrated on ways of reducing the vulnerability of the ICBM squadrons. Site configuration was an important element. At first it was planned to site missiles according to the 9 × 1 scheme, with all nine missiles on launchers controlled from a single launch control center. This configuration presented an attractive target for the enemy inasmuch as he had only to destroy the control center to incapacitate all nine missiles. Thus the Air Force revised this configuration into a 3 × 3 arrangement, which indicated three complexes—each with three missiles—and with each complex controlled by a single launch center.

Under the 3 × 3 arrangement, a potential enemy would have to target three different control centers in order to destroy nine missiles. At the next stage, the Air Force devised the so-called unitary configuration beginning

---

*The President's budget had limited Atlas new obligational authority (NOA) funds to $750.7 million, Titan to $677.5 million, and Minuteman to $347.2 million.

†The strategy of attacking an enemy's military forces and war-making potential.

with the 1×9 layout. The 1×9 indicated nine missiles on launchers, each with its own launch control center. Under the unitary arrangement the enemy was forced to target each missile individually to destroy it.[17]

The impediments to the unitary siting configuration were not solely technical. Clearly, changes in equipment and facilities were required for implementation, but unitary siting implied additional funding as well. The Air Force succeeded in justifying the unitary configuration as the most economical in light of increased wartime effectiveness under this system. At the same time, the AF–BMC sought to upgrade the "hardness" of the seventh and subsequent Atlas squadrons to 100 pounds per square inch. OSD's indecisiveness forced deferral of the hardening for both the seventh and eighth Atlas squadrons, and both remained at the original 25 pounds per square inch.[18]

Rushed into service to head off the so-called missile gap, the Atlas D series was the first operational ICBM deployed. The Atlas Ds were initially located on above-ground gantry-type launch pads at Vandenberg AFB. Subsequently, the missiles were placed into unprotected "coffins" which also were located above ground. The coffins simplified maintenance but provided no additional hardness. The missiles still had to be fueled and raised into a vertical position for firing. Most of the D series depended upon dispersion to survive an enemy attack. The Atlas E missiles also were placed into coffins, but were covered with earth that was said to provide the missiles with 25 pounds per square inch protection against overpressures. As with the D series, the Es had to be raised and fueled before launching. The most advanced series were the Atlas Fs. At first the Fs sat atop elevators housed inside underground concrete and steel silos. Covered by massive doors, these silos were designed to survive 100–pounds per square inch overpressures.[19]

Air Force plans had called for achieving an emergency operational capability in June 1959, when the first complex of three Atlas D missiles would be placed on alert at Vandenberg AFB. (It was to be a combined missile training and operational site.) This goal remained on schedule until about mid-April 1959, when a series of flight tests beginning with the first Atlas D, went awry. Although BMD and the ICBM Scientific Advisory Committee* assessed the mishaps as random failures, the need to evaluate and resolve the problems that prevented the missiles from successfully completing their flight tests deferred the operational date to September 1959.[20]

The Air Force sought to improve the survival and reaction characteristics of the Titan, just as it had done with the Atlas. On July 18, 1958, the AF–BMC had approved changing the Titan from an undispersed 9×1 to a 3×3 configuration for all eleven squadrons planned. Other measures

---

*See page 123.

An Atlas lies in its unprotected coffin at Vandenberg AFB, 1961.

contemplated during 1958 included shifting from radio-controlled to all-inertial guidance; changing to the 1 × 9 configuration; launching from inside the silos; and employing storable or noncryogenic* propellants. Shifting to the all-inertial guidance system would facilitate the change to the 1 × 9 configuration. The Air Force also contemplated eliminating the elevator and launching the Titan† directly from the silo. This launch mode would reduce missile exposure time, eliminate the cost and maintenance of elevators, and speed reaction time. The Air Force formally incorporated these changes into its April 1959 proposal and offered it as a supplement to the Fiscal Year 1960 development plan.[21]

In July 1959 the AF–BMC adjusted the Atlas–Titan plans in several ways. First, it increased the hardening criteria of the eighth Atlas squadron from 25 to 100 pounds per square inch and raised to 10 the number of Atlas squadrons. Next, the committee pared $25 million from the Titan budget through reduction of certain training facilities and requirements. It also

---

*A cryogenic propellant is a fuel or oxidizer kept at an extremely low temperature, generally below −50°C. For example, liquid oxygen is a cryogenic oxidizer. The primary drawbacks of such materials were that they could not be stored easily and, due to high volatility, posed extreme handling problems.

†Refers to Titan II; see page 194.

approved the technique of launching ICBMs from the vertical position inside the silo. Finally, the committee eliminated the twelfth Titan squadron from the Fiscal Year 1960 plan and submitted a proposal for 28 ICBM squadrons to the OSD-BMC.[22]

At about the same time, Secretary McElroy, apparently reacting to pressures generated by the missile gap, asked the Air Force whether the Titan could be rushed into operation sooner than scheduled. Air Force Secretary Douglas passed the request to Maj. Gen. Osmond J. Ritland, who had succeeded Schriever as BMD Commander in April 1959.* The missile division studied the question and concluded that, for $168 million in Fiscal 1961 and $229 million in 1962, a total of fifteen Titan squadrons could be sited. But Ritland vetoed the idea, because of the greater funding and the manning and training requirements entailed by this change. Instead, he recommended substituting two Titan squadrons for two less advanced Atlases.[23]

With the missile gap controversy focusing national attention on the enemy threat, the Air Force exploited the situation by seeking acceptance of a larger force. It had proposed a twenty-nine-squadron force of seventeen Atlas and twelve Titan squadrons (Chart 7-1) to become operational by June 1963.[24] The force would have progressively greater capabilities in terms of operational characteristics and hardening.[25]

Earlier, General Ritland had alerted the Air Staff to a possible delay in deploying the initial Atlas squadron. The reasons for the anticipated delay were a nationwide steel strike, which began on July 15,† and the lack of a decision by the OSD-BMC. Consequently, the Air Force again revised its long-range plans to be consistent with budgetary limitations, and in September offered a twenty-six-squadron ICBM program comprising twelve Atlas and fourteen Titan squadrons. Under this option the number of Atlas squadrons was reduced and the number of Titan squadrons was raised by two.[26]

A more advanced version of the Titan, designated the Titan II, was conceived for the last 8 squadrons. Its second stage would have a 10-foot diameter, compared with Titan I's 8 feet, thus enabling it to house a larger engine, to fly 600 miles farther, and to carry a heavier payload.‡ Titan II also would assume a 1 × 9 configuration and would be sited underground.

---

*On April 25, 1959, General Schriever succeeded General Anderson at ARDC. Anderson assumed command of AMC. Schriever retained command when ARDC became Air Force Systems Command in April 1961.

†The steel strike lasted 116 days and contributed to delaying Atlas's deployment.

‡The payload was increased in accordance with a Rand study, which recommended larger strikes against cities and hardened targets. The increase also enabled it to carry penetration aids, decoys, multiple warheads, and electronic countermeasures. A 7,500-pound, 9-megaton warhead was contemplated.

Chart 7–1

Proposed ICBM Force, June 1959

ATLAS Plan

No. of Squadrons	Type of Guidance	Site Config- uration*	Degree of Hardening	Operational Dates
2 Atlas D	radio-inertial	6 × 1	none	Jun 59–Mar 60
2 Atlas D	radio-inertial	3 × 3	none	Aug 60–Nov 60
4 Atlas E	all-inertial	1 × 9	25 psi	Jun 61–Jan 62
9 Atlas F	all-inertial	1 × 9 (silo lift)	100 psi	Mar 62–Jun 63

TITAN Plan

6	radio-inertial	1 × 9 (silo lift)	100 psi	Jun 61–Aug 62
6	all-inertial	1 × 9 (in silo)	100 psi	Oct 62–Jun 63

* The first digit indicates the number of complexes per squadron and the second the number of launch centers per complex. Thus 6 × 1 signifies six missiles controlled by one center, 3 × 3 signifies three complexes of three missiles each, controlled by three centers, and 1 × 9 indicates one missle per complex, nine missiles total, each controlled by its own center.

Instead of riding an elevator to the surface before firing, the Titan II would be fired directly from inside the silo. The new missile used a storable, non-cryogenic hydrazine fuel and a storable oxidizer (nitrogen tetroxide) that improved its reaction time and reduced its vulnerability. The change-over in production from Titan I to Titan II was estimated to cost $2 million in Fiscal Year 1960 and an additional $9 million in Fiscal Year 1961, and it would delay operational readiness for those squadrons by about 5 months each. Both the financial and schedule costs, however, foreclosed this option.[27]

Throughout the fall of 1959, Air Force and Defense Department officials reviewed a great variety of long-range plans for Atlas and Titan squadrons. These plans represented various degrees of hardening, combinations of models, launch modes, and schedules. Among the major issues considered were the effects of different operational dates on the "missile gap"; consequences of overlapping between the liquid-fueled Atlas and Titan and the solid-fueled Minuteman; and budgetary considerations. The latter exerted powerful control over many issues, including technical decisions. For example, the Air Force achieved considerable cost savings simply by adjusting the site separation distances between missile silos rather than providing a separate control facility for each.[28]

Under the December 1959 development plan—which evolved from the fall review—there would be 4 Atlas D squadrons, 1 each at Vandenberg and Offutt, and 2 squadrons at Warren Air Force Base. Three Atlas E squadrons were projected, 1 each at Fairchild, Forbes, and Warren Air Force Bases. The E series featured 9 launchers per squadron and an 18-mile dispersion distance between launchers. Atlas E's missiles would be hardened to 25 psi and would employ all-inertial guidance. Six Atlas F squadrons were proposed, 1 each at Schilling, Lincoln, Altus, Dyess, Walker, and Plattsburgh Air Force Bases. Again, 9 launchers were contemplated per squadron, but dispersion would only be 7 to 10 miles. The all-inertial Atlas Fs were to be hardened to 100 pounds per square inch. One Atlas E training launcher was planned for Vandenberg AFB's 576th Strategic Missile Squadron, but no Atlas F training site had been approved.[29]

A forest of USAF missiles. Maj. Gen. Osmond J. Ritland displays models of R&D programs being managed by the Air Force Ballistic Missiles Division.

On January 4, 1960, Defense Secretary Thomas S. Gates ruled that, under the new force objectives, Atlas and Titan would be increased from the currently approved program of twenty to twenty-seven squadrons (thirteen Atlas and fourteen Titan), with the last squadron of each becoming operational in December 1962 and February 1964 respectively. The National Security Council supported the new force objectives, and President Eisenhower approved them on January 30.[30]

With respect to the Titan squadrons, a controversy developed over whether to continue the Titan I or the advanced Titan II. The OSD–BMC had recommended against continuing with the Titan II because of the high cost—up to an additional $200 million—required to deploy the planned eight Titan II squadrons. Secretary Gates overruled the OSD–BMC in January 1960, but the missile's future remained uncertain because of flight test difficulties. After four consecutive successful launchings in early 1959, a Titan I test missile exploded in August 1959 and then another blew up in December 1959. An investigation by the Air Force Scientific Advisory Committee cleared the Titan of any basic design flaws. The committee attributed the launch failure to faulty test procedures and shortcomings in ground equipment facilities.[31]

In January 1960 another Congressional session convened, and missile reliability joined earlier concerns over the missile gap and rising ICBM costs. Congressmen asked whether a parallel ICBM program—the Titan—was necessary, and the words "duplication and waste" rang out once more on Capitol Hill. Some legislators favored canceling the Titan in favor of the "proven" Atlas, whereas others sought to expand the bomber force instead.[32]

Proponents stressed Titan's advantages over the Atlas. Besides holding a performance edge—including quicker reaction time, higher reliability, and greater range and payload—an operational Titan required less manpower and continuing financial support. Also, the advanced Titan was expected to aid the nation's space program.* But canceling the Titan invited many disadvantages. The cost of accelerating the Atlas might cause a loss of three to five Titan squadrons during the critical 1961–1962 period. Canceling the Titan would reduce the ICBM production base, result in the loss of more than $2 billion already sunk into the program, and dislocate the Martin Company's engineering staff. Finally, adapting Atlas missiles to Titan facilities would require an enormously difficult and costly effort.[33]

Responding to charges of the exorbitant cost of the ICBM program, the Air Force pointed out the highly compressed nature of the program's

---

*General Schriever had envisioned moving military research from ballistic missiles to space satellites. [Speech, Feb 1957, San Diego, CA, quoted in R. F. Futrell, *Ideas, Concepts, Doctrine: A History of Basic Thinking in the United States Air Force, 1907–1964* (Maxwell AFB, Alabama, 1974), p 277.]

development, testing, procurement, and construction. Testifying before Congressional committees on these issues, Air Force and Defense officials consistently supported the Titan program in terms of both its technical and military soundness.[34]

Even as the Congressional hearings continued, the AF–BMC refined the ICBM program based on the force objectives approved in January 1960 by Secretary Gates. In other efforts to trim costs, the Air Force committee shortened dispersal distances between missile sites, limited training launches to ten per year per missile squadron, and recommended that the last six Atlas squadrons—all Atlas Fs—use a 1 × 12 configuration instead of the planned 1 × 9. The latter change would add eighteen missiles to the Atlas force. The AF–BMC also favored accelerating the operational readiness dates of some squadrons, despite objections by General Ritland* that the practice was unrealistic.[35]

In March 1960 the OSD–BMC approved the Atlas development plan for Fiscal Year 1960 and the proposed Fiscal 1961 plan. Funding reservations, as amended, were as follows:[36]

Fiscal Year 1959 .... $641.5 million
Fiscal Year 1960 .... $971.3 million
Fiscal Year 1961 .... $676.6 million

Similarly, the AF–BMC reduced the dispersal distances between Titan sites and limited annual training launches to ten per squadron. The committee deferred building the Titan training facility at Vandenberg AFB from 1961 to 1962. Also, as a means of cost reduction, it required collocating two nine-missile Titan II squadrons at each support base, thereby creating a 1 × 18 configuration. Finally, it reaffirmed the need for the ten-foot diameter Titan II second stage. The OSD–BMC approved Titan development funding in April 1960 as follows:[37]

Fiscal Year 1959 .... $495.4 million
Fiscal Year 1960 .... $763.4 million
Fiscal Year 1961 .... $1,002.1 million

The above changes were later reflected in revised Atlas and Titan development plans. In June, based on the findings from a nuclear test series,† the Ballistic Missile Division raised the hardness requirement for Atlas

---

*Ritland warned that the schedules were far too compressed. He was urged to proceed because the dates had been approved by the Air Staff and OSD and were submitted to Congress.

†The Hardtack I and II tests were conducted both in the Pacific and at the Nevada test site from April to October 1958.

facilities from 100 to 150/200 pounds per square inch and for Titan II from 100 to 300/350 pounds per square inch.[38]

In May 1960 a committee under Dr. Charles C. Lauritsen completed a technical and management appraisal of the ICBM which had been conducted at the request of General Schriever. Concerned about Soviet advances in missiles and rocketry, Lauritsen urged Schriever to accept some degradation—in either missile range, or accuracy with respect to the initial ICBM squadrons—to ensure meeting deployment schedules. This plan would provide a timely interim capability until the Minuteman became operational.[39]

The OSD-BMC did not share Lauritsen's concern, and on August 15 had approved a Fiscal Year 1961 ICBM budget considerably below what the Ballistic Missile Division had requested.* The Air Force budget had cited several factors in support of its request, including higher-than-expected construction costs; a higher missile production rate to support additional reliability testing, space projects, and the Nike–Zeus air defense project; additional facilities for hydrazine fuel production; additional planning for Titan II; and research and development costs for mobile Minuteman systems and penetration aids.[40]

On December 13, 1960, the OSD-BMC approved a Fiscal Year 1961 budget of $788.8 million for Atlas and $1,055.8 million for Titan. Both figures exceeded those approved by the committee in August, but totalled some $29 million less than the Air Force had requested. The heaviest cuts were applied to the installation and checkout of missile sites and to the proposed expansion of production facilities.[41]

The Concurrency Concept

Debate over the missile gap diminished, but did not die, after the first session of the 86th Congress ended in September 1959. Dr. Herbert F. York, Director of Defense Research and Engineering, conceded that the Russians were leading in rocket technology. York also acknowledged the possible existence of a missile gap, but he believed that it was being closed. In December 1959 Thomas S. Gates, who had succeeded McElroy as Secretary of Defense that month, asserted that the United States and USSR were about even in the arms race. At the same time, Gates claimed that the Russians were building up their missile stockpile faster than the United States and concluded that a missile gap might exist by the early 1960s. In his book, *The Uncertain Trumpet*, former Army Chief of Staff Maxwell Taylor warned that the United States would remain at a disadvantage in missiles for

---

*The Atlas budget was about $120 million less than requested, and the approved Titan budget was $20 million short.

the next five years. Meanwhile, continued Russian achievements in missiles and space (the Soviets had hit the moon in September 1959, photographed it in October, and launched two ICBMs into the Pacific in January 1960) sustained the missile gap debate into 1960.[42]

Part of the Congressional debate centered on a newspaper account that erroneously attributed to Secretary McElroy the statement that the Soviets would hold a 3:1 advantage in ICBMs during the 1960s. The debate also focused on a recent series of Titan test failures that fueled pressures to cancel the Titan program in favor of the Atlas.[43]

Nonetheless, the Administration continued to deny the existence of a military crisis. In his January 1960 State of the Union address, President Eisenhower sought to allay Americans' fears about the missile gap and at the same time to warn Russia against underestimating U.S. power. The President's message highlighted the fourteen consecutive successful Atlas test launches that had followed a series of five test failures between February and June 1959. He also announced that the first complex of Atlas ICBMs was operational, and in subsequent weeks top military officials publicly emphasized Atlas's accuracy and operational status.[44]

Defense Secretary Gates and the new Secretary of the Air Force, Dudley C. Sharp,* testified before Congressional committees in January 1960. These officials observed that, although the Russians might enjoy a temporary numerical edge in missiles, intelligence estimates of Soviet missile inventories, performance, and production rates indicated that no "deterrent gap" existed. Other Defense Department witnesses, including Joint Chiefs of Staff Chairman Gen. Nathan F. Twining, assured Congress that America's retaliatory power could not be destroyed, even in a surprise attack. The press refused to accept these intelligence appraisals and accused the Administration of "mind reading" the Soviets' intentions rather than assessing their capabilities.[45]

In March 1960 President Eisenhower launched a campaign to allay public fears about the missile gap. In a 17-page letter sent to some 600 business leaders, Eisenhower stressed that critics of his Administration had confined discussion on the controversial issue to a single element—the ICBM. But national security did not rest solely on matching the Soviets in missiles. Rather, the test of military adequacy depended on its overall deterrent strength. Air Force Secretary Sharp backed this theme by minimizing the significance of the missile gap. When asked by Congress whether the ICBM program should be accelerated, the Air Force Chief of Staff, General White, replied: "I cannot say that it would be vital to do so. I can only say more weapons would be more insurance." White also observed that the U.S. lead in aircraft obviated the need for a crash missile program.

---

*Sharp succeeded James H. Douglas on December 11, 1959.

Finally, even General Power, the SAC Commander, agreed that a crash program for missiles was unnecessary. "Deterrence," he said, "is composed of a great many things."[46]

Emplacing the ICBMs in launch facilities had always represented a considerable engineering task. But with the added pressure of the missile gap controversy, it became a monumental one. General Schriever attacked the problem through what later came to be called "concurrency." Under this concept, site construction, installation and checkout, flight testing, and training were all undertaken as rapidly as possible and within a very narrow and overlapping schedule. Concurrency aimed at having missiles, sites, equipment, and crews all ready at the same time.

This method saved much valuable time but also increased costs considerably, often resulted in unrealistic training, and turned out systems that required extensive modification and refinement. Site construction costs, for example, soared well beyond their original projections because of the numerous changes incorporated to improve missile survivability through silo hardening and site dispersal. By the fall of 1961, Atlas construction costs exceeded their original budget by $125 million, and Titan I costs were $80 million above projections.[47]

Site Activation

The Ballistic Missile Division was responsible for developing concepts and criteria for technical facilities, designing and constructing those facilities, and monitoring construction to ensure compatibility with the weapon systems. BMD also prepared detailed plans for installation and checkout, technical direction, and validation of the total system performance. Finally, BMD placed the entire system in a fifteen-minute operational readiness condition, capable of responding to emergency war order launching, prior to transferring the site to the Strategic Air Command.

Air Materiel Command—represented by its Ballistic Missile Office— performed contract management and administration for missile production, delivery of spare parts, quality control, and logistic support. Air Training Command was responsible for training of individual missile personnel. Crew training, preliminary to operational readiness, was assigned to the Strategic Air Command, which also developed missile operational concepts. Through its Corps of Engineers Construction Agency, the Army was assigned to administer and manage site construction.[48]

During 1957 the typical siting activity involved a joint effort by BMD, SAC, and the Corps of Engineers. The team first mapped areas adjacent to the support bases where the missiles were to be sited. Concurrently, soils analyses and topographical and geological surveys were conducted prior to the selection of individual sites for the operational squadrons. Throughout this phase, numerous design changes were incorporated as a result of site survival studies and missile guidance system developments.

These changes—first applied to the operational/training complex at Vandenberg AFB—included the use of horizontal storage launchers, which afforded only minimal additional protection but simplified missile maintenance and servicing. For instance, it was found that the General Electric Mod III guidance system required only 2 instead of 4 rate stations.* Use of this system reduced the distance between the stations and guidance buildings, and thus permitted siting the Atlas D squadrons on 900 acres of land instead of the 1,960 acres previously planned.[49]

Civilian contractors constructed the facilities. Their work was monitored by the Army Corps of Engineers, which administered the contracts and supervised construction. A Ballistic Missile Division field office, established at each construction site, ensured weapon system compatibility, provided technical interpretation, and expedited the incorporation of modifications and change orders. Similarly, a Ballistic Missile Office field unit of AMC provided on-site support.[50]

The ICBM construction represented the largest and most extensive building program of its kind at that time. In addition to the "brick and mortar" tasks, the construction phase included road building, water systems development, electrical power generation and distribution, sanitation, air conditioning, security fencing and lighting, and propellant loading.[51]

The primary facilities for missile operations included the launch and service buildings, guidance building, remote rate stations, and boresight towers.† Construction delays at the Warren AFB sites postponed completion of the technical facilities until October 1959, and the propellant loading systems were not finished until just prior to SAC's acceptance of the sites. The compressed schedule also obliged the construction contractor and Convair—the installation and checkout contractor—to occupy the sites jointly for about three months.[52]

Probably the most exacting and troublesome construction phase involved the propellant loading system. The quick-reaction feature for the Atlas required that the missile be fueled and fired within 15 minutes. Even though it had taken years to upgrade aircraft refueling to a rate of 600 gallons per minute, now propellant loading for missiles required flow rates that were far greater (5,000 gallons per minute for liquid oxygen at -500 degrees F), under 6,000 pounds per square inch pressure, and with nearly surgical cleanliness to prevent contamination. Even a minute amount might

---

*These were stations equipped with guidance antennas, which received radio signals reporting a missile's rate of speed.

†Used to align directional antennas by optical procedure.

A construction site for Titan launchers, near Denver, Colorado.

cause an explosion. Moreover, as LOX could not be stored inside the missile, each launch was preceded by the transfer of the liquid from the storage tanks to the missile. This was an extremely delicate and hazardous operation because of the tendency of LOX to sustain combustion when combined with alcohol, kerosene, or hydrazine. A chance spark or "combustion instability" in the engine could trigger an explosion.

The propellant loading system used mainly "off-the-shelf" components, but many modifications, such as new valves, had to be developed to meet specifications. The Atlas missile held approximately 11,500 gallons of RP–1 fuel and 18,600 gallons of LOX. During countdown, the fuel tanks were filled in 4 minutes and 45 seconds (from T minus 12:15 to T minus 7:30) at a rate of 3,500 gallons per minute. The LOX tanks were loaded in 4 minutes and 50 seconds (from T minus 6:00 to T minus 1:10) at a rate of 5,500 gallons per minute. Next, the operational procedure called for an hour's "hold" before launch, and then "topping off" the tanks during the countdown with an additional 0.5 percent of fuel.[53]

The installation and checkout phase consisted of a demonstration of all the weapon system components except the missile itself. BMD's Atlas Program Director was responsible for the overall management and technical direction, but Convair performed about seventy percent of the tasks. Prior to January 1958, when SAC assumed responsibility for the IOC, contractor engineers employed research and development equipment used at Cape

Canaveral. After SAC assumed responsibility, the program was reoriented toward achieving operational capability with military personnel. Emphasis turned to automatic launch and maintenance equipment and standardized replacement units. In July 1959—three months after the first Atlas D flight test—installation and checkout began on the first launcher at Warren AFB's 564th Strategic Missile Squadron.[54]

Initially, ICBM training was based on use of contractor-furnished maintenance and launch capability and was the responsibility of BMD and contractor personnel. Again, Air Training Command was charged with individual training and SAC was responsible for the overall crew training program. Personnel requirements and integrated weapon system training were formulated in early 1958, and the initial class of Atlas supervisors and planners graduated in July 1958. Subsequently, an integrated training plan was issued, and preparations were made to conduct training at Vandenberg AFB. In May 1959 Convair started its "over-the-shoulder" factory training program for individuals. Integrated weapon system training began at Vandenberg AFB later that year.

Once a crew* had completed integrated training and was declared combat ready, it received two additional types of instruction: recurring and corrective training. Recurring training, scheduled every six months, dealt with subjects vital to fulfilling the unit's mission. Corrective training, by contrast, was administered to correct deficiencies uncovered during periodic missile inspections.[55]

At first SAC avoided conducting unscheduled operational inspections of missile sites—the so-called "no notice" type familiar to aircrews. General Power felt that missile crews were not yet sufficiently familiar with the new weapons, and he was reluctant to remove more than a few missiles from strategic alert at one time. In place of "no notice" inspections, SAC instituted a system of "shakedowns" which had been proposed by Lt. Gen. John D. Ryan, the Air Force Inspector General. Limited to one missile per squadron at any one time, the shakedown required two consecutive, successful propellant-loading countdowns. The purpose of such an exercise was to determine that all systems were in working order and to identify minimum actions needed to maintain launch reliability. These exercises quickly revealed the inherent unreliability of rockets fueled with non-storable cryogenic liquid fuel. Later operational and follow-on flight tests tended to substantiate this conclusion.[56]

---

*An Atlas D crew consisted of twelve members: a launch control officer, a missile system analyst, a power distribution system technician, a missile electrician, three missile maintenance technicians, a missile engine mechanic, a ground support equipment specialist, a propulsion system technician, a guidance system analyst, and a hydraulics technician. The number of guidance personnel varied with the type of guidance system used. Atlas E and F crews had only five members.

Flight Testing *

Because ballistic missiles were unmanned and essentially unrecoverable, flight testing presented a unique situation that required a new test philosophy. Accordingly, maximum testing of components was conducted in laboratories and captive facilities in order to obtain sufficient confidence in the missiles before proceeding to actual flights.

The MA–3 propulsion system, for example, underwent 15 months of ground testing prior to its initial launch in the Atlas E test program in October 1960. Three engines were subjected to captive testing at General Dynamics's facility in Sycamore Canyon, California, and another 3 were tested at Edwards AFB. All told, approximately 50 tests were run— consuming more than 8,000 seconds of firing time—before the first launch. By 1962 the Air Force had spent about $250 million for ground test facilities † in the ballistic missile program.[57]

The Atlas flight test program began on June 11, 1957, at Cape Canaveral, Florida. Generally the tests were run by series, with the experimental series Atlas A, B, and C preceding the operational Atlas D configuration on the launch pads. The 8 Atlas A missiles launched were in minimal flying configuration, using only the booster and vernier engines (instead of the complete propulsion system) and a nose fairing in place of a reentry vehicle. Initial thrust on the A–series flights was raised from 270,000 to 300,000 pounds; the maximum range and altitude were 600 nautical miles and 57.5 nautical miles respectively. The Atlas A tests ended in June 1958 with 3 successes.[58]

Nine Atlas series B flight tests were conducted between July 1958 and February 1959. All of the basic subsystems were tested in this series, including the MA–1 propulsion system, the Mod 1 radio guidance system, and the Mark 2 heat-sink reentry vehicle. The Atlas B tests demonstrated booster staging and reentry vehicle separation, and attained 5,500 nautical miles range and 500 nautical miles altitude. The most memorable flight in this series was Project Score. Launched on December 18, 1958, it placed an entire missile (Atlas 10B) in earth orbit. A recorder aboard the vehicle relayed President Eisenhower's Christmas message to the world. The missile remained aloft until the orbit decayed in January 1959.[59]

The Atlas C series tests emphasized weight reduction and improved accuracy. Only six missiles were flown in this series between December 1958 and August 1959. The tests marked the use of thin-skinned fuel tanks and

---

* See also page 130.

† Major facilities included engine test stands at North American Aviation's site at Santa Susana, California, and launch stands and assembly buildings at Camp Elliott and Edwards AFB, California.

the Mod 2 and Mod 3 guidance systems. During the Atlas C series tests, the first flights were made into the Atlantic Missile Range Impact Locator System net and the first recovery of a reentry vehicle was achieved.[60]

The Atlas D flight tests aimed at verifying the operational configuration missile. Beginning in April 1959 and running through the end of the year, 15 Atlas D flights were conducted. There were 3 successive failures before the program began producing positive results. This test series demonstrated that the missile's accuracy was considerably better than the 1 nautical mile circular error probable expected. Also, the Mark 3 ablative type reentry vehicle was shown to be operationally sound, and Atlas D missiles flew to an extended 7,800 nautical miles range. Seven of the flights provided initial testing of the all-inertial guidance system designed for the Atlas E.

On September 9, 1959, the Air Force first successfully launched a model of the Mercury–Atlas vehicle, thus paving the way for manned orbital space flights.* Other tests included biomedical and space environment experiments aided by the use of telemetry and recoverable reentry vehicle

---

* On February 20, 1962, Atlas 109D boosted Lt. Col. John Glenn into orbit. In April Atlas 133D launched the Ranger IV spacecraft from Cape Canaveral, thus becoming the first American package to land on the moon.

Flight test of an Atlas ICBM at Cape Canaveral, August 1958.

An Atlas missile on its
launching platform,
flanked by its service
tower, Cape Canaveral,
1958.

Transporting a new nose cone, to be flight tested on an Atlas missile, 1959.

capsules. Unfortunately, an attempt to orbit the moon with an Atlas–Able IV vehicle failed on November 26, 1959.[61]

Construction

On September 1, 1959, the Air Force accepted the Atlas. A week later—after a SAC crew had successfully launched an Atlas training missile—General Power declared the ICBM operational. As a result, one of the three missiles in Complex 576A at Vandenberg AFB was placed on strategic alert.*

Considering that the event occurred only two months later than the completion date that had been established four years before, this represented a remarkable achievement. But few other ICBMs would be placed on alert for many months to come. Delays were caused by various factors, including propellant loading difficulties, late deliveries of equipment, and flight testing problems at Cape Canaveral. Complex 576B at Vandenberg AFB experienced similar delays, and also required the incorporation of major design changes to accommodate a new missile nose cone. Despite the slippage, training proceeded on schedule.[62]

The next 3 Atlas squadrons were scheduled to become operational at Warren AFB, Wyoming, and Offutt AFB, Nebraska, during March, August, and November 1960. Additional Atlas and Titan I squadrons were to be activated on a regular basis until the entire force was in place by June 1963. By late 1959, however, the effects of the 116-day nationwide steel strike were being felt. Delays also were caused by underestimation of the project, with slippages averaging about 90 days behind schedule.[63]

Siting the 564th Strategic Missile Squadron at Warren AFB was initially postponed from March to April 1960. Then additional problems arose, including facility changes, propellant contamination, and the integration of certain programming and checkout equipment. Late completion of the 576th Strategic Missile Squadron at Vandenberg also affected the Warren squadron and prompted Headquarters USAF to adopt a new procedure, whereby Atlas sites were transferred to SAC in increments rather than as complete squadrons. This procedure was subsequently applied elsewhere. On April 30, 1960, a single Atlas was placed on strategic alert at Warren AFB.[64]

Two days before the Warren AFB deadline, General Power advised General White that, although SAC crews were combat ready, the missiles were not. General Schriever's on-site inspection had disclosed a host of problems, including managerial inadequacies, delays in implementation of

---

*Formally called Emergency War Order plan alert.

tasks, and shortcomings in organizational procedures and manning. Consequently, Warren's alert status was postponed. Finally, on August 9, 1960, SAC declared operational Warren's first complex—three missiles and launchers.[65]

Warren's second squadron, the 565th Strategic Missile Squadron, also encountered construction problems that were blamed on overextended or incompetent contractors. While the Air Force and Corps of Engineers investigated alternative actions, General LeMay appointed a board of senior officers under Brig. Gen. Richard D. Curtin to study the situation and to recommend solutions. Submitted in July, General Curtin's report attributed site activation problems to many factors. In essence, the project had been grossly underestimated in terms of its difficulty. Labor strife, including frequent and widespread strikes, also delayed construction. Numerous facility changes were made, either to correct shortcomings or to improve capability. Moreover, certain contractors were found to be incompetently managed and organized—a situation that was aggravated by the lack of clear division of responsibility between the Corps of Engineers and Air Force agencies. General Curtin recommended creating a single manager within the Air Materiel Command.[66]

General LeMay acted quickly and decisively. Effective July 11, 1960, he transferred site activation responsibility from ARDC to AMC except for sites already underway at Vandenberg, Warren, and Offutt AFBs. Under the reorganization, ARDC's and AMC's field offices were merged into a site activation task force at each construction site. A specially selected senior colonel commanded each task force. Maj. Gen. Thomas P. Gerrity was appointed chief of the new Ballistic Missile Center (AMC) in Los Angeles, and was assigned responsibility for site selection, facility design, installation and checkout, and turnover of sites to SAC. Construction responsibility remained with the Army Corps of Engineers, with AMC exercising surveillance.[67]

At the end of July, Defense Department officials (including Secretary Gates) and more than fifty industrialists reviewed the site activation program and recommended a complete reorganization. Management was tightened once more, with responsibility for site construction transferred from the Corps of Engineers district offices to a new entity with headquarters in Los Angeles. Designated the Corps of Engineers Ballistic Missile Construction Office, the organization was commanded by Brig. Gen. Alvin C. Welling. OSD also assigned undivided authority to contracting officers, eliminated multiple site inspections, stationed an architect-engineer at each site, expedited payments to contractors for site changes, and clarified management responsibilities between the Army and Air Force. Confident that these actions would prevent delays, Secretary Gates attributed past difficulties to the inexperience of contractors and to the fact that "a wartime operation was undertaken under peacetime conditions with only peacetime authority.'' [68]

The changes in construction management and supervision were implemented only gradually. On September 15, 1960, the sites for the first two Titan squadrons at Lowry AFB, Colorado, were transferred to the Corps of Engineers Ballistic Missile Construction Office. In subsequent months, other Atlas and Titan sites also were transferred. By year's end there were definite indications that the much-revised but more realistic site activation schedules would be met. [69]

Aerospace Corporation

Although managing ICBM construction occupied its most immediate attention, the Air Force did not neglect other interests. A study issued in the spring of 1958 attempted to chart policy on the future of the missile complex at Los Angeles—composed of the Ballistic Missile Division, Ballistic Missile Office, SAC–MIKE, and the Space Technology Laboratories.[*] The study emphasized centralized program control, management, coordination, and expert staffs at the complex. It also recognized the uniqueness of the missile complex in providing an entry into the outer space field. [70]

At this time there was considerable interest in outer space activities throughout the government. In January 1958, President Eisenhower had assigned top priority to the development of satellite and missile defense systems, thus placing these systems on a par with ICBMs and IRBMs. Various military and civilian agencies vied for control of space projects,[†] particularly in view of the confused jurisdiction among the agencies. Anxious to carve out a role in manned space flight, BMD represented the Air Force conviction "that superiority in space is a fundamental requirement since on it will depend the entire future position, prestige, and indeed, the welfare of the U.S." Although BMD was permitted to organize for space systems development, it did not become actively involved in new space programs until 1960, because the Advanced Research Projects Agency (ARPA), an OSD agency, conducted initial work on all advanced military programs. [71]

. In the midst of these futuristic concerns, BMD faced a more mundane problem: the dual interest of Ramo-Wooldridge as the profit-making parent of the Space Technology Laboratories. While the laboratories provided the Air Force with systems engineering services for the ballistic missiles

---

[*] In December 1957, Ramo-Wooldridge's Guided Missiles Research Division was renamed Space Technology Laboratories and was separated from the company, presumably to placate critics.

[†] Explorer I, the first American satellite, had been launched on January 31, 1958.

Titan missile Site 1A, under construction at Lowry AFB, Colorado, February 1960.

program, Ramo-Wooldridge had been approached to undertake consulting, development, and production of space-related projects. The proposal to Ramo-Wooldridge drew criticism from both governmental and industry sources, who were opposed either to the company's systems engineering concept or to the details of its involvement. Some objected to the high salaries of Ramo-Wooldridge officers; others attacked the company's privileged position within the Air Force and its relationship with Thompson Products. Competitors in the ballistic missile field feared that Thompson Products would monopolize the supply of structural parts for missiles and that Ramo-Wooldridge would capture the electronics market.[72]

From the start, the Air Force had attempted to mitigate industry suspicions by banning Ramo-Wooldridge from hardware production. A contract clause forbade the company from "development or production of any components for use in the ICBM field . . . except with the express approval of the Assistant Secretary of the Air Force (Materiel) or his authorized representative."[73]

Thompson Products and Ramo-Wooldridge merged on October 31, 1958, to form Thompson-Ramo-Wooldridge (TRW). Subsequently, Space Technology Laboratories became an independent but wholly owned subsidiary of TRW, and James H. (Jimmy) Doolittle was named Chairman of the Board. The Air Force extended the hardware exclusion clause to TRW and to STL. When charges of conflict of interest continued to be expressed,

General Schriever concluded that the only way to maintain STL and to avoid suspicion was to accomplish a complete separation from TRW.[74]

A September 1959 Congressional report recommended converting STL to a nonprofit institution like the Rand Corporation or other private and university-sponsored organizations. TRW objected at first to losing a valuable financial asset, but then saw the advantage of eliminating its hardware ban. The Air Force assigned a committee, headed by Dr. Clark B. Millikan of Caltech, to study the matter. Millikan's report of January 1960 supported the need for a "basically non-competitive" civil contractor to conduct advanced planning, systems design, and technical evaluation of programs. It also recommended that STL continue to oversee the Atlas, Titan, and Minuteman programs.[75]

The Air Force accepted the recommendations. It purchased facilities and capitalized a new nonprofit organization for $5 million. On June 3, 1960, the Aerospace Corporation was established "to engage in, assist and contribute to the support of scientific activities and projects . . . for the United States Government."[76]

Deploying the First Generation

Before the advent of the Kennedy Administration, the United States engaged in a crash project to deploy as many ICBMs as possible to offset an assumed Russian ICBM advantage. Afterward, as the nature of the "missile gap" became clearer, the concern shifted from the number of missiles to their flexibility and reliability. Accordingly, the Air Force incorporated extensive modifications to its first-generation, liquid-fueled missiles and reexamined its growing ICBM arsenal to determine which ones it would keep, improve, or replace.[77]

Because the missile gap had been an important issue in his election, President John F. Kennedy lost no time in directing Secretary of Defense Robert S. McNamara to examine the ICBM program. While the reappraisal was in progress, the new Administration concentrated on improving management and reducing waste. In January 1961 the new Air Force Secretary, Eugene M. Zuckert, met with top Air Force officials to consider a proposal to relocate the Ballistic Missile Division from Inglewood to San Bernardino Air Materiel Area at Norton AFB, California. In February the Air Force Ballistic Missile and Space Committee* proposed to expand the ICBM program by adding 3 Atlas and 2 Titan squadrons at a cost of some $480

---

*In October 1960 AF–BMC had been redesignated the Air Force Ballistic Missile and Space Committee. For simplicity, the term AF–BMC will continue to be used here. On July 25, 1961, the committee was again renamed the Designated Systems Management Group (DSMG).

million. SAC opposed this plan, fearing that it might jeopardize the 1964 objective force of 805 Minuteman missiles as well as SAC's B–70 program and space plans.[78]

In March 1961—as part of the Administration's sweeping review of strategic forces—Secretary McNamara issued a list of ninety-two major programs and issues for the services to comment upon. Included on this list were the following topics: substituting fixed-base Minuteman sites for mobile Minuteman squadrons; increasing missile production; retiring Atlas; settling the status of Titan II; and requiring additional ICBM training and reliability testing. Later that month, with only a few studies completed, McNamara decided to defer plans for three mobile Minuteman squadrons and to cancel two of the eight Titan II squadrons that had been programmed. The approved Atlas–Titan force structure comprised thirteen Atlas and twelve Titan squadrons, as shown in Chart 7–2.[79]

Both decisions were contrary to Air Force recommendations, and McNamara appeared before a Congressional committee to defend his actions. The Defense Secretary stressed the advantages of shifting from the costly, cumbersome, liquid-fueled Atlas and Titan to the solid-fueled Minuteman and Polaris missiles. The Atlas comprised some 40,000 parts, including many delicate electronics components that overburdened maintenance and operational crews. Also, the extreme caution necessary in fueling

President John F. Kennedy tours Vandenberg AFB, accompanied by Secretary of Defense Robert S. McNamara (left), SAC Commander Gen. Thomas S. Power (right), and Lt. Gen. Howell M. Estes, Jr. (right background), March 1962.

Chart 7-2

Atlas–Titan Force Structure

ATLAS

No. of Squadrons	Series	Guidance	Config- uration	Hardness	Operational Squadrons
1*	D	Radio-inertial	3 × 1	—	Aug 60–Jul 62
	E	All-inertial	1 × 1	25 psi	
	F	All-inertial	1 × 2	—	
1	D	Radio-inertial	3 × 2	—	Sep 1960
2	D	Radio-inertial	3 × 3	—	Mar 1961
3	E	All-inertial	1 × 9	25 psi	Aug 61–Dec 61
6	F	All-inertial	1 × 12	100 psi	Jul 62–Dec 62

TITAN

No. of Squadrons	Series	Guidance	Config- uration	Hardness	Operational Squadrons
6	Titan I	Radio-inertial	3 × 3	150/200 psi	Aug 61–Aug 62
6	Titan II	All-inertial	1 × 9	300/350 psi	Mar 63–Nov 63

---

*The 576th Strategic Missile Squadron at Vandenberg AFB consisted of six training and operational missiles. In February 1961, Complex 576A—holding three Atlas Ds—was converted to support the Nike–Zeus and penetration aids programs.

---

the missile immediately before launch prevented it from meeting the required 15-minute reaction time. (In contrast, these same missiles, when slightly modified, were perfectly suitable as boosters for launching space satellites. In the space role, reaction speed was not important, and technicians had ample time to inspect the missile's numerous fittings, switches, and valves.)

McNamara's accelerated program would add 220 solid-fueled missiles—160 Polaris and 60 Minuteman—to those proposed in Eisenhower's January 1961 budget. Although tempted to cancel Atlas, the Defense Secretary concluded that the program was too far along to yield any savings. But he claimed that the decision to eliminate 2 Titan II squadrons saved about $270 million.[80]

Air Force plans to phase out its first-generation ICBMs hinged on the availability of substantial numbers of Minuteman missiles. The "soft" configuration Atlas Ds were scheduled for inactivation beginning in 1966. Secretary Zuckert supported the Air Force's long-term strategic concept of a diversified force. Thus, there would always be a need for large numbers of manned heavy bombers "even beyond the point at which total effectiveness of missiles [had] been totally proven." The Air Force would never rely solely on a single type of weapon and opposed plans to reduce the B-52 * force.[81]

In June 1961 Secretary McNamara clung to the Administration's view of a missile gap, but was confident that there was no "deterrent gap"—the same terminology that President Eisenhower had used years earlier. Also, McNamara predicted that the United States would either match or surpass the Soviet Union in ICBMs by 1963. As McNamara spoke, there were twenty-eight operational Atlas missiles, including three Atlas Ds and one Atlas E at Vandenberg, fifteen Atlas Ds at Warren, and nine Atlas Ds at Offutt AFB. Of these, twenty-two were on daily alert and three had an emergency combat capability.† There were also three Titan I missiles on launchers at Vandenberg and three at Lowry AFB, but none of these was combat ready.[82]

Reliability Problems

As noted earlier, the missile gap controversy had obscured the ICBM reliability problems that had plagued the Atlas from the beginning. There were various component deficiencies, many of them related to the propellant loading system. Corrective measures proved largely ineffective, because reliability problems multiplied during the first half of 1960.

In March a disastrous explosion—blamed on the propellant loading system—tore apart an Atlas missile and its facilities at Vandenberg AFB. In May and July, two flight test missiles experienced flight control problems and had to be destroyed shortly after lift-off. And the start of reentry and warhead testing introduced a new set of problems. Construction design problems, compounded by missile unreliability, delayed the operational readiness dates of ICBM squadrons.[83]

---

*Uncertainties surrounding the B-70 program motivated the Air Force to insist on the requirement for 13 B-52 wings by 1970.

†A reaction time of 4 to 50 hours.

Some of the missile shortcomings could be attributed to the need to speed the initial operational capability. The rush to reach operational status had compressed testing too much. Normally, the contractor conducted Category I subsystem development tests, followed by R&D subsystem and component integration or Category II tests. The operational command performed Category III tests to ensure a system's readiness, accuracy, and reliability. Lastly, Category IV operational tests ensured that objectives were being maintained. But owing to pressures to attain an early IOC, ICBM testing now proceeded directly from Category I to IV, without sufficient Category II and III trials.

Reviewing the program in July 1960, General Power, the Commander in Chief of SAC, warned that high reliability depended on an expanded test program. He urged the immediate adoption of a one-year, sixteen-missile Category III test program beginning in August. All available Atlas missiles, including spares from operational squadrons, were needed to complete the test. Air Force Headquarters approved Power's proposal.[84]

The high-priority test program began in September at Vandenberg AFB's Complex 576B. Despite a concerted Air Force and industry attack on the problems, two launch attempts (designated Golden Journey and High Arrow) failed. Although discouraged, General Power contended that reliability problems should receive the same level of attention as had site activation. Another unsuccessful launch attempt in October underscored the seriousness of the problem.[85]

Headquarters USAF encouraged SAC to coordinate its testing with BMD, suggesting that, in light of the concurrency concept, the missiles were being overexercised. But General Power observed that, one year after the Atlas had been declared operational, no deployed missile could be considered fully reliable; hence, its chance of being launched was zero. Moreover, of the sixteen latest Atlas launches from Vandenberg, just three had impacted in the target area. The others had either aborted, been destroyed after lift-off, or fallen considerably short of their targets.* Power again urged intensive Category III testing and the exercise of stricter quality control over components. For example, some switches had been manufactured without any standard specifications and could malfunction unexpectedly. Power insisted that certain basic performance criteria be established before declaring the missiles operational.[86] He also opposed reducing the Atlas operational requirements as a means of achieving higher missile reliability, and recommended additional Category II and III tests for the Titan. Meanwhile—considering the unreliability of the Atlas and the

---

*Paradoxically, after 5 research and development failures during the first half of 1959, 23 of 25 subsequent Atlas D launches from Cape Canaveral (between August 1959 and October 1960) were successful, including 7,000- and 9,000-mile flights.

planned phase-out of the B–47—Power favored increasing B–52 production to attain a sixteen-wing force as quickly as possible.[87]

General White blamed configuration changes and inaccurate cost estimates—which resulted in frequent and drastic reprogramming actions— for Atlas's unreliability. General LeMay had formed an intercommand board, consisting of representatives from SAC, AMC, and ARDC, to investigate the causes for missile failure and to recommend corrective actions.[88]

In its November 1960 report, the board attributed reliability problems to many factors, including inadequate testing, facilities, technical data, training, and configuration and quality controls. Although the board concluded that most flight failures were random, it recommended establishing a combined Category II and III test exercise at Vandenberg AFB. Designated Golden Ram, the test attempted to complete the integration of the Atlas missile and its equipment, personnel, and procedures. Running for about one year, Golden Ram disclosed numerous shortcomings in the Atlas and in its maintenance procedures. Solutions to specific problems were later incorporated into deployed missiles.[89]

Meanwhile, the Atlas E and Titan I also experienced technical problems including several flight test failures. The Atlas E failures were attributed to hydraulic and control system malfunctions caused by the difficulty of integrating major configurational changes. Titan I problems were dramatized in December 1960, when the operational system test facility at Vandenberg was destroyed in a spectacular explosion just before the first scheduled launch. Later investigation traced the cause of the accident to an elevator system malfunction and inadequate safety measures in propellant loading.[90]

Disturbed by the continuing difficulties, in December 1960 Secretary Gates asked for a review of all ballistic missile launches. When General White designated a Joint Staff office to undertake the analysis, an inter-service dispute erupted over the terms of reference and the extent of participation. Ultimately, the Weapon Systems Evaluation Group, an OSD agency, evaluated missile launches, but the Joint Staff—in cooperation with the services—passed judgment on the findings and made recommendations to the Joint Chiefs of Staff.[91]

Continued reliability problems attracted the attention of Kennedy Administration officials. In January 1961, Zuckert warned McNamara that recent Atlas E flight test failures—combined with missile site construction problems—threatened to delay missile deployments by up to sixty days. Reliability problems also threatened to slow Titan I deployments at Lowry AFB. To resolve the problems, Zuckert recommended increasing missile procurement to permit additional flight tests. In April and May 1961 testimony before the House Appropriations Subcommittee, Secretary Zuckert decried the "numbers game" that had been used in debating the missile gap. He charged that missile reliability was a serious problem and estimated that it would take about five years to correct. Zuckert urged the Air Staff to establish clearer test criteria, standardize test results, and perform better statistical analysis.[92]

In May 1961 a Director of Defense Research and Engineering report highlighted the exorbitant costs of missile testing, estimated at between $1 and $3 million per missile. Besides the difficulty of simulating realistic wartime configurations, there was an inordinate variety of missiles, including three different types of Atlas, two Titan, and three Polaris—all sufficiently different to require separate operational tests. Reviewing preliminary results of the Golden Ram * exercise, the Director concluded that it had been a mistake to proceed from Category I to IV testing without completing integrated Category II and III tests.[93]

The Golden Ram exercise had uncovered numerous hardware deficiencies in ground equipment, facilities, missiles, technical data, and operational and maintenance procedures. Despite two successful flight tests in December 1960 and May 1961, the Atlas continued to be beset by problems, and a $20 million retrofit program was started in June. The Air Force hoped thereby to improve Atlas's reliability to between fifty and seventy-five percent. During the retrofit, half of the Atlas D squadrons were to be downgraded from alert readiness to emergency combat status.[94]

The Atlas E and F also experienced testing problems. By June 1961, only three of ten Atlas E test flights had been successful. Of the seven failures, three were attributed to design deficiencies and four others were blamed on random failures. The damage sustained by the test facility at Vandenberg AFB in early June further set back the Atlas E training and test program. Construction delays in readying the test facility for the Atlas F required compressing the program's testing and training and postponed scheduled operational dates.[95]

Meanwhile, the Titan program was producing slightly better results. By the end of June 1961, twenty-three of thirty-five Titan missiles launched were rated as fully successful, nine were partial successes, and three were failures. Two of the successes marked milestones in developing the Titan II: The May 3 launch was the first conducted from inside a silo, and the June 23 launch was the first to use the all-inertial guidance system. Unfortunately, the program still suffered from the effects of the Vandenberg training facility explosion on December 3, 1960, which had caused extensive revisions in the test and training programs. Also, the Titan program lacked funding to procure more missiles than originally programmed and to retrofit

---

* Golden Ram sought to stabilize the Atlas D design, which had been altered during the flight test program. See page 217.

the missiles at their operational bases. Titan site activation at Lowry AFB also was hampered by late deliveries of ground equipment and by requirements to redesign and modify the propellant loading system and the silo elevator.[96]

As with site activation, missile reliability problems soon invited a Congressional investigation. In the spring of 1961, the Senate Preparedness Investigating Subcommittee held hearings on the question and visited SAC, AFSC, and other Air Force agencies. Based on these hearings and visits, the committee concluded that the announced operational readiness dates were overly optimistic. Reviewing the site activation experience, Generals Power and Schriever noted that the Soviet threat had made it imperative to attain the earliest possible missile capability. Given the complexity and magnitude of the site activation task, the generals declared themselves satisfied that the ICBM program was successful. General Schriever readily admitted a need for additional flight testing and predicted that, within a few years, missile reliability would improve to eighty percent.[97]

Final Deployments

In January 1961 Dr. Jerome B. Wiesner, the President's designated science advisor, submitted a report on the U.S. missile and space programs which had been requested by President-elect Kennedy. The Wiesner Report found the missile program lagging and recommended accelerating missile development and procurement as well as base construction. It also found an overriding need for additional funds and for "reestablishing an effective, efficient, technically competent management." The report blamed many of the management difficulties on distractions within both the Department of Defense and industry, caused by an influx of new space projects.[98]

Representative Harry R. Sheppard, Chairman of the House Military Construction Subcommittee, held hearings on the ICBM construction program in March 1961. Focusing on construction costs, the Sheppard Committee was distressed to find that Minuteman construction costs—as experienced at its first site, near Malmstrom AFB, Montana—were no easier to control than the Atlas and Titan costs had been. The causes were familiar: lengthy negotiations due to split responsibilities for construction between the Air Force and the Army Corps of Engineers, gross underestimation of the tasks involved, and the inability to stabilize missile designs.

Citing the expenses generated by the numerous technical change orders, the committee suggested that the Air Force and its contractors were using the concurrency concept to cover up mistakes. The Office of the Secretary of Defense, however, supported the Air Force strongly in this matter. In its June report to the Sheppard Committee, OSD stated: "It is our opinion that the purposes achieved have justified the concept. Time is the key to national security and concurrency has saved a great deal of time."[99]

Still another investigation—by the Senate Subcommittee on Government Operations—also vindicated the Air Force's program management. Reviewing labor walkouts at ICBM sites, the subcommittee found that, from the start of construction in 1956 until March 31, 1961, there had been 327 work stoppages by construction workers at 19 operational and test sites, and 162,872 man-days had been lost. Moreover, half of the strikes occurred at Patrick, Edwards, and Vandenberg AFBs—the 3 sites where research and development presented the most critical and difficult problems.[100]

Meanwhile, Secretary Zuckert announced that the Air Force would reorganize its site activation program to ensure faster settlement of contractor claims. The action came partly in response to directives from the President and the Secretary of Defense and from the findings of the Sheppard Committee. It also acknowledged the need for new management to control the growing space program.[101]

In May 1959, a weapon systems study had been initiated under a group headed by Gen. Samuel E. Anderson of AMC, General Schriever of ARDC, and Maj. Gen. Mark E. Bradley, Acting DCS for Materiel. The study group

A ten-story Titan II, ready for launching from its underground silo at McConnell AFB, Kansas.

Attending ceremonies marking operational readiness of a Titan site near Lowry AFB are (left to right) Gen. Bernard A. Schriever, Maj. Gen. Thomas P. Gerrity, Lt. Gen. Archie J. Old, and Lt. Gen. Howell M. Estes, Jr., May 1962.

advanced three plans. Bradley proposed to extend the BMD/BMC dual-responsibility approach to aeronautical and electronics systems. General Anderson wanted to recombine AMC and ARDC. Schriever supported Bradley's plan, but also proposed creating two commands: one to manage weapons acquisition and the other responsible for logistical support. General LeMay, who commissioned the study, favored Bradley's version.

Various reorganizations were considered over the next two years, but nothing substantive resulted. In early 1961 Roswell L. Gilpatric, the new Deputy Secretary of Defense, suggested that the Air Force might win the space mission if it straightened out the AMC–ARDC relationship. Gilpatric had been Undersecretary of the Air Force and a board member of the Aerospace Corporation.[102]

General White immediately convened the Air Force Council and announced a new command arrangement. The details of the reorganization were worked out over the next few months. To facilitate the changeover, General Anderson—who had opposed Schriever's plan—was assigned to Europe, and Gen. William F. McKee was installed as Commander of the new Air Force Logistics Command. General Schriever was promoted to four-star rank and continued as the chief of the new Air Force Systems Command. Effective April 1, 1961, the Air Force combined elements of ARDC and AMC into AFSC; the remainder became AFLC. As part of this reorganization, the Air Force Ballistic Missile Division and the Ballistic Missile Center were divided between two new AFSC organizations—the Ballistic Systems Division and the Space Systems Division. Also, the Office of Deputy Commander for Aerospace Systems, in Inglewood, California, was created and placed organizationally atop the two divisions to facilitate decision making. Lt. Gen. Howell M. Estes, Jr., was named the first Deputy Commander. The Army's Corps of Engineers Ballistic Missile Construction Office came under the Ballistic Systems Division for operational control, but remained under the Army for administration and support. This reorganization marked the first time that a single agency was assigned to manage the entire program, including development, testing, procurement, evaluation, production and installation of ballistic missiles.[103]

In May 1961 President Kennedy expanded the Administration's involvement in the missile program by creating a special commission under the Secretary of Labor. Called the Missile Site Labor Commission, it was responsible for developing policies, procedures, and methods for addressing labor problems. A Labor Department labor relations committee also was organized and established field offices at each construction site. The Army and Air Force appointed labor relations advisors at each site, while the site activation task force members represented the DOD on the committees.[104]

By the end of 1961, four Atlas D squadrons were operational—one each at Vandenberg and Offutt Air Force Bases, and two at Warren Air Force Base. In addition, three Atlas E squadrons were on alert at Fairchild, Forbes, and Warren Air Force Bases. The entire Titan I force, comprising six squadrons of nine missiles each, became operational between April and August 1962 (see Chart 7-2). These events were followed by the equally rapid deployment of the six Atlas F squadrons—consisting of twelve missiles each—between September and December 1962. The thirteenth and final Atlas squadron was turned over to SAC at Plattsburgh AFB, New York, on December 9, 1962. The milestone was achieved nineteen days ahead of schedule, and culminated a remarkable eight-year effort.[105]

IRBM Squadrons

Prospects for expanding the Air Force's IRBM program brightened in January 1958 as Gen. Lauris Norstad, Supreme Allied Commander, Europe, reported a need for ten IRBM squadrons in addition to the four Thor units already scheduled for deployment to the United Kingdom. In February

1958, Air Force Secretary Douglas presented the proposal for sixteen IRBM squadrons to Mr. McElroy. This plan was frustrated when the Joint Chiefs of Staff refused to advance the readiness date for the sixteen IRBM squadrons from June 1962 to June 1961.[106]

In April, Douglas attempted to eliminate the Jupiter program when he asked Secretary McElroy to postpone Jupiter deployment plans pending additional tests. General White also wanted to foreclose on the Jupiter, but was restrained by the intense Congressional pressure brought to bear on the issue. Finally, Air Force and Defense officials agreed to field a twelve-squadron IRBM force, comprising nine Thor and three Jupiter squadrons. President Eisenhower approved these plans "for planning purposes only" and on the condition that they would not consume additional Fiscal Year 1958 or 1959 funds.[107]

Meanwhile, in February, the British Ambassador to the United States, Harold Caccia, and American Secretary of State Christian A. Herter signed a preliminary understanding on the subject of basing the Thors in Britain. It was followed by a bilateral agreement in June and by technical U.S. Air Force–Royal Air Force arrangements in July. The agreements provided that the four Thor squadrons to be based in Great Britain would be manned by British crews. The United States would retain custody of the nuclear warheads, and both governments had to consent to any so-called "anger" launching.[108]

The four Thor squadrons were scheduled to be deployed to the United Kingdom * between December 1958 and March 1960. The five other Thor squadrons were tentatively earmarked for Italy, Turkey, Okinawa, and Alaska at unspecified dates. It was planned that the three squadrons of Jupiter missiles would become operational in France sometime between February 1959 and March 1960. When Gen. Charles DeGaulle assumed power in June 1958, however, he refused to accept the Jupiters, and Air Force attention turned to alternate sites in Greece and Spain.[109]

The reluctance of the Europeans to accept the American missiles continued through the summer of 1958. Coupled with the budgetary crisis in the United States, this obstacle led to a reconsideration of the IRBM force size. At first the Joint Chiefs of Staff urged keeping all twelve IRBM squadrons, on the grounds that these missiles represented the smallest and most austere program possible. But with the continued financial problems at home and the bleak outlook overseas, the JCS reversed their position and recommended reducing the IRBM force to eight squadrons.

Secretary McElroy stated publicly that the nearer the United States ICBM came to attaining operational status, the less attractive did overseas IRBM deployment seem. Nonetheless, in December the National Security

---

* The Thor activation was called Project Emily.

Council recommended deploying five Thor* and three Jupiter squadrons. President Eisenhower approved this plan and also provided for an expansion of the force if the Europeans changed their minds. This decision ended a two-year-long suspense over which missile—the Army's Jupiter or the Air Force's Thor—would go into quantity production. The answer was both. It was a familiar pattern of prolonged procrastination ending in compromise.[110]

In August 1958 the United States launched a massive airlift of supplies and equipment (aboard C-124 Globemasters) to the United Kingdom in support of the Thor deployment.† Between December 1958 and March 1960, several problems occurred which wrecked the original schedule for deploying the Thor force. One of these concerned site construction, a British responsibility. Also, the normal equipment installation and checkout time of 165 days was compressed to an incredible 15 days, and the time allotted for crew training was grossly inadequate. Most significant was the provision in the bilateral agreement that the British would decide exactly when a squadron was operationally ready. Thus, when the U.S. Air Force turned over the first missile complex to the RAF, the British relegated it to training status.[111]

Failure to appreciate these procedural details caused embarrassment for Defense officials appearing before Congress. For example, in December 1958 Secretary Douglas informed the Senate that a Thor missile squadron would become operational within thirty days. In January 1959 General Twining told a House committee, "We have them [Thors] sitting there ready to go." But, in April, Defense Secretary McElroy was forced to admit that "none of those missiles is ready for immediate countdown and firing." McElroy observed that only the British could declare the Thor operational.[112]

Actually, by the end of December 1958 the Americans had installed seven Thor missiles out of the fifteen programmed‡ for the first British unit, the 77th Strategic Missile Squadron at Feltwell. If necessary, two of these missiles could have been fired after several hours of preparation. But the objective of bringing these missiles to combat readiness within fifteen to twenty minutes of an alert could not be accomplished until after the British completed crew training and returned the missiles to operational status. Thus, it was not until June 1959—six months behind schedule—that the Air Force turned over the first complete Thor squadron to the RAF.[113]

---

*Subsequently, only four Thor squadrons were approved.

†To monitor the Thor deployment to the United Kingdom, Headquarters SAC activated the 705th Strategic Missile Wing (SMW) at Lakenheath RAF Station on February 20, 1958, but it soon moved to South Ruislip. As the deployment was completed, SAC's 7th Air Division assumed responsibility for USAF's part of the program, and the 705th was inactivated.

‡The Thor site configuration had three missiles per launch complex. Five complexes thus made up one fifteen-missile squadron.

Subsequent Thor deployments also slipped by several months. The second RAF squadron, the 97th Strategic Missile Squadron at Hemswell, was declared operational in September and the third squadron, the 98th SMS at Driffield, in December. Thor deployment was completed on April 29, 1960, when SAC turned over the fourth and final squadron to the 144th SMS (RAF) at North Luffenham, bringing to sixty the number of IRBMs poised on strategic alert. (See Chart 7–3).[114]

Jupiter's status remained murky, as the U.S. Air Force tried to negotiate a joint services agreement with the Italian Air Force for basing of Jupiter missiles in that NATO country. Meanwhile, in May 1959, 37 Italian airmen had arrived at the Redstone Arsenal in Huntsville, Alabama, for missile training by Chrysler engineers. The U.S.-Italian base rights agreement, however, stalled for some time, and the Air Force could assert only that the Jupiter would be deployed 190 days after a go-ahead decision.[115]

Two fifteen-missile Jupiter squadrons were to be deployed to Italy, with the first missile scheduled for installation in March 1960. In August 1959 the U.S. and Italian Air Forces signed a technical agreement to deploy two Jupiter squadrons to Gioia del Colle, near an airfield in southern Italy. Designated NATO I, the thirty Jupiters were to be manned and placed on alert by Italian crews. Although the Italians provided launch crews, the missiles would remain in U.S. custody until released by an execution order.

In August 1959 the U.S. Air Forces in Europe (USAFE) Commander recommended deploying the third Jupiter squadron (NATO II) of fifteen missiles to Cigli Airfield near Izmir, Turkey. An agreement between the Turkish and U.S. governments was concluded in September. A major manning problem arose, however, because many Turkish personnel were undergoing training for fighter units, and their manpower had been consumed in that effort. Consequently, it was agreed in April 1960 that U.S. Air Force personnel would man the Jupiters until Turkish crews became available. Turkish personnel completed crew training, but apparently did not man the Jupiter sites. Missile combat crew training for both the Italians and the Turks was conducted at the Redstone Arsenal; training launches for NATO I and NATO II crews were conducted from Cape Canaveral, beginning in April 1961.[116]

On July 14, 1960, one three-missile Jupiter complex became operational at Gioia del Colle. Facilities construction began at Cigli in late October 1960. From the end of 1960 through early 1961, the Jupiter missiles and ground equipment stationed in Italy experienced serious corrosion problems. This situation delayed the installation and checkout of some sites by sixty days and required concerted study to find a solution.[117]

In addition to the corrosion problem, the unprotected missiles were subjected to wind and electrical storms requiring corrective engineering changes. Nonetheless, siting the missiles progressed at an acceptable rate,

Chart 7-3

IRBMs in Europe

Squadrons	Support Base	Number and Type	SAC Turnover to Host Nation	Operational	First IRBM Off Alert	Last Off Alert	Last IRBM Shipped
77th RAF SMS	Feltwell	15 Thor	Jun 22, 1959	Jun 30, 1960	—	Jul 1, 1963	—
7th RAF SMS	Hemswell	15 Thor	Sep 11, 1959	—	—	May 15, 1963	—
8th RAF SMS	Driffield	15 Thor	Dec 22, 1959	—	Nov 29, 1962	Apr 1963	—
44th RAF SMS	North Luffenham	15 Thor	Apr 29, 1960	—	—	Aug 15, 1963	Sep 27, 1963
NATO I (2 squadrons)	Gioia Del Colle	30 Jupiter	*	Apr 14, 1961 Jul 1961	Apr 1963	Apr 1963	Jul 1963
NATO II	Cigli	15 Jupiter	†	Mar 5, 1962	Apr 1963	Apr 1963	Jul 1963

* First Jupiter emplaced on July 11, 1960.
† First Jupiter emplaced May 25, 1962; warhead in SAC's custody.
— Exact dates unknown.

and by mid-February 1961, four of the ten launch positions of the Italian Jupiter squadrons were turned over to the host nation. On April 14, 1961, the first Italian Jupiter squadron was declared operational with the turnover of the fifth three-missile complex to the Italian Air Force. A week later, the Italians successfully launched their first training missile from Cape Canaveral. In July 1961 the tenth and last Jupiter launch position in Italy became operational.[118]

In mid-August 1961, after completing the Italian sites, 275 Chrysler technicians moved to Turkey, where they began to install the 15-missile NATO II squadron. The first launch positions became operational as scheduled on November 6, 1961. A second position came on alert the following month,* and the fifth and final position became operational on March 5, 1962.[119]

Minuteman

Even as the Air Force accelerated the deployment of its liquid-fueled ICBMs, it had an extensive effort in progress to develop a more effective, more flexible, and cheaper alternative. Named Minuteman † (originally Weapon System Q), it was a project to develop a small, 3-stage, solid-fueled ICBM to be deployed in large quantity. Minuteman studies began in late 1955 and by the end of 1957 had progressed to a point at which the OSD–BMC recommended the start of program development.‡ On February 21, 1958, Minuteman became part of the Air Force's objective force. Plans called for 100 Minuteman missiles to be deployed by 1964 and 400 more the following year. At the end of June, Defense Secretary McElroy approved Minuteman but limited the effort to an R&D program. Subsequently, the Air Force prepared a development plan and a contractor team. Also, OSD expanded rocket engine test facilities to accommodate the new missile, but withheld assigning Minuteman a top priority on its Master Urgency List.[120]

For Fiscal Year 1959 the Air Force budgeted $210 million for Minuteman, planning to achieve limited operational status by July 1962.

---

*At this time there were six Atlas D and E squadrons operational in the United States. Also, SAC successfully launched the first of a series of fifteen Atlas D missiles under the Category III test program from Vandenberg AFB. On March 22, 1962, shortly after the Jupiter deployment was completed, the first Titan I complex at Lowry AFB, Colorado was turned over to SAC.

†The name was changed in September 1957.

‡By 1957, sufficient progress had been made in propellant mixtures, casing, and thrust vector control and termination to justify proceeding with the solid-fuel program. In Schriever's estimation, any presumed Russian lead in missiles was erased with the advent of the solid-fueled Minuteman. [Interview, Gen. Bernard A. Schriever with Lt. Col. Lyn R. Officer and James C. Hasdorff, Washington, June 20, 1973, p 8.]

Production facilities, however, were not included in the budget submission, and the Air Force noted that this omission limited its production to 150 Minuteman missiles by 1965. In July 1958 the AF–BMC approved the Minuteman plan. The plan also gained approval of the OSD–BMC, the ICBM Scientific Advisory Board, and the Weapon Systems Evaluation Group; the latter called the Minuteman superior to any other missile system in terms of cost effectiveness. Finally, Congress backed the Minuteman by increasing its appropriation from $50 to $140 million.[121]

In August 1958, Air Force Secretary Douglas stated that the Air Force was willing to reprogram $70 million to attain the $210 million required for Minuteman development. Despite the Air Force's enthusiasm, however, William Holaday remained unconvinced. He questioned the need for a multiplicity of missiles—all to become operational at about the same time—and asked the Joint Chiefs of Staff for a recommendation.[122]

As had happened so often before with regard to missiles, the Joint Chiefs were unable to agree. Air Force planners blamed lack of consensus on Army and Navy stalling tactics, which included proposals for drastic changes in the Minuteman operational mode such as hardened underground silos.[123]

On September 17, 1958, Holaday abruptly slashed the Air Force's

A Minuteman ICBM, ready for testing at the Air Force Missile Test Center, Florida, January 1960.

Minuteman budget proposal by limiting development to $100 million, with half to come from Air Force reprogramming funds. Holaday also directed the Air Force not to spend a $90 million supplemental, which had been approved by Congress for the Minuteman.[124]

The Air Force, however, could not be dissuaded. Secretary Douglas appealed over Holaday's head—directly to Secretary McElroy—and succeeded in gaining OSD's approval in October 1958.[125]

With General White and Secretary Douglas solidly united on maintaining the Minuteman budget, the Air Force pressed on. Following a November 1958 briefing, White and Douglas persuaded Holaday to designate Minuteman as a "weapon system," thereby securing a high priority for its development. Nonetheless, Holaday cautioned that he was approving only planning and not actual production, training, or deployment. Acting unilaterally, the Air Force reprogrammed the additional funds needed to raise the missile's budget to $184 million. In January 1959 the AF–BMC approved and, although Holaday again cautioned the Air Force against establishing a definite operational schedule, the Air Force aimed for July 1962 as the IOC date.[126]

At the JCS level, Minuteman generally enjoyed the support of the Army, provided the Air Force was willing to sacrifice the Titan. But the Army did not consider Minuteman development to be urgent and refused to commit large sums of money for production. The Navy did not believe that Minuteman could be deployed before 1965, and promoted its own Polaris IRBM as being the superior solid-fuel ballistic missile. For its part, the Air Force was well aware that "the Polaris was making knots" and General Twining reportedly urged General LeMay "to get it [Minuteman] into the inventory . . . we've got to have a good solid-propellant missile to compete with the Polaris program." In February 1959 the JCS opposed a crash program for Minuteman and recommended that no specific operational date be established for its deployment.[127]

Congressional hearings in early 1959 concerning the "missile gap" provided the Air Force with an ideal forum to promote accelerating the Minuteman program. In April Secretary Douglas promoted a plan calling for 3 Minuteman squadrons—a force of 150 missiles—in addition to the 27 squadrons of Atlas and Titan missiles programmed. Under this proposal, the Air Force envisioned 445 Minuteman missiles by January 1965 and 800 by June 1965. These plans represented a substantial increase over the original missile force and added more than $2 billion to the 1959–1964 Minuteman budget projections. The AF–BMC approved the plan in May, and Secretary McElroy—en route to the Geneva disarmament conference— gave verbal approval except for production.[128]

General White considered it urgent to develop the Minuteman as a major weapon system. He established an objective force of 60 Minuteman squadrons—at 50 missiles per squadron, this force constituted 3,000 missiles—through Fiscal Year 1970. In early June 1959, Congress signaled its support of the Minuteman by approving supplemental Fiscal Year 1960 funds to expand the program, and Secretary McElroy informed Congress of the Administration's concurrence.[129]

Although the Air Force had originally envisioned siting the Minuteman in underground silos, it also initiated action to place the missiles aboard railroad cars. In part, the Air Force action was motivated by Navy criticism of Minuteman's vulnerability to pinpoint attack, in contrast with the mobility of the Polaris. Strategic Air Command led the campaign to improve Minuteman mobility. On February 12, 1959, SAC issued a Qualitative Operational Requirement, asking for a mobile Minuteman unit to be operational within four years. General Power proposed assigning first priority to the railroad version of Minuteman.[130]

Although the railroad mobility idea seemed quite attractive, additional technical and operational studies conducted by BMD and SAC disclosed a number of serious operating and logistical problems. In May 1959, the AF–BMC approved the mobility concept but made it complementary to the primary objective of a hardened and dispersed underground Minuteman force. The committee also endorsed the January 1, 1963, operational readiness date for the first mobile unit, but asked for additional study on the size of the mobile force. On June 1 OSD–BMC approved the Air Force committee's action.[131]

Phase-out–Phase-in

The first seven operational Atlas squadrons were installed over a fifteen-month period from August 1960 to November 1961. Deployment was essentially on the schedule established in March 1957 and only slightly behind the crash effort that evolved in reaction to Sputnik. The Sputnik launch had alarmed the nation, and had raised fears that U.S. strategic forces faced imminent destruction because they were hopelessly inferior to the Russians. A controversy erupted over the so-called missile gap, in which the Eisenhower Administration tried to allay public fears by asserting that no deterrent gap existed. The Democrats charged that a missile gap did indeed exist and that the United States would remain behind for at least five years.[132]

The missile gap controversy spawned myriad studies which generally supported the case for an enlarged or accelerated ICBM force. The studies also spilled into related areas and promoted interest in developing the solid-fueled Minuteman ICBM, an air-launched ballistic missile called Skybolt, and various outer space technology projects. The military, especially the Air Force, seized upon the public outcry for more ICBMs as an opportunity to accelerate its programs. And despite reservations expressed by several military leaders—including General Schriever—that an acceleration was unrealistic, the Air Force pressed on.[133]

Consequently, although the Air Force was said to have won the race with the Russians to deploy ICBMs in quantity, its achievement proved extremely costly in terms of resources and reliability. After completing the Golden Ram retrofit of Atlas, the Air Force instituted a regular "updating" program to modify missiles after they had attained operational status. In fact, the Atlas D, E, and F all required extensive modifications * as missile systems continued to experience numerous shortcomings in guidance and flight control systems, air conditioning, elevators, and so on. The Titan also experienced its share of problems, engendered in large part by the rush to completion.[134]

Initially, missile test firings were conducted to identify and correct technical problems. Although the flight tests proved invaluable in that regard, beginning in January 1962 they also became a means to help validate operational reliability. The JCS instituted new types of tests for the Air Force and Navy to obtain reliability data used in preparing the war plan—the Single Integrated Operational Plan. The ICBM test program evolved into a four-stage cycle beginning with research and development, the former Category I and II subsystem development and integration tests. The second phase, called Demonstration And Shakedown, corresponded to the former Category III operational tests. These were followed by Operational Testing, or Type III, aimed at measuring reliability; and Follow-on Operational Testing, or Type IV, which sought to ensure that readiness, accuracy, and reliability were preserved.[135]

Ground test procedures were generally similar to the Operational Testing and Follow-on Operational Testing, although there were differences to match the characteristics of the system being tested. Testing began with countdown exercises at the operational site, after which the test missile was shipped to Vandenberg AFB for the operational crew to launch. The number of launches required to establish reliability and to make certain that the missile was properly maintained varied with the size of the inventory, the intended life of the system, and the viewpoint of the various organizations.

SAC favored a large amount of reliability data and generally supported a large test program. For the 1963 to 1965 period, General Power proposed a $103.9 million flight test program, including the launch of seven Atlas D, twenty-two Atlas E, twenty-two Atlas F, and twenty-two Titan I missiles. The Air Staff modified this proposal into a long-range plan and

---

*One modification program, called Clean Sweep, required updating of some fifty-four critical items and ran from September 1962 to 1964.

provided that five missiles of each type would be launched in the demonstration and shakedown phase. In addition, operational testing was scheduled for eight Atlas E, twenty-five Atlas F, and twelve Titan I missiles. There were to be six Follow-on Operational Tests annually for the Atlas E and twelve for the Atlas F and Titan I. This test program was modified, however, with the withdrawal of some versions from the inventory.[136]*

Retiring Thor and Jupiter

Strategic Air Command had never been very enthusiastic about the intermediate range ballistic missiles. In January 1959—before SAC deployed four Thor squadrons in the United Kingdom and three Jupiter squadrons in Italy and Turkey—General Power had recommended terminating the IRBMs. Power felt that the money saved on the IRBMs could be better used in the ICBM program. Because of their highly volatile liquid fuels, the IRBMs had to be carefully loaded just prior to firing and proved too slow in alert reaction. Also, because of their unprotected above-ground positioning, the missiles were subject to environmental hazards and vulnerable to enemy attack. More significant, the steady introduction of Atlas and Titan ICBMs into the SAC inventory—and the rapid development of the faster-reacting, hardened, and dispersed solid-fueled Minuteman and Polaris missiles—rendered the IRBMs obsolete. Despite all of these shortcomings, however, the IRBMs for a time demonstrated America's resolve to defend its allies and represented the only display of strategic missiles in Europe.[137]

By 1962, a comprehensive reevaluation of the Thor program had been conducted by SAC, Headquarters U.S. Air Force, and OSD. As a result, Secretary McNamara informed British Defence Minister Peter Thorneycroft, in May 1962, that the United States intended to end logistic support for the Thor when the bilateral agreement expired in November 1964. The British were unwilling to wait until then, and on August 1, 1962, Thorneycroft informed Parliament that he planned to phase out the Thor during the spring and summer of 1963.[138]

The first Thor was removed from alert on November 29, 1962, at the 98th SMS, Driffield, and over the next nine months the missile complexes were gradually phased out. The last missile came off alert on August 15, 1963, at the 144th SMS, North Luffenham. The Thors were returned to the

---

*Ballistic Systems Division's responsibility was now limited to completing the Atlas E and F Category II testing at Vandenberg AFB, extended through August 1963. The division was also responsible for completing the Atlas E and F updating programs, scheduled to end in 1964. Contracting and programming of Atlas missiles for the space program was transferred in July 1962 to the Space Systems Division.

United States by September 27, and the facilities and ground equipment were disposed of by December 20, 1963. During the four years of USAF–RAF Thor operations, the IRBMs displayed a progressively improved in-commission rate, rising to eighty-four percent in 1962 and to ninety-eight percent in 1963.[139]

Along with the withdrawal of the sixty Thor missiles from the United Kingdom, the forty-five Jupiters deployed in Italy and Turkey were removed from alert during the spring of 1963, little more than one year after the last of them had become operational. The Jupiter phase-out proved as mysterious as its deployment had been. By the summer of 1962, the Air Force closed its liaison office at the Redstone Arsenal; completed Project Wrap Up, a series of reliability modifications; and closed USAFE's liaison office in Rome, transferring its duties to a military assistance advisory group in Gioia del Colle. During the October 1962 Cuban Missile Crisis, "the USSR proposed a trade-off of Jupiter missiles in Turkey for their missiles in Cuba, but the proposal was summarily rejected." [140]

In February 1963, the JCS designated the Air Force as executive agent for withdrawing Jupiter missiles from Europe. Nicknamed Pot Pie I and II, the withdrawals began on April 1. By April 23, all of the missiles and equipment from Italy were disassembled. The Jupiters departed from Turkey on July 26.[141]

Retiring Atlas and Titan I

In the spring of 1963, an Air Staff study group—which had been assigned to examine the question of missile reliability—recommended the early retirement of the Atlas D, Atlas E, and Titan I ICBMs. The Atlas D was scheduled to remain in service until 1967, but the group recommended its retirement two years sooner, and also proposed removing the Atlas E in 1967 and Titan I in 1968. SAC endorsed the early retirement of the Atlas D and E, on the condition that the money saved would be applied to buy additional Minuteman missiles. SAC, however, favored keeping the Titan I through the 1970s. The Air Staff, General LeMay, and Secretary Zuckert supported the early retirements and submitted a formal plan to the JCS. [142]

After review and revision of these plans by the JCS and OSD staffs, the Air Force emerged with an orderly retirement schedule: the Atlas D would be retired in 1964, the Atlas E in 1966, and the Titan I in 1967. In May 1964—almost concomitant with the retirement of the Atlas D—Secretary McNamara directed accelerating the Atlas E and Titan I phase-out to 1965, but indicated that the Atlas F would remain in operation until 1969. After the November 1964 election, however, McNamara announced the retirement of all first-generation missiles in 1965 "because of their obsoles-

Chart 7-4

Atlas Squadron Milestones

Squadron	Support Base	Number and Type	Organized *	Turnover to SAC	Operational	1st ICBM Off Alert	Last ICBM Off Alert	Last ICBM Shipped	Squadron Inactivated
576 SMS	Vandenberg California	6 Atlas D 1 Atlas E 2 Atlas F	Apr 1, 1958	Jan 15, 1959	—	May 1, 1964	—	—	Apr 2, 1966
564 SMS	F.E. Warren Wyoming	6 Atlas D	Jul 1, 1958	Aug 30, 1960	Sep 2, 1960	May 15, 1964	—	Jun 23, 1964	Sep 1, 1964
565 SMS	F.E. Warren Wyoming	9 Atlas D	Dec 1, 1958	Mar 4, 1961	Mar 7, 1961	Jul 1, 1964	—	Aug 1, 1964	Dec 1, 1964
566 SMS† (549 SMS)	Offutt Nebraska	9 Atlas D	Aug 15, 1959	Mar 30, 1961	Mar 30, 1961	Oct 1, 1964	—	Oct 22, 1964	Dec 15, 1964
567 SMS	Fairchild Washington	9 Atlas E	Apr 1, 1960	Sep 28, 1961	Sep 28, 1961	Feb 17, 1965	Mar 31, 1965	Apr 5, 1965	Jun 25, 1965
548 SMS	Forbes Kansas	9 Atlas E	Jul 1, 1960	Oct 10, 1961	Oct 10, 1961	Jan 4, 1965	Jan 28, 1965	Feb 8, 1965	Mar 25, 1965

Squadron	Location	Missiles						
549 SMS† (566 SMS)	F.E. Warren Wyoming	9 Atlas E	Oct 1, 1960	Nov 20, 1961	Nov 20, 1961	Jan 4, 1965	Jan 30, 1965	Feb 8, 1965	Mar 25, 1965
550 SMS	Schilling Kansas	12 Atlas F	Apr 1, 1961	Sep 7, 1962	Sep 9, 1962	Feb 1, 1965	Mar 5, 1965	Mar 11, 1965	Jun 25, 1965
551 SMS	Lincoln Nebraska	12 Atlas F	Apr 1, 1961	Sep 15, 1962	Sep 15, 1962	Mar 10, 1965	Apr 12, 1965	Apr 20, 1965	Jun 25, 1965
577 SMS	Altus Oklahoma	12 Atlas F	Jun 1, 1961	Oct 9, 1962	Oct 9, 1962	Dec 30, 1964	Feb 4, 1965	Feb 10, 1965	Mar 25, 1965
578 SMS	Dyess Kansas	12 Atlas F	Jul 1, 1962	Nov 4, 1962	Nov 15, 1962	Dec 1, 1964	Feb 3, 1965	Feb 10, 1965	Mar 25, 1965
579 SMS	Walker New Mexico	12 Atlas F	Sep 1, 1961	Nov 30, 1962	Nov 30, 1962	Jan 5, 1965	Feb 4, 1965	Feb 9, 1965	Mar 25, 1965
556 SMS‡	Plattsburgh New York	12 Atlas F	Oct 1, 1961	Dec 7, 1962	Dec 20, 1962	Mar 12, 1965	Apr 10, 1965	Apr 13, 1965	Mar 25, 1965

* Before 1960 this term was synonymous with "activated."
† On Jul 1, 1961, the Atlas D squadron at Offutt and the Atlas E squadron at Warren exchanged designators.
‡ Activated as 556 (Snark) Dec 15, 1957; inactivated Jul 16, 1959; assigned to 702 SMW Apr 1–Jul 16, 1959.

Chart 7-5

Titan Squadron Milestones

Squadron	Support Base	Number and Type	Activated	Turnover to SAC	Operational	1st ICBM Off Alert	Last ICBM Off Alert	Last Shipped	Inactivated
848 SMS * (724 SMS)	Lowry Colorado	9 Titan I	Feb 1, 1960	Apr 18, 1962	Apr 18, 1962	Feb 17, 1965	Mar 26, 1965	Apr 15, 1965	Jun 25, 1965
849 SMS * (725 SMS)	Lowry Colorado	9 Titan I	Aug 1, 1960	May 4, 1962	May 10, 1962	Feb 17, 1965	Mar 26, 1965	Apr 15, 1965	Jun 25, 1965
850 SMS	Ellsworth South Dakota	9 Titan I	Dec 1, 1960	Sep 28, 1962	Sep 28, 1962	Jan 4, 1965	Feb 1, 1965	Feb 12, 1965	Mar 25, 1965
851 SMS	Beale California	9 Titan I	Feb 1, 1961	Sep 8, 1962	Sep 8, 1962	Jan 4, 1965	Jan 22, 1965	Feb 10, 1965	Mar 25, 1965
568 SMS	Larson Washington	9 Titan I	Apr 1, 1961	Sep 26, 1962	Sep 26, 1962	Jan 4, 1965	Feb 2, 1965	Feb 8, 1965	Mar 25, 1965
569 SMS	Mt. Home Idaho	9 Titan I	Jun 1, 1961	Aug 16, 1962	Aug 16, 1962	Feb 17, 1965	Apr 1, 1965	Apr 8, 1965	Jun 25, 1965

*On July 1, 1961, the 848th SMS and the 849th SMS were discontinued. They were replaced by the 724th SMS and the 725th SMS respectively.

cence." He explained that the action was motivated by economic considerations and expected that the phase-out would save $117 million. Apparently
sensing that the first generation of ICBMs had run its course, the Air Force
did not appeal the decision. One analyst observed tersely that SAC "evinced
little nostalgia at their passing. These complex systems, fueled by volatile
liquid oxygen, and in relatively soft configuration had been difficult and
expensive to maintain on alert." [143]

Minuteman did not receive OSD's top priority for facilities until the
fall of 1959. Conceding that the missile held great potential, the JCS
nonetheless refused to initiate yet another crash project. Then, on February
1, 1961, the first Minuteman flight test from Cape Canaveral—a "full up"
configuration—proved a complete success, and its obvious value could no
longer be denied. In March 1961 McNamara visited the Air Force ballistic
missile complex at Los Angeles, and soon thereafter Minuteman was made
into a crash effort.

A more flexible and safer system than Atlas or Titan, the solid-fueled
Minuteman enabled the Air Force to retire its first-generation ICBMs earlier
than expected. The first Minuteman flight, of 10 missiles, became operational at Malmstrom AFB, Montana, on October 24, 1962, at the time of
the Cuban Missile Crisis.* The first complete Minuteman wing, composed
of three 50-missile squadrons, became operational in July 1963. Each
squadron had 50 launchers and there were 5 launch control centers, one for
every 10-missile flight. Both the launchers and the launch control centers
were dispersed and hardened to survive nuclear blast overpressures. By July
1964 there were 12 operational Minuteman squadrons, for a total of 600
missiles. The entire ICBM inventory, pending retirements and excluding the
Vandenberg AFB† sites, included 821 missiles: [144]

18 Atlas D	54 Titan I	600 Minuteman
27 Atlas E	54 Titan II	
68 Atlas F		

During the first stages of the phase-out, SAC was responsible for
removing the missiles, reentry vehicles, and fuels and preparing them for
shipment. SAC also identified equipment to be salvaged.‡ Air Force
Logistics Command organized a site deactivation task force at each SAC
support base and assumed responsibility for closing launch and support

---

*Flight A, 10th Strategic Missile Squadron, 341st Strategic Missile Wing.

†Operational/training units at Vandenberg included the 576th SMS (Atlas), the 395th
SMS (Titan), and the 394th SMS (Minuteman).

‡Of 196 diesel generators removed from the missile sites, half were shipped for use in
Vietnam as of the end of 1966.

facilities, and for finding uses for the excess missiles and equipment and for the installations themselves. AFLC acted as caretaker until the properties were either turned over to the General Services Administration or assigned to another command.[145]

All of the Atlas Ds were phased out between May and October 1964. From January through March 1965, SAC removed the Atlas Es and Fs, and by June 1965 had deactivated all of the Titan I missiles as well. The Atlas ICBMs were shipped to San Bernardino Air Materiel Area, Norton AFB, for storage; the Titans were stored at Mira Loma Air Force Station, near Vandenberg AFB.[146]

Surplus Atlas missiles were modified for use in support of advanced ballistic missile reentry research and also to help the Army with its anti-ballistic missile program. There was no demand for surplus Titan I missiles, however, and in the spring of 1966 the Aerospace Corporation advised against their continued storage.[147]

In December 1964, Secretary Zuckert ordered a study on the disposition of the excess missile launch sites. The study group considered only Atlas F and Titan I sites; the Atlas E sites were too compact to be of value. There was a total of seventy-two Atlas F and fifty-four Titan I silos. Water seepage had eliminated all of the Plattsburgh AFB silos from consideration, and four Atlas F sites had been damaged by fires. It was also decided not to reuse any sites that were near SAC bases scheduled for closing. In all, only forty-four Atlas F and forty-five Titan I sites remained. Due to personnel and funding limitations, however, OSD rejected making new assignments for these sites. By 1966, only three Titan I sites had been proposed for new missions. The Air Force retained the Atlas and Titan I sites at Vandenberg AFB.[148]

Epilogue

By 1965, the Air Force had at last emerged from its ICBM growing-pain years and had attained maturity. The first generation of operational ballistic missiles, the Atlas series and the Titan 1 (both liquid-fueled), had given way to the Titan IIs and the solid-fueled Minuteman series. From a force of fewer than 50 Atlases and Titan Is in 1960, the number of Air Force ballistic missiles grew to 1,000 operational Minuteman missiles and 54 Titan IIs by the end of the decade. Despite various problems associated with liquid-fueled missiles, the Titan IIs remained in service for some 25 years until they were finally removed from operational service in 1987. The latest generation of ICBM, the MX or Peacekeeper, became operational late in 1986.

This ICBM maturity, however, was not gained easily. From the beginning, there was controversy regarding the feasibility, necessity, and control of ballistic missiles among the armed services and even within the Air Force. Although the Air Force had shown some interest in guided missiles (or "pilotless aircraft," as they were also called) as far back as 1917, many in that service were not very enthusiastic about them. In arguments remarkably reminiscent of comments by Army officers observing the airplane for the first time, prior to World War I, Air Force purists regarded anything without wings or pilots as unworthy of interest.

World War II and German efforts to produce long-range missiles (notably the V–2) sparked renewed U.S. interest in these weapons in the United States. The seeds of a "turf war" were sown in late 1944: the Navy began looking into missile development, and the AAF and the Army's Ordnance Department were directed to develop aerodynamic lift (cruise) missiles and momentum (or ballistic) missiles respectively. Among the first to realize the potential of these new weapons was H. H. Arnold, AAF Commanding General, who directed that some twenty-eight projects encompassing four missile categories—air-to-air, air-to-surface, surface-to-air, and surface-to-surface—be awarded study contracts. A total of $34 million in Fiscal Year 1946 funds was committed for missile research.[1]

After the war, the reduction of military forces resulted in discontinuation of ten of these studies and a reduced guided missile budget of $13 million.[2] Only those projects that seemed likely to bear fruit the soonest

First flight of a Minuteman ICBM, launched at the Air Force Missile Test Center, Florida, 1961.

were retained. Convair's MX–774B ballistic missile project survived the first cuts but did not survive a second reduction in funding in early 1947. Nevertheless, Convair continued to test the missiles, using unexpended project funds and its own money. The Air Force, faced with a lower budget, dropped ICBM research to eighth place on its priority list, where it languished for some time.

Meanwhile, fierce struggles were taking place, both within the Air Force and between the services, over which organization would dominate the missile program. Although the Russian atomic bomb test in August 1949, followed by the start of the Korean War in June 1950, tended to increase missile research spending once more, these events in themselves did not lead to a coherent ICBM policy. Each service saw the ICBM, and all missiles, in relation to its own particular perspectives.

In January 1951, the increased funding led to the award of a long-range missile study contract to Convair. Originally called the MX–1593 project, it would soon be known as Atlas. From this study, Convair and Air Force engineers concluded that a ballistic approach would be the best choice for an ICBM. Even though the study showed that a long-range ballistic missile was a viable concept, authorization for full-scale development of the Atlas was not forthcoming. Funding was authorized for the Atlas, but at such low levels—as compared to that for both the Snark and Navaho aerodynamic cruise missiles—that development and testing would have extended to 1963.

Several events combined to accelerate both the funding and the development and testing of the Atlas. The U.S. test of a thermonuclear device in November 1952 was followed by the test of a Russian hydrogen bomb in August 1953. Military experts believed that the Russians were far ahead of the United States in ICBM development and rocket technology. Finally, Trevor Gardner, as Special Assistant for Research and Development to the Secretary of the Air Force, came upon the scene to push the ICBM program ahead.

Goaded on by Gardner, and seeing the potential of the Atlas, in the spring of 1954 the Air Force accelerated the Atlas program and gave it the highest developmental priority. It was believed then that a preliminary operational capability could be obtained by June 1958. In the meantime, the Air Force awarded contracts to study two-stage missile configurations, which proved to be so successful that an alternate ICBM configuration was planned as a backup to the Atlas. This missile, the Martin-built Titan, later received increased funding and eventually became operational alongside the Atlas. The JCS believed that a third missile—the Thor, an IRBM—also occupied an important place in U.S. missile planning and assigned it a priority equal to that of the ICBMs.

Yet, despite the high priority given to the ICBM and IRBM programs, they were soon to feel another budget crunch. In mid-1956, the Secretary of the Air Force rejected the proposed ICBM initial operational capability budget. He recommended reducing funding to stretch out the IOC time, or even deleting the Atlas or Titan programs completely. Later, when the FY 1958 budget was submitted, another $200 million bite was taken out of the missile program. One of the few bright spots for the Air Force during this time was the fact that it was assigned the operational responsibility for IRBMs, including control of the Army's Jupiter IRBM.

The Eisenhower Administration was in the throes of further budget cuts, which affected both the ICBM and IRBM programs, when Sputnik I spun around the earth. Surprised and stunned, the Administration reversed itself and accelerated the programs once again. In Sputnik's wake came the cries of "missile gap." Although there probably never was such a gap, this highly publicized affair served to push the Air Force's ICBM program forward despite objections from the other services.

Whereas the Atlas and Titan squadrons had been proposed in January 1958 to be deployed by June 1963, now the process was speeded up considerably. The first Atlas models went on alert in August 1960, and the Titan I and Atlas F became operational beginning in April 1962. The Thor and Jupiter IRBMs also were operational earlier than planned, but had relatively brief service lives. Additionally, a new generation of ICBMs—the Minuteman and Titan II—was developed so rapidly that the first of these units, a Minuteman squadron, became operational in October 1962.

The Air Force ICBM program hiccuped along rather erratically in its early stages, but the groundwork had been laid. When it appeared that a national crisis was at hand in the late 1950s, the first ICBMs were deployed operationally in a remarkably swift and efficient manner. This deployment was not without cost. Tremendous expenses, estimated at close to $17 billion, were incurred in the Air Force's ballistic missile program.[3] Not all of this spending involved the relatively expensive technological development of a completely new system, including such components as liquid and solid propellants, missile airframes, guidance systems, and so on. There were also the more mundane costs of constructing the facilities to produce these new technologies and also those of building the many missile sites to house the ICBMs.

The industry portion of the ICBM program was gigantic. Subcontracting was not a new concept in the aircraft industry. Since World War II, numerous subcontractors had built aircraft components or even complete aircraft. But the ICBM program elevated subcontracting to a grand scale. For example, at the end of 1955 some 56 major contractors were working on the Atlas. Two years later, there were more than 150 major contracts for the same program. Having two ICBM designs underway at the same time also increased the magnitude of the task. In the late 1950s, about 2,000 contractors were working on all phases of the ballistic missile program—a number that does not include all the work done by various Air Force commands.[4]

Most of the industry's work—but not all—was of good quality. Much of this work was at the limits of technology, requiring greater reliability and closer tolerances than many firms had previously achieved. Some of the contractors simply did not have the necessary expertise. For example, although Convair was believed well qualified to build the Atlas airframe, the Air Force considered the company weak in several areas and recommended other contractors for those tasks. Thus, this program initially strained the aircraft industry to the limit. The technology was there, in rudimentary form, but at the outset there were not enough trained personnel, not enough modern manufacturing complexes, and not enough testing facilities. In time these would appear, but their absence presented serious problems at the start.

This massive program also had a great impact on the Air Force, not just monetarily but also in terms of its role in the defense of the United States. The success of the ICBM and IRBM programs forced the Air Force to rethink its position regarding aircraft and missiles. It was obvious that missiles of all types would play an increasingly important role in the service. But it took many years of high-level thought to determine how these missiles would be integrated into the force structure. If the Air Force did not lay claim to control of strategic missiles, someone else—the Army or Navy—surely would.

By 1958, the Air Force was projecting itself as an "aerospace power," utilizing both manned and unmanned air-breathing vehicles, ballistic missiles, spacecraft, and satellites. For the Air Force, the mechanics and strategy of aerial warfare took a quantum leap. Planning began to include fighting not just in the atmosphere, but also in outer space. Naturally, this view of the service as an aerospace power was not shared by the Army or Navy, nor by some individuals in the Department of Defense. Nonetheless, aerospace power became a cornerstone of the Air Force's continuing search for a basic doctrine that accommodated weapons operating inside and outside the atmosphere.[5]

Although the ICBM ushered in a new age of warfare, the Air Force did not convert entirely to missiles. The belief persisted that a manned aircraft was the "proper" vehicle for the service. Those with a more logical bent, however, reasoned that a mixed force of missiles and aircraft would provide the greatest flexibility for all types of conflicts. This view has prevailed. For FY 1964, Air Force procurement funds for aircraft totalled somewhat over $3.5 billion; for missiles, a little more than $2 billion. Aircraft procurement funds soared in FY 1985 as compared to missile procurement, but estimated FY 1989 appropriations show about the same ratio between the two as in FY 1964 (although the total appropriations are much greater).[6]

BALLISTIC MISSILES

Ever since the ICBM force became operational in 1960, the missiles have sat and waited for what some (although not many in the Air Force) believe will be the final war. An uneasy half-peace has settled over the world. Many low-intensity conflicts have come and gone, but no nuclear war has broken out. American and Russian ICBMs have been upgraded and refined over the years to ensure their ability to inflict "unacceptable damage" upon the enemy under any conditions. The ICBMs have become a paradox—thousands of them waiting to unleash total destruction, but the very fact of their presence ensuring their non-use.

Appendices

Appendix 1

The Tea Pot Committee Report

THE RAMO-WOOLDRIDGE CORPORATION
6316 West 92nd Street
Los Angeles 45, California

February 1, 1954

Dr. Hendrik Bode
Dr. Louis Dunn
Dr. L. A. Hyland
Prof. George B. Kistiakowsky
Prof. C. C. Lauritsen
Dr. Clark Millikan
Prof. John von Neumann
Dr. Allen E. Puckett
Prof. J. B. Wiesner

Gentlemen:

Enclosed is a copy of what is intended as the final recommendation of the Tea Pot Committee. It differs from the most recent draft sent to all of you as described below.

A number of you have expressed the opinion that the previous draft was entirely satisfactory precisely as it stood, and all of you have made some suggestions for improvements here and there, about some of which you have said you did not have strong feelings. In general, we have introduced each improvement suggestion, unless it appeared to have possibilities of inadvertently causing some differences in opinion to arise between the members upon a minor point where no difference was previously noted.

It has now become urgent that Mr. Gardner have our final recommendations. Accordingly, we would appreciate it if, promptly upon reading the enclosed document, you would inform immediately both Mr. Gardner's office and us of your approval. If you feel that you cannot do this because of disagreement with one or another statement, please make your conditional approval and simultaneously send both to Mr. Garnder's office and to us proposed new wording for that particular statement. Obviously, it will be extremely helpful if you can avoid the latter step, unless you are positive that the wording does not describe thoughts close to your own.

The changes are as follows:

BALLISTIC MISSILES

1. Section I, Paragraph 2, has been changed, starting with the second sentence. It previously read:

> "Intelligence data have been made available to the Committee, which indicate that the Soviet are active in the development of ballistic missiles. While this evidence is necessarily incomplete, it is disturbing to notice that most of the members of this Committee, on the basis of available evidence, believe that the Russians are probably significantly ahead of us in long-range ballistic missiles, and no member of the Committee believes this possibility should be ruled out. While this Committee cannot attempt a definitive judgment on the political or psychological importance of matching the enemy in developing such intercontinental weapons, his apparently high rate of progress in this field is a strong argument for an increase in our own interest in similar projects."

About half of the members of the Committee have expressed concern over this wording, because upon further deliberation it suggests very strongly that data were presented to us of a much more positive nature than was actually the case. In attempting to state correctly the fears of the majority of the Committee of what the Soviets might be doing, we ended up in an inaccurate statement. The new version, which is now believed to be factual, does not frighten the casual reader as much as the statement which it replaces. However, for the proper reader, it probably accomplishes all that we should seek to accomplish with the available facts.

2. Section I, Paragraph 3. In the first sentence, the words, "Important aspects of," have been inserted; the sentence as it was sounded almost as though nothing about the present three projects was satisfactory.

3. Also, in Section I, Paragraph 3, Item (c) has been raised to Item (a) and has been elaborated upon somewhat. It has been moved to the first position, because Committee members have expressed the belief that is is the most important of all factors in causing changes in the program to be recommended at this time. Furthermore, an opportunity exists here to be more tactful than in the previous short single sentence.

4. Section I, Paragraph 5. Having previously demoted these two peripheral items to this late paragraph of the introduction, we probably went too far in using such short description of the thoughts that it is difficult for a new reader to comprehend our meaning. The additional material added makes clearer what were understood to be the Committee's intentions.

5. Section II, Paragraph 6. The addition of the word, "specifically,"

in the first sentence (together with the second sentence left unchanged) is believed to be sufficient to alleviate some minor concern that North American's celestial guidance work (now partially dependent on Snark money) might get cut off prematurely.

6. Section III, Paragraph 1. The first sentence was previously too brief to express the Committee's thoughts. (It was previously merely, "The Committee believes that the present Navaho program should be continued, with program extension in those phases noted below.")

7. Section IV, Paragraph 5. A bad double colon sentence structure was revised, with no change in wording or meaning.

8. Section IV, Paragraph V, Item (a). The previous discussion of Convair hardware had an involved sentence about not removing from the Atlas project any member of the "technical" team. Such a statement appeared confusing in view of various other remarks we make about curtailing hardware, certain aspects of guidance, and certain aspects of production engineering planning. We merely omitted the unclear reference to maintaining the "technical" members of the team and did the minimum revising of the sentence then required.

9. Section IV, Paragraph V, Item (c). Several Committee members called attention to the fact that the previous statement was unclear. It appeared that the only way to improve this was to put a more adequate statement in place of the previous single sentence:

> "All guidance work should be halted where not specifical-
> ly required in connection with instrumenting flight-test
> facilities."

Dean and I both expect to be in Washington on Thursday and Friday, February 4 and 5, which is probably about when you will be reading this document. We can probably be reached through Mr. Gardner's office.

Sincerely,

Si

Simon Ramo

SR
aj
enclosure

DEPARTMENT OF THE AIR FORCE
HEADQUARTERS UNITED STATES AIR FORCE
Washington, D.C.

OFFICE OF THE SECRETARY   February 16, 1954

MEMORANDUM FOR ASSISTANT SECRETARY OF DEFENSE
(RESEARCH AND DEVELOPMENT)

On June 16, 1953, a Department of Defense Study Group on Guided Missiles was established by the Armed Forces Policy Council to make a technical evaluation of the missiles programs of the military services. Our Study Group determined that intercontinental ballistic missiles could best be evaluated by a special group of the nation's leading scientists. Such a group was formed and their report is attached. I am in complete agreement with its general conclusions.

In my opinion, the fact that these eminent scientists validate the technical feasibility of attaining an intercontinental ballistic missile capability in a reasonable time period is of major importance. The report points out that such a weapon system might be operationally available within six years. It is my strong belief, and that of several members of the Committee, including Drs. von Neumann, Kistiakowsky and Wiesner, that a "PhD type" operational capability is attainable within approximately four years provided that:

a. The Secretary of the Air Force direct that this be accomplished and assign an extremely high priority to the project.

b. A management structure be established within the Air Force which would permit the work to be accomplished through a centralized authority.

A presentation has been made to the Secretary of the Air Force who has directed that:

a. A mid-1958 preliminary intercontinental ballistic missile system operational capability be attained.

b. An extremely high priority be assigned to the project.

The Secretary has instructed me to draft an implementing plan which will be forwarded to you upon completion.

We believe this matter to be of sufficient importance to be brought to the attention of Mr. Wilson and Mr. Kyes and the Armed Force Policy Council. Secretary Talbott would like to discuss this with you at your convenience.

cc: Secretary Talbott   signed
    U/Secretary Douglas
    Gen Craigie, DCS/D   Trevor Gardner
    Gen Brentnall, DCS/O   Special Assistant
                                   (Research and Development)

BALLISTIC MISSILES

February 1, 1954

RECOMMENDATIONS OF THE TEA POT COMMITTEE

I. INTRODUCTION—SOME GENERAL REMARKS ON THE LONG-RANGE MISSILE PROGRAMS

1. The Committee's assignment has been limited to that of studying long-range intercontinental strategic missiles under development by the Air Force and making suitable recommendations for improving this program. Specific recommendations are made of changes for the improvement of the present Snark, Navaho, and Atlas programs.

2. Unusual urgency for a strategic missile capability can arise from one of two principal causes: a rapid strengthening of the Soviet defense against our SAC manned bombers, or rapid progress by the Soviet in his own development of strategic missiles which would provide a compelling political and psychological reason for our own effort to proceed apace. The available intelligence data are insufficient to make possible a positive estimate of the progress being made by the Soviet in the development of intercontinental missiles. Evidence exists of an appreciation of this field on the part of the Soviet and of activity in some important phases of guided missiles which could have as an end objective the development by the Soviet of intercontinental missiles. While the evidence does not justify a conclusion that the Russians are ahead of us, it is also felt by the Committee that this possibility certainly cannot be ruled out.

3. Generally speaking, important aspects of the present long-range missile program consisting of the three projects, Snark, Navaho, and Atlas, are believed to be unsatisfactory. While specific recommendations for improving each of these programs are made in the following sections of this memorandum, certain weaknesses generally common to all programs are noted here.

    a. It is believed that all three missile systems have thoroughly out-of-date military specifications on target C.E.P.'s. This results from the very recent progress toward larger yield warheads which could hardly have been predicted when these specifications were originally established.

    b. The problem of reduction of base vulnerability needs much more careful study, particularly with respect to the influence on missile design that might be exerted by a better handling of this base vulnerability matter.

    c. Closely related to base vulnerability is the problem of readiness and firepower; in general, the present plans for each of the three missiles result in discouragingly low-rate single and multiple missile launchings in view of the importance of destroying enemy SAC bases quickly at the start of the war.

4. The specific recommendations made by this Committee on the long-range intercontinental missiles have been based on the conviction that only nuclear warheads are appropriate, and that the designs of the missiles should not be made more difficult by the added requirement to accommodate other types of warheads.

5. Two peripheral items seem to require mention as exceptions to the policy of this Committee not to make recommendations on programs other than the intercontinental missile programs.

    a. Certain recommendations are made, in connection with the Snark program, for the use of Simplified Snarks as an aid to the SAC manned-bomber program. Generally speaking, any program proposals that offer possibilities of prolonging the use of manned bombers are worthy of serious consideration. This has not been an assignment of this Committee; these recommendations merely developed naturally out of the Committee's search for means of modifying the Snark program to permit it to lead to useful results in a reasonable time.

    b. There is to the Committee's knowledge no current Air Force program for ballistic missiles of medium range (say, 200–1500 miles). Whether or not this is a serious ommission in the over-all Defense Department plans has not been studied by this Committee, but should be considered by some qualified agency. It is pertinent for this Committee to note that such missile capability is not necessarily automatically attained, nor most rapidly and economically attained, by the development of the longer-range missiles.

6. In the investigations leading to the recommendations in this memorandum, the Committee acknowledges the aid received from the latest Rand proposals on an intercontinental ballistic missile system (IBMS).

II. RECOMMENDATIONS ON THE SNARK PROGRAM

1. The Snark program as now constituted is regarded as leading to an overly complex weapon at a substantially later time than presently scheduled. This program is in need of major simplification.

2. It is recommended that this program be altered to have as its objective a "Simplified Snark." This missile would be essentially that now under early tests and consist of the present Snark air frame, engines, autopilot, and radio-command guidance equipment, but with elimination of all complex guidance equipment namely, the automatic celestial navigator, the doppler radar, and the beacon radar. This simplified missile should be

given an early production go-ahead. The new program should provide early operational missiles to serve in one or more of the following capacities:

a. Area decoys. For this purpose, simple preset navigation may be adequate to bring the Snarks into the desired corridor in proper time relation to SAC manned-bomber attacks. The Committee believes that, compared with any other area decoy missile capable of traveling 5500 N.M., the Simplified Snark would not be appreciably more complex or expensive, and should certainly be available sooner.

b. Local decoy and saturation missiles.

c. Dispensers of chaff ahead of and around the mother bomber to confuse area and local defenses.

d. Carriers of automatic E.C.M.

e. Carriers of bombs, radio-commanded to the neighborhood of the target by the mother bomber, which could then stay away (100 to 200 miles) from the local target defenses.

f. Reconnaissance vehicles.

For all of the foregoing applications except the first and, possible, the last, the Snarks would be herded into the general neighborhood of the target by radio-command guidance from manned bombers.

3. The use of Snarks in the foregoing manner would extend and prolong the usefulness of SAC manned bombers while providing a step in training with, and operational use of, guided missiles by the Air Force. The proposed program has the major virtue that it should permit an operational capability within four to five years. The Committee believes that such a result will not be attained without such a simplified program.

4. For Snarks used as strike vehicles, the military requirements on C.E.P. should be changed from 1500 feet to three to five nautical miles.

5. Because of the very high priority which the Simplified Snark program described above should have in the Northrop effort, the Committee recommends that the additional, active Northrop proposal to design a new high-altitude Snark should not be considered at the present time.

6. The Committee recommends the immediate cancellation of both the Northrop and North American celestial navigation, doppler radar, and beacon radar systems now being designed specifically for Snark. North American is expected to continue research and development in celestial and inertial guidance, because of the need of these techniques in the Navaho and other North American development programs. This guidance work should

constitute an adequate insurance program, should some requirement later develop for similar guidance systems specifically tailored for the Snark vehicle.

III. RECOMMENDATIONS ON THE NAVAHO PROGRAM

1. The Committee believes that at this time the Navaho program would not benefit from a broad attempt at acceleration of the entire program. It recommends that the present program be continued with program extension in those phases noted below. The Navaho missile offers the following special capabilities:

> a. It will be difficult to defend against, thereby constituting a highly formidable weapon, although not so invulnerable as the IBMS.

> b. It has the capability of carrying a larger warhead than the presently envisioned IBMS. This feature appears to make the Navaho a complementary weapon to the IBMS and not necessarily an interim approach.

2. The Committee concurs in present emphasis on a medium-range (about 3500 miles) first step of the Navaho development program and, further, wishes to emphasize that this may also be a logical first-step operational range for the Navaho missile. More specifically, in view of the special technical problems of Navaho, insistence on 5500 miles as the operational range may delay availability of a highly-valuable lesser-range missile system.

3. The military requirement on Navaho C.E.P. should be increased from 1500 feet to three nautical miles.

4. The Committee strongly recommends that an additional source be provided for the development of Navaho ramjets, so as to decrease the doubt that now exists that ramjets of adequate performance and reliability will be available when required. Any additional contractor selected should definitely be one that has a background of successful ramjet experience.

5. Provision should be made to increase the North American rocket engine testing facilities, in order to permit this contractor to meet the engine requirements of both the Navaho and IBMS programs. Production planning for the rocket motor should be accelerated.

6. Present preparations for production of the difficult precision guidance components are regarded as insufficient to insure meeting the present schedules. The Air Force should make a prompt decision on the

production source for the difficult Navaho guidance components; then, production planning should be immediately initiated.

IV. RECOMMENDATIONS ON THE ATLAS PROGRAM

1. While much credit is due Convair for pioneering work on the IBMS in the years immediately following the war, it is the conviction of the Committee that a radical reorganization of the IBMS project considerably transcending the Convair framework is required if a militarily useful vehicle is to be had within a reasonable span of time. Specifically, the Committee believes that the design must be based on a new and comprehensive weapons systems study, together with a thorough-going exploration of alternate approaches to several critical phases of the problem, adequately based on fundamental science. In addition, some decisive parts of the military specifications, which are entirely outdated and are critically hampering the progress of the project, should be reviewed in the light of current warhead technology. Issuance of the general directives asked for above should be the first task of the new IBMS development group, which we propose should be given directive responsibility for the entire project.

2. The Committee judges that at this moment the project could not be effectively accelerated by heavy financial commitments, early freezing of the design, and production planning. However, the Committee expects that the new group referred to above will within a year be in a position to recommend in full detail a redirected, expanded, and accelerated program, which is likely to call soon for increased financial support and high project priority.

3. The Committee sees no technical reason why by such a procedure, assuming proper direction and support, a period of six to eight years should not permit the attainment of the beginnings of an operational capability.

4. The Committee's own considerations in this area have already led it to certain conclusions, namely:

a. The military requirement on C.E.P. should be relaxed from the present 1500 feet to at least two, and probably three, nautical miles.

b. The warhead weight might be reduced as far as 1500 lbs., the precise figure to be determined after the Castle tests and by missile systems optimization. Warhead diameter should also be considered as an available, somewhat flexible parameter.

c. The re-entry problem should be reinvestigated with special attention to "detachable drag- skirt" considerations. This will involve a study of the interplay of re-entry heating, choice of trajectory, resulting aiming precision, and terminal vulnerability considerations. Without this, no impact Mach number should be rigidly specified, and in particular the present specification (M = 6) should be discarded.

d. The guidance problem should be re-examined in the light of the radically relaxed C.E.P. In particular, more serious consideration should now be given to entirely missile-contained inertial guidance.

e. The present concept of launching base system and supporting facilities for the IBMS leads to too vulnerable an operation. The design of the missile and the nature and layout of the supporting facilities should be adjusted to provide an optimum combination of low vulnerability, high firepower, and short starting time.

5. While it is urgent that the new IBMS development group be set up as recommended, it is necessary to make some interim decisions with regard to the work going on and planned for the immediate future at Convair. The Air Force is urged to review this program immediately, with the recommendation that all decisions for the immediate future be regarded as temporary and subject to the later overriding control by the new systems management group. It is believed that such temporary decisions should include the following:

a. The Convair hardware program should be curtailed as regards actual fabrication of specific structures for full-scale flight tests. The building of a limited number of static test structures should be permitted.

b. The North American work on rocket propulsion should continue.

c. Guidance work should be halted where it consists of detailed design work on the present Atlas system and continued only as required for (1) gathering of fundamental data useful in evaluating candidate guidance systems for the new decreased accuracy requirements, or (2) instrumenting flight-test facilities at the long-range proving ground.

d. All production engineering effort by Convair should be halted.

6. The most urgent and immediate need in the IBMS program is the setting up of the above-mentioned new IBMS development-management agency for the entire program, including the Convair effort. This program can then be subsequently extended and accelerated in some optimum manner to be determined by the studies of this new group. The setting up of

various parallel projects as required will then also follow. The nature of the task for this new agency requires that over-all technical direction be in the hands of an unusually competent group of scientists and engineers capable of making systems analyses, supervising the research phases, and completely controlling the experimental and hardware phases of the program—the present ones as well as the subsequent ones that will have to be initiated. The type of directorial team needed is of the caliber and strength that may require the creation of a special group by a "drafting" operation performed by the highest-level government executives on university, industry, and government organizations.

7. While the main responsibility of this new group will be to attain an IBMS capability in as short a time as possible, this group should also be given responsibility for and authority over the advanced research phases of a continuing IBMS program, such as investigation of nuclear propulsion.

8. To attain the IBMS capability in the six to eight years referred to hereinbefore, it is clear that the operation of this new group must be relieved of excessive detailed regulation by existing government agencies.

V. SUMMARY OF ESTIMATED AVAILABILITY DATES

The following estimates by the Committee of availability of the three missile systems must be regarded as very approximate. However, it is believed by the Committee that something like these dates should be possible if the programs are altered as recommended in the foregoing.

Missile	Date of First Successful Production Item	Date of Attainment of Sufficient Operational Numbers to Constitute a Threat
1. Simplified Snark, for decoys, ECM, and radio-commanded bombing	1957	1958–1959
2. Navaho, 3500-mile range	1958–1959	1960–1961
3. Navaho, 5500-mile range	1960–1961	1962–1963
4. IBMS	1960–1961	1962–1963

February 10, 1954

Mr. Trevor Gardner
Special Assistant of the Secretary of the Air Force
Pentagon Building
Washington 25, D. C.

Dear Mr. Gardner:

Confirming our telephone conversation, enclosed is a copy of Recommendations of the Committee on Strategic Missiles. It is identical with the copy transmitted to you and the members of the Committee last week, with the following exceptions:

(1) The title of the Committee has been changed.

(2) An appendix has been added, with additional comments by two Committee members. These comments, as stated in the appendix, have not been coordinated with our Committee members because of lack of time.

(3) An asterisk has been added to the text on Page 2, referring to the appendix.

It is my understanding that this completes the activities of the Committee.

Sincerely yours,

Simon Ramo

RS
aj
enclosure

February 10, 1954

RECOMMENDATIONS OF THE STRATEGIC MISSILES
EVALUATION COMMITTEE

I. Introduction—Some General Remarks on the Long-Range Missile
Programs

II. Recommendations on the Snark Program

III. Recommendations on the Navaho Program

IV. Recommendations on the Atlas Program

V. Summary of Estimated Availability Dates

VI. Appendix—Additional Comments by Committee Members

VI. APPENDICES

Appendix A

All of the recommendations have been unanimously approved by all Committee members, with the exception that Section I, Paragraph 2, has not been approved by Professor von Neumann, who has submitted the following proposed new paragraph to express his views. Lack of time has precluded coordination with other Committee members, to determine if any other members might also prefer Professor von Neumann's proposed paragraph to the present text.

"Unusual urgency for a strategic missile capability can arise from one of two principal causes: a rapid strengthening of the Soviet defenses against our SAC manned bombers, or rapid progress by the Soviet in his own development of strategic missiles which would provide a compelling political and psychological reason for our own effort to proceed apace. The former is to be expected during the second half of this decade. As to the latter, the available intelligence data are insufficient to make possible a precise estimate of the progress being made by the Soviet in the development of intercontinental missiles, but evidence exists of an appreciation of this field on the part of the Soviet, and of activity in some important phases of guided missiles which it is natural to connect with the objective of development by the Soviet of intercontinental missiles. Thus, while the evidence may not justify a positive conclusion that the Russians are ahead of us, a grave concern in this regard is in order."

Appendix B

The following comments have been submitted by Dr. Ramo.

"While some of the Committee's recommendations are for a change in the present Air Force program, I believe that other recommendations constitute a concurrence with or emphasizing of present Air Force intentions, as indicated by Air Force directives, budgets, and plans. To avoid misunderstanding on this point, I suggest that a paragraph such as the following might be added to the introduction.

" 'The recommendations of the Committee are not to be understood as calling, in every case, for a change in the present program of the Air Force. Certain of the recommendations will be recognized as endorsing a course of action presently intended by the Air Force.' "

Lack of time has precluded coordination with other Committee members to determine their reactions to the question of including the suggested paragraph.

Appendix B - List of Committee Members

Professor Clark B. Millikan	California Institute of Technology
Professor Charles C. Lauritsen	California Institute of Technology
Dr. Louis G. Dunn	California Institute of Technology
Professor John von Neumann	Institute for Advanced Study
Dr. Hendrik W. Bode	Bell Telephone Laboratories
Dr. Allen E. Puckett	Hughes Aircraft Company
Dr. George B. Kistiakowsky	Harvard University
Professor J. B. Wiesner	Massachusetts Institute of Technology
Mr. Lawrence A. Hyland	Bendix Aviation Corporation
Dr. Simon Ramo	Ramo-Wooldridge Corporation
Dr. Dean Wooldridge	Ramo-Wooldridge Corporation

Appendix 2

The Gillette Report

DEPARTMENT OF THE AIR FORCE
WASHINGTON

OFFICE OF THE ASSISTANT SECRETARY

September 13, 1955

MEMORANDUM FOR MR. GILLETTE

Consistent with the over-riding priority for the ICBM development program recently established by the National Security Council and as reaffirmed and emphasized by the President's letter to Senator Anderson of September 6th, it is requested that you serve as chairman of a working group to evaluate the administrative management and control procedures incident to this program. This evaluation should have as a primary objective the reduction of administrative interference and delays which impede achievement of the earliest possible ICBM operational capability. This would include studies of the organizational structure, financial procedures, procurement policies and any other aspect which, in your judgement, would have a bearing on the acceleration of this program.

It is requested that the working group prepare a report containing its findings and recommendations by September. The report should be transmitted to a review committee which is being established with myself as chairman and which will be responsible for making final recommendations to Secretary Quarles for his indorsement for Secretary Wilson.

Trevor Gardner

DEPARTMENT OF THE AIR FORCE
Washington

November 14, 1955

OFFICE OF THE SECRETARY

MEMORANDUM FOR THE CHIEF OF STAFF
SUBJECT: Implementation of Approved Management Procedures and
Concepts Related to the Management of the ICBM and
IRBM Programs

The attached Air Force plan for simplifying administrative procedures for the ICBM and IRBM Programs, prepared in conjunction with the Air Staff and representatives of my office, is approved. It is requested that necessary action be taken to issue the appropriate directives which will implement the procedures and organizational arrangements contained in the plan.

My memorandum to you, dated November 14, 1955, established the Air Force Ballistic Missiles Committee. There is included with the Air Force Plan copies of the memorandums providing the necessary delegation of authority and establishing a compatible management environment in the Office of the Secretary of Defense for implementation of the plan.

It is requested that the plan be implemented with all possible speed. I would appreciate being advised of the actions taken in connection with this request.

Donald A. Quarles

AIR FORCE PLAN (REVISED)
FOR SIMPLIFYING ADMINISTRATIVE PROCEDURES
FOR THE ICBM AND IRBM PROGRAMS

(This is the Air Force plan dated October 21, 1955 as submitted to the Department of Defense, revised to reflect DOD Directives dated November 8, 1955 pertaining to the Air Force ICBM Program and the additional Air Force responsibility for the IRBM Program)

November 10, 1955

BALLISTIC MISSILES

TABLE OF CONTENTS

Part I

Part II

PART I

BALLISTIC MISSILES

INTRODUCTION

1. By memorandum from the Deputy Secretary of Defense dated September 17, 1955, the Secretary of the Air Force was directed in effect to:

    a. Prosecute within his assigned responsibilities the ICBM research and development program with maximum urgency.

    b. Recommend to the Secretary of Defense such additional actions or administrative arrangements as he considers necessary on the part of the Secretary of Defense to implement this (the Secretary of the Air Force's) responsibility.

    c. Keep the Secretary of Defense currently informed on the progress of the program.

2. Anticipating requirements upon the Air Force of the nature described in "a" and "b" above, a Working Group was established by memorandum dated September 13, 1955 by The Assistant Secretary of the Air Force (Research and Development). This Group was to evaluate the administrative and control procedures incident to the ICBM Program, with the objective of reducing any administrative delays which might impede achievement of the earliest possible ICBM operational capability. Additional guidance stressed the importance of considering unprecedented emergency-type actions wherever required to keep program progress up with technological progress. The report was to be transmitted to The Assistant Secretary of the Air Force (Research and Development), as chairman of a review committee which would make final recommendations to the Secretary of the Air Force.

3. The Working Group was established, with representation from the Office of the Secretary, the Air Staff and Air Research and Development Command, the Western Development Division, and Special Aircraft Project Office, AMC (SAPO). It held a number of meetings both in HQ USAF and at the Western Development Division in Los Angeles. The findings and recommendations were submitted to the Secretary of the Air Force. The original Report of the Working Group, as amended by staff action, resulted in the "Air Force Plan for Simplifying Administrative Procedures for the ICBM Program" dated October 21, 1955 which was submitted to the Department of Defense. The present Plan (Revised) amends the foregoing to reflect the resultant directive of the Secretary of Defense dated November 8, 1955 pertaining to the ICBM Program, and the new responsibilities given to Air Force for the IRBM Program. (See Tab A for above Department of Defense memoranda.)

These Department of Defense memoranda reflect the consideration and degree of implementation by the Office of the Secretary of Defense of those recommendations made relative to that office in the original Plan. In addition, the memoranda assign the management responsibility for the development of a land based Intermediate Range Ballistic Missile (IRBM #1) to the Air Force and direct the use of the same streamlined management structure in the prosecution of both programs.

Although the Secretary of Defense has already acted upon the recommendations pertaining to that office contained in the original October 21 Plan, these recommendations have been left in the present Plan (Revised) for background information in considering proposed new Air Force procedures. The general effect of the recommendations in simplifying the administrative procedures for the ICBM/IRBM is shown in Tab B.

The following highlights of the 8 November 1955 DOD memoranda are reflected in the revised recommendations on Air Force procedures, contained herein:

1. The DOD proposes to recommend to the National Security Council that the IRBM research and development program be given an equal priority to the ICB program but with no interference to the valid requirements of the ICBM program. Pending clarification by the National Security Council, the IRBM program will be carried on at a priority second only to the ICBM program.

2. The Air Force is assigned management responsibility for the ICBM Development Program and for the conduct of a land based Intermediate Range Ballistic Missile (IRBM #1) Development Program.

3. The management responsibility for an additional Intermediate Range Ballistic Missile Development Program (IRBM #2), having the dual objective of achieving an early shipboard capability and also providing a land based alternate to the Air Force IRBM #1 Program, is assigned jointly to the Army and Navy. Appropriate liaison channels will be established immediately between the Air Force and joint Army–Navy programs at various levels to assure a full and complete interchange of information.

4. The two programs for achievement of an Intermediate Range Ballistic Missile capability will be accorded equal priority.

5. An OSD Ballistic Missiles Committee (OSD–BMC) will be created for the purpose of reviewing the overall Department

of Defense Ballistic Missile Program for approval of the necessary supporting effort.

General Observations and Summary of Recommendations

General Observations

Examination of administrative procedures in the light of actual or potential effects on the progress of the Ballistic Missile Program brought into clear focus four important basic premises that should be recognized, and in the opinion of the Working Group, generally accepted.

1. That the Air Force be recognized as the Executive Agent of the Department of the Defense for the development and operation of the ICBM system and a land based IRBM (IRBM #1). On the basis of this premise and the NSC established priority of the program it is recommended that (a) the other Services be clearly requested by the Secretary of Defense to require their contractors to give preference to work on these programs, and their commands to afford maximum cooperation, and (b) Industry be apprised of the national interest in and the urgency of these Air Force programs.

2. That present successive levels of review place an onerous burden upon personnel actually administering the ICBM and IRBM #1 programs and obviously extend the time required for program approvals; that therefore, to assure program acceleration commensurate with technological progress maximum authority for program approval and implementation should be delegated to the lowest possible echelon consistent with the ability of that echelon to obtain and apply the necessary resources within its assigned responsibilities. (See section on Organization and Command Relationships.)

3. That the responsibility of ARDC must be clearly extended to include all steps in establishing an initial operational capability within the limits of approved USAF operational and logistic concepts for the creation and use of long-range missile system. The operational control of the initial units will be transferred to the operational command at an appropriate time by Headquarters USAF. The intimate relationship of research and development with preproduction items, prototype bases, and training and operational procedures in a program of maximum urgency in a completely unique envi-

ronment, call for a single authority to assure time phasing of all elements. (See Section on Planning and Programming.)

4. The ARDC–AMC relationship is essentially that of a Weapons System Project Office (WSPO) for a weapon system where ARDC is the executive agent. AMC supports ARDC with contractual services and advice based on AMC's broad experience in programming, pricing, production, maintenance ànd supply. Full support by AMC will be provided for the ballistic missile program in consonance with its very high priority. Inasmuch as ARDC is the executive agent for this program, AMC will be fully responsive to ARDC's management direction. All aspects of the ICBM and IRBM #1 Programs, including operational, logistic, training, and installations plans for initial units, will be included in Development Plans to be submitted by ARDC. These plans must be made and kept current by ARDC with assistance as necessary from other Major Air Commands. Approval of these plans will be given by the Secretary of the Air Force supported by Air Staff reviews. Upon approval of the program Hq. USAF will direct the execution and administration thereof as hereinafter prescribed. (See Section II – Planning and Programming.)

Summary of Recommendations

Section I – Organization and Command Relationships

It is recommended that the Secretary of Defense:

1. Establish an OSD Ballistic Missiles Committee (OSD–BMC) chaired by the Deputy Secretary of Defense and including the interested Assistant Secretaries, such as Research and Development, Applications Engineering, Comptroller and Properties & Installations. A responsible representative of the Bureau of the Budget should be invited to participate as a member of this body. This committee will serve as a single point of contact to which the Secretary of the Air Force will report and as a single program review and approval authority at the OSD level.

2. Delegate his responsibility for management of the ICBM and IRBM #1 Programs to the Secretary of the Air Force subject to final review and guidance by the OSD–BMC. Such broad delegation will include unusual authority pertaining to the

areas of facilities, procurement, funding and the composition of the technical program.

It is recommended that the Secretary of the Air Force:

1. Establish an Air Force Ballistic Missiles Committee (AF-BMC) to review, approve and direct implementation of the Ballistic Missile Program. The Committee will be chaired by the Secretary of the Air Force and include the Assistant Secretaries for Research and Development, Financial Management, Materiel and the Assistant Chief of Staff for Guided Missiles. The Assistant Secretary for Research and Development will serve as the Vice Chairman of the committee to establish a functional liaison between this committee and the OSD-BMC and will be the central control point within OSAF for all matters related to the program. The Assistant Secretary of Defense for Research and Development will be invited to attend such meetings as may be appropriate. (See Tab C)

It is recommended that the Chief of Staff, USAF: (Tab D)

1. Expand the responsibilities of the Office of the Assistant Chief of Staff for Guided Missiles to include responsibilities for controlling ballistic missile matters in Headquarters, USAF and providing a secretariat for the AF-BMC.

2. Delegate to the Commander, ARDC the primary responsibility for creating an initial ICBM operational capability in the closest harmony with AMC, SAC, ATC and other commands concerned. The responsibility for establishing the initial operational capability for the IRBM #1 is under study and will be delegated at a later date.

3. Direct the establishment of a Ballistic Missile office in each specific Air Command concerned. This office will be directly responsible to the commander as a point of contact and expediting agency for all ICBM and IRBM matters related to that command.

4. Direct the major organizational elements in the management structure of the ICBM and IRBM #1 Programs to coordinate with their counterparts in the management structure of the IRBM #2 Program to establish effective liaison for exchange of information and resolution of interrelated problems.

Section II – Planning and Programming

It is recommended that:

1. The ICBM and IRBM #1 Development Plans, submitted to the AF–BMC by 1 September of each year, be the basis for authorization for actions in the following areas:

    a. Programming

    b. Facility planning

    c. Budgeting

    d. Apportionment actions

    e. Test Schedules

    f. Allocation of personnel

    g. Allocation of aircraft

    h. Financial planning

    i. Status reporting

2. Procedures be established to use the Air Force BMC as the single reviewing and approval authority within the Department of the Air Force.

3. ARDC be assigned primary responsibility for creating the initial ICBM operational capability which will be in consonance with the approved USAF operational and logistic concepts for long-range missile systems.

4. The Development Plans as approved by the Secretary of the Air Force will constitute the only authority under which all other actions of the Air Force, including programming, budgeting and financing actions, would be implemented and no actions would be authorized that were not included in an approved Development Plan.

5. The following outline of basic procedural steps in the area of ARDC (WDD)–AMC relationships will assure continued mutual understanding.

    a. ARDC (WDD) will determine and develop requirements for Industrial Facilities and production quantities of missiles and components thereof for implementation of the Development Plans.

    b. ARDC (WDD) will obtain assistance from AMC on requirements for Industrial Facilities, missiles, and components thereof, where necessary in the judgment of Commander, WDD.

    c. ARDC (WDD) will include the requirements together with any AMC endorsement in the Development Plan.

    d. Hq. USAF will implement the approved Development Plans for these requirements by issuing Procurement Directives and funds through AMC to WDD for total approved requirements.

    e. ARDC (WDD) will execute the program as approved, using AMC as the contracting agency.

Section III – Budgeting and Funding

It is recommended that the Secretary of Defense:

1. Prescribe that the dollar requirements for the ballistic missile program are separate from the dollar requirements or limitations applicable to any other Air Force program and will be justified separately.

2. Exempt the dollar requirements for the ICBM and IRBM #1 Programs contained in Air Force budget and apportionment requests, from review by offices within the Office, Secretary of Defense other than the single review by the OSD–BMC.

3. Accept the Budget Annex of the Development Plans and the Air Force appropriate component dollar requirements as included in classified "line items" in the appropriate Air Force appropriation request as the source of estimates for the President's annual budget.

It is recommended that:

1. The Budget Annex to the Development Plans be maintained current on a monthly basis strictly in consonance and keyed to the definitive program details.

2. The Air Force financial plans be derived exclusively from the Financial Plan portion of the Budget Annex of the Development Plans.

3. Air Force apportionments include ICBM and IRBM #1 fund requirements as sum totals derived from the Financial Plan portion of the Budget Annex of the Development Plans.

4. Funds be authorized and allocated in amounts and for the purposes shown in the Financial Plan to ARDC and AMC and WDD, or to the Air Force construction agent, as designated by Headquarters USAF for identified portions of the Program.

Section IV – Procurement Policies and Procedures

It is recommended that the manning of the office responsible for ICBM and IRBM #1 procurement action be given a high priority to insure an adequate number of highly qualified personnel.

Section V – Industrial Facilities

It is recommended that:

1. The Secretary of Defense delegate to the Secretary of the Air Force full authority to approve all ICBM and IRBM #1 facility requests. This requires waiver of the provisions of DOD Directive 4275.2 as it applies to the Ballistic Missile Program.

2. Air Force review of Industrial Facilities at the Secretarial and Headquarters level be limited to approval of the Industrial Facility Program Addendum of the Development Plans.

3. Facility expansion authority in connection with the Ballistic Missile Program be delegated to Commander AMC in the same manner as the present delegation for facility expansion for less than $100,000.

4. ARDC (WDD) execute the program as approved, using AMC as the contracting agency.

Section VI – Military Construction

It is recommended that:

1. ICBM and IRBM #1 construction requirements as included in the approved Development Plans be programmed for lump sum authorization and appropriation.

2. The Assistant Secretary of Defense (Comptroller) memorandum of 17 February 1954 be waived and all construction funds appropriated for support of ICBM and IRBM #1 be released in one bulk sum.

3. Construction funds be allocated promptly to designated construction agencies.

4. DOD Directive 4270.5 be waived and the Air Force authorized to designate the agency for construction best able to meet program objectives for the Ballistic Missiles Program.

5. The provisions of Assistant Secretary of Defense (P&I) memorandum of 2 February 1954 regarding approval of construction criteria and standards be waived and the Air Force be authorized to proceed immediately with studies and design of facilities required to support this program.

6. OSD delegate authority to the Air Force to establish completion dates of facilities to meet requirements of the ICBM and IRBM #1 Programs.

7. ARDC (WDD) develop construction requirements and cause them to be included in the Development Plans in compliance with AFR 80-30 (see Planning and Programming, Section II).

Section VII – Scientific Advisory Committee

It is recommended that:

1. The Scientific Advisory Committee, which reports to the Secretary of the Air Force, be considered also as the Scientific Review Committee for the Office of the Secretary of Defense.

2. The Scientific Advisory Committee meet each quarter and submit quarterly technical status reports to the Office of the Secretary of Defense.

3. The members of the Scientific Advisory Committee spend additional time as needed between quarterly meetings in order to delve more deeply into technical matters which prove of concern to them during the presentation at the quarterly meetings. Such additional time then will be used to clear up misunderstandings in presentation and to delineate clearly technical problems before they are reported in detail to the Secretary of the Air Force and the Secretary of Defense.

PART II

BALLISTIC MISSILES

SECTION I

ORGANIZATION AND COMMAND RELATIONSHIPS

GENERAL

Above the level of the Major Air Commands in the Air Force, the Ballistic Missile Program has been handled within the machinery established normally to review and implement the entire program of the Department of Defense. Because of the special requirements for acceleration of the ICBM and IRMB #1 Programs it is proposed to lift it out of intermediate routine reviews centralizing authority to the maximum feasible extent in the Commander, ARDC at the operating level, and in the Secretary of the Air Force at the final Air Force review and policy level.

The Office of the Secretary of Defense:

To expedite administrative procedures under emergency-type conditions, it is believed warranted to request the Secretary of Defense to delegate unusual review and approval authority for matters concerned with the early attainment of a ballistic missile capability to the Secretary of the Air Force. At the present time justifications and clearances are required on various aspects of the Program from the offices of at least five Assistant Secretaries of Defense. Further, the Secretary of Defense should be requested to establish an OSD Ballistic Missiles Committee for such matters related to the ICBM and IRBM #1 Programs as would come to the Secretary of Defense for his information or resolution. This OSD committee would accept information in the form of periodic briefings and reports to permit the Secretary of Defense to fulfill his responsibilities to the President and the NSC, and provide the Air Force with overall program guidance.

RECOMMENDATIONS

It is recommended that the Secretary of Defense:

1. Establish an OSD Ballistic Missiles Committee chaired by the Deputy Secretary of Defense and including the interested Assistant Secretaries, such as Research and Development, Applications Engineering, Comptroller and Properties & Installations. A responsible representative of the Bureau of the Budget should be invited to participate as a member of this body. This committee will serve as a single point of contact to which the Secretary of the Air

Force will report and as a single program review and approval authority at the OSD level.

2. Delegate his responsibility for management of the ICBM and IRBM #2 Programs to the Secretary of the Air Force subject to final review and guidance by the OSD–BMC. Such broad delegation will include unusual authority pertaining to the areas of facilities, procurement, funding and the composition of the technical program.

The Office of the Secretary of the Air Force:

To discharge properly and with efficiency the review responsibilities proposed to be delegated to him, the Secretary of the Air Force must streamline procedures in respect to the ICBM AND IRBM #1 Programs within his office, and direct that special procedures also obtain in the Air Staff at Headquarters, USAF, and in the Major Commands. In his own office, at least three Assistant Secretaries have responsibilities for review, often consecutive in nature. To consolidate these Secretarial reviews at one time and place, and to provide his office with the coordinated information needed to permit final decision on all ICBM matters, a top level Secretary's review group is proposed with membership from both the Office of the Secretary and the Air Staff.

RECOMMENDATIONS

It is recommended that the Secretary of the Air Force:

1. Establish an Air Force Ballistic Missiles Committee to review, approve and direct implementation of the ICBM and IRBM #1 Programs. The committee will be chaired by the Secretary of the Air Force and include the Assistant Secretaries for Research and Development, Financial Management, Materiel, and Assistant Chief of Staff for Guided Missiles. The Assistant Secretary for Research and Development will serve as the Vice Chairman of the committee to establish a functional liaison between this committee and the OSD–BMC and to provide a single control point within OSAF for all matters related to the program. The Assistant Secretary of Defense for Research and Development will be asked to attend such meetings as may be appropriate. (See Tab C)

The Air Staff (Headquarters, USAF):

A single office in the Air Staff is required to provide comprehensive control of all Ballistic Missile matters that come to Headquarters, USAF, to assure timely staff work on the Development Plans and changes thereto, and to afford the AF–BMC an adequate and competent secretariat. More specifically, the functions of the office would include: (a) serving as a receiving and dispatching agency for all correspondence related to ICBM and IRBM #1, (b) establishing suspense dates on matters requiring action, (c) following up on all matters referred to the Air Staff or OSAF to insure that suspense dates were met, (d) serving as a focal point for consolidation of the Air Staff position in respect to the overall Development Plan, including program budget and financial plan and reporting this position to the AF–BMC, and (e) serving as secretariat of the AF–BMC under the direction of the Committee Chairman. In performing these functions this office would have access to all of the capabilities of the various elements of the Air Staff. Delays now inherent in multiple consecutive reviews would be avoided by arranging the concurrent review by all interested elements. Inherent in the functions of this office would be the housing of the Liaison Officer representing WDD at Headquarters, USAF. (See Tab D)

RECOMMENDATION

It is recommended that the Chief of Staff expand the responsibilities of the Office of the Assistant Chief of Staff for Guided Missiles to include responsibilities for controlling Ballistic Missile matters in Headquarters, USAF and providing a secretariat for the AF–BMC.

Major Air Commands:

The alignment of organization and command responsibilities for most effective prosecution of the ICBM and IRBM #1 Programs must be considered in the environment of certain basic principles:

1. Applying the basic premise stated in the Introduction, that maximum authority must be delegated to the lowest possible echelon to insure expedition in an emergency program, primary authority should be delegated to the Commander, ARDC for the actual development of an initial ICBM operational capability within the limits of approved USAF operational and logistic concept for the creation and use of long-range missile systems and subject to such review procedures as may be prescribed by the Secretary. The responsibility for establishing the initial operational capability for the IRBM #1 is under study and will be delegated at a later date.

2. The principal operating organization of the ICBM and IRBM #1 Development Programs is the Western Development Division, an

integral part of the Air Research and Development Command in that its Commander is Deputy Commander of ARDC for this program. Because of the high priority assigned to the program, and the extreme complexity of the technical problems associated with acquiring operational capability, unusual technical and management competence has been assembled by the Air Force under ARDC, through the Western Development Division and its prime contractor, the Ramo-Wooldridge Corporation, with counsel from a special Scientific Advisory Committee. It is believed that this competence in ARDC should be fully recognized by the assignment of primary authority and responsibility for prosecution of the development program to that command.

3. There should be one formal review authority established at Headquarters USAF, the Air Force Ballistic Missiles Committee. This authority is the only one empowered to approve or disapprove any development program matter submitted for decision by ARDC (WDD). All intermediate echelons between ARDC (WDD) and the final review authority would retain only authority to review, approve, and implement if such was consistent with their available resources, and within assigned authority, or review, comment and forward to higher authority if needed.

4. Each major organizational element should establish a single office to serve as a point of contact on all matters pertaining to the ICBM and IRBM #1 Programs. This office would insure the full availability of the organization's capabilities in furthering the programs at the same time avoiding all delays. To accomplish successfully this function the office would need to be closely associated with the Commander of the organization.

Within the WDD no problems were found which appeared to warrant an organizational change. The Commander of WDD as a Deputy Commander of ARDC has adequate latitude in dealing with the various Centers of the ARDC which have support responsibilities to the ICBM and IRBM #1 Programs. The arrangement also provides immediate access to the Commander, ARDC for assistance in performing lateral coordination with other major air commanders. The ARDC–AMC agreement appears to be operating satisfactorily with AMC supporting the Program to the fullest extent by unusual delegation of procurement authority to its Special Aircraft Project Office (SAPO) located at WDD. It should be noted, however, that the Commander, WDD, has command and administrative authority over WDD, and not over the Field Office. The latter embraces WDD, SAPO, and Ramo-Wooldridge Corporation.

BALLISTIC MISSILES

In recognition of the coexistence of a joint Army–Navy IRBM Development Program (IRBM #2) and the Air Force Ballistic Missile Program (ICBM, IRBM #1) to minimize mutual interference and assure the attainment of the earliest operational capability for each weapon, the utmost in cooperation between the programs is required. Effective liaison is required at the working level to accomplish the necessary exchange of technical information and to resolve interrelated problems.

RECOMMMENDATIONS

It is recommended that the Chief of Staff: (Tab D)

1. Delegate to the Commander, ARDC, the primary responsibility for creating an initial ICBM operational capability within the limits of approved USAF operational and logistic concepts for the creation and use of long-range missiles and in closest harmony with AMC, SAC, ATC and other commands concerned.

2. Direct the establishment of a Ballistic Missile Office in each specific Air Command concerned. This office will be directly responsible to the commander as a point of contact and expediting agency for all ICBM and IRBM #1 matters related to that command.

3. Direct the major organizational elements in the management structure of the ICBM and IRBM #1 Programs to coordinate with their counterparts in the management structure of the IRBM #2 Program to establish effective liaison for exchange of information and resolution of interrelated problems. (See Tab for suggested Directives.)

SECTION II

PLANNING AND PROGRAMMING

There appear to be certain inherent delays in the present methods of planning and programming in the Ballistic Missile Program.

It would be highly advantageous if the ICBM and IRBM #1 Development Plans, as amended periodically by management reports, could be employed as single action documents for planning, programming, budgeting and reporting. These documents, prepared in accordance with ARDC Manual 80-4 in compliance with AFR 80-30 are comprehensive in nature, carrying detailed tabs on each facet of the program; i.e., budget, personnel, industrial facilities, military construction, training, etc. At present the documents, although approved by Headquarters, USAF, serve little actual use since separate individual processing and approval actions are required for many of the various items contained in the Plans. In effect, although a Plan has been officially approved, such approval now provides no authority or basis for implementation. Yet, the Development Plan is certainly the most logical and practical vehicle to define and justify the program.

Consistent with other portions of this report which recommend maximum delegation of authority and waiver of normal intermediate reviews, a step by step procedure has been considered whereby maximum speed and emphasis can be delivered to the ICBM and IRBM #1 Programs, by use of the Development Plans as the basic program documents. Basically this procedure requires (1) the use of the AF-BMC chaired by the Secretary of the Air Force as the single reviewing authority, and (2) using the Development Plans as the basis for such review and approval. The detailed procedures are described in Tab E.

Of prime importance to adequate and timely planning and programming is the definition of the parameters of ARDC's responsibility to the program. The present directives to ARDC call generally for a program to "achieve the earliest possible operational capability." However, a major task in the ICBM and IRBM #1 Programs is the initiation and implementation of an initial operational plan at an early stage in the development program. Since these weapon systems are unique in many operational aspects, the implementation of the initial operational capability must be very closely integrated with the development program. This intimate relationship requires close cooperative coordination among diverse Command and Air Staff agencies and indicates it would be advantageous to designate a single authority in this respect.

In this connection ARDC is charged with submission of a recommended Operational Concept and Operational Plan. Since the initial operational capability for the IRBM #1 involves a remote launching site the responsibility for establishing the initial operational capability for this weapon is under study and will be delegated at a later date. Early decision on an initial operations plan is vital to the desired achievement of an operational capability at the earliest possible date. Since it is assumed that at least one or two operational bases will be established, it is essential that basic decisions (including location, construction, and funding) leading to this initial operations capability be made at the earliest possible moment. Evolution of the Concept and Plan is progressing, but unless basic decisions regarding the initial installation(s) are forthcoming in the immediate future, there appears to be a real chance of delay in effective weapon employment.

It is felt that ARDC should be given primary responsibility for the development program to obtain initial operational capability for both the ICBM and IRBM #1 within the limits of approved USAF operational and logistics concepts for the creation and use of long-range missile systems and that all other commands be directed to support ARDC to the maximum extent necessary. Subsequent to gaining initial operational capability, operational control will be transferred to the operational Command. (See Tab D)

The flow of programming procedures as related to the ARDC (WDD)–AMC relationship should be based essentially on the Weapons System Project Office (WSPO) arrangement wherein ARDC (WDD) is executive agent, as generally described in numbered paragraph 4 under General Observations on page 6. The specific steps in the relationship are recommended in detail below to avoid misunderstanding. (See also Tab F)

RECOMMENDATIONS

It is recommended that:

1. The ICBM and IRBM #1 Development Plans, submitted to the AF–BMC by 1 September of each year, be the basis for authorization for actions in the following areas:

  a. Programming

  b. Facility planning

  c. Budgeting

  d. Apportionment actions

  e. Test Schedules

  f. Allocation of personnel

  g. Allocation of aircraft

h. Financial Planning

i. Status reporting

2. Procedures be established to use the AF–BMC as the single reviewing and approval authority within the Department of the Air Force.

3. ARDC be assigned primary responsibility for creating the initial ICBM operational capability which will be in consonance with the approved USAF operational and logistic concepts for long-range missile systems.

4. The Programs as approved by the Secretary of the Air Force will constitute the sole authority under which all other actions of the Air Force, including programming, budgeting and financing actions, would be implemented and no actions would be authorized that were not included in the approved Development Plans.

5. The following outline of basic procedural steps in the area of ARDC (WDD)–AMC relationships will assure continue mutual understanding.

a. ARDC (WDD) will determine and develop requirements for Industrial Facilities and production quantities of missiles and components thereof for implementation of the Development Plans.

b. ARDC (WDD) will obtain assistance from AMC on requirements for Industrial Facilities, missiles, and components thereof, where necessary in the judgment of Commander, WDD.

c. ARDC (WDD) will include the requirements together with any AMC endorsement in the Development Plans.

d. Hq. USAF will implement the approved Development Plans for these requirements by issuing Procurement Directives and funds through AMC to WDD for total approved requirements.

e. ARDC (WDD) will execute the program as approved, using AMC as the contracting agency.

SECTION III

BUDGETING AND FUNDING

The findings and recommendations of the preceding portions of this report specifically delineate command responsibility and authorities incident to the ICBM and IRBM #1 Programs. To summarize for these purposes, they cover the following pertinent points:

1. A Development Plan as a prerequisite, includes a complete and definitive time-phased program covering all aspects of the ICMB and IRBM #1 Programs. As a part of the Development Plans, there will be a Budget Annex embracing a long term, time-phased dollar forecast by each Air Force appropriate, correlated directly to the definitive program as set forth in the Development Plan. In addition the Budget Annex will include a Financial Plan covering the short term financial requirements by Air Force appropriations, correlated directly to the definitive program as contained in the Development Plan.

2. The Secretary of the Air Force will review and approve the definitive program in all of its aspects as contained in the Development Plan. This would include the Budget Annex of the Development Plan. This approval will constitute the sole authority under which all other actions of the Air Force, including budgeting and financing actions, would be authorized and no actions would be authorized that were not included in the approved Development Plan.

3. A maximum delegation of authority will be obtained from the Office, Secretary of Defense, and delegated to the fullest feasible extent to successive lower echelons within the Air Force chain of command. This delegation of authority would clearly exempt any and all aspects of the ICBM and IRBM #1 Programs from review by offices within the Office, Secretary of Defense, with the exception of the Secretary of Defense himself and the OSD–BMC.

Since it has been recommended that the Secretary of the Air Force have full responsibility and authority for these programs and in view of the overriding priority of the Programs, it is believed that the ICBM and IRBM #1 Budget should be presented and considered as a separate package, outside and additive to any dollar requirements, goals or limitations applicable to the remainder of the Air Force Program. This would insure that the ICBM and IRBM #1 Programs would not be interfered with by other programs and also would permit the ICBM and IRBM #1 Programs to follow a much shorter budget cycle than the rest of the Air Force programs, in that the number of review levels could be reduced. Additionally, since final funding requirments for the ICBM and IRBM #1 are not yet known, programming for the rest of the Air Force would otherwise have to be conditional pending exact knowledge of the ICBM and IRBM #1 needs.

RECOMMENDATIONS

It is recommended that the Secretary of Defense:

1. Prescribe that the dollar requirements for these programs be justified separately from the dollar requirements for the rest of the Air Force program.

2. Exempt the dollar requirements for the ICBM Program contained in Air Force budget and apportionment requests, from review by offices within the Office, Secretary of Defense in lieu of final review and approval by the OSD–BMC.

3. Accept the Budget Annex of each Development Plan, substantiated as a package, with Air Force appropriation component dollar requirements included as classified line items in the Air Force appropriation request as the sole source of estimate for the President's Budget.

It is further recommended that:

1. The Air Force financial plans be derived exclusively from the Financial Plan portion of the Budget Annex of each Development Plan.

2. Air Force apportionments include ICBM and IRBM #2 fund requirements as sum totals, as derived from the Financial Plan portion of the Budget Annex of each Development Plan.

3. Funds be authorized and allocated in amounts and for the purposes shown in the Financial Plan to ARDC and AMC for WDD, or to the Air Force construction agent, as designated by Headquarters USAF for identified portions of the Program.

SECTION IV

PROCUREMENT POLICIES AND PROCEDURES

To insure adequate contract support in consonance with the overriding priority of the ICBM Program, the Air Materiel Command established the Special Aircraft Project Office (SAPO), located with the Western Development Division. The Commander, AMC has delegated broad contracting authorities now vested in the Directorate of Procurement and Production to the Chief of the Special Aircraft Project Office. The scope of this delegation is outlined in detail in a memorandum signed by General Baker, dated 28 July 1954. Of particular significance is the extension of authority to the SAPO to issue letter contracts irrespective of dollar amount and without prior approval.

This unlimited letter contracting authority permits the Air Force to put the necessary contracts to work immediately and in general obviates the effect of any delay that accrues in the review proceedings that take place during the negotiation of definitive contracts. Definitive contracts involving more than $350,000 are forwarded to Headquarters, AMC for approval by the Procurement Review Committee. It is considered that this remains a necessary step for the protection of the Government and should not be eliminated.

The delegation of authority by the Director of Procurement and Production, Headquarters, AMC to the Chief, SAPO includes the limitation that actions of the delegee are bound by the Armed Service Procurement Regulations and the Air Force Procurement Instruction. These regulations and instructions have been established as a guide to the contracting office and as a protection of the interests of the Government. It would not be in the National interest to grant or request complete deviation authority for this field agency. In general these regulations and instructions are sufficiently broad as to permit the exercise of good judgment. In those instances where a deviation my be considered prudent an adequate organizational mechanism exists for gaining a specific deviation and the request will be handled in accordance with the Program priority. It is not technically practical to search the ASPR's and the AFPI's for provisions that may in the future require deviations. These procurement policies and procedures originally established for the ICBM Program will also be used in carrying out the IRBM #1 Program.

SECTION V

INDUSTRIAL FACILITIES

The present system for processing requests for industrial facilities from the Western Development Division is time consuming and has a delaying effect on the Program. The current procedure requires WDD to transmit requests to the AMC Facilities Review Board. After review by the Board, the request is then forwarded to Deputy Chief of Staff (Materiel), Hq. USAF. Subsequently the request is forwarded to the Assistant Secretary of the Air Force, Materiel, for his approval. Additionally, if the request for expansion is estimated to cost in excess of $1 million, Department of Defense Directive 4275.2 requires that the request be reviewed by the Assistant Secretary of Defense (Properties & Installations). Each of these echelons has several lateral elements which review all or part of each request. This procedure can take, and sometime has taken, from two to three months. Most of this time has been consumed in satisfying Hq. USAF, Secretary of the Air Force, and OSD review requirements. It is considered imperative that the procedure be streamlined to a major extent.

Timely availability of test support and operational facilities is important to the ICBM and IRBM #1 Programs. The Weapon System is unique and many of the required facilities are of a special nature not available in the Air Force controlled inventory. The development schedule has been compressed to the limit of technological achievement. Failure to provide adequate and timely facilities could result in directly relating the operational date to facilities availability rather than to technical capabilities.

To facilitate the attainment of the important objectives of this program, it is necessary to restrict the OSD, Hq. USAF and Secretarial review to that incident to the review of the Development Plan. The technical service of AMC should be available as needed by ARDC (WDD) and full delegation of all facility expansion authority, as has been delegated for expansions under $100,000, should be made to AMC.

RECOMMENDATIONS

It is recommended that:

1. The Secretary of Defense delegate to the Secretary of the Air Force full authority to approve all ICBM and IRBM #1 facility requests. This requires waiver of the provisions of DOD Directive 4275.2 as it applies to these Programs.

2. Air Force review at the Secretarial and Headquarters level be

295

limited to approval of the Industrial Facility Program Addendum of each Development Plan.

3. Facility expansion authority in connection with the ICBM and IRBM Programs be delegated to Commander, AMC in the same manner as the present delegation for facility expansion for less than $100,000.

4. ARDC (WDD) execute the program as approved, using AMC as the contracting agency.

SECTION VI

MILITARY CONSTRUCTION

In reviewing the potential sources of delay to the timely completion of the ICBM and IRBM #1 Programs, the lack of facilities is identified as one of primary concern. Substantial relaxation of controls and streamlining of action channels are required to permit rapid and orderly implementation of construction. Under routine procedures, specific projects must be identified 18 months prior to the date funds are appropriated for construction. During the first 12 months of that period, preliminary planning is undertaken, the projects are carefully screened in Hq. USAF, through the Ad Hoc Committee, the Installations Board, the Budget Advisory Committee, the Air Council, and the Air Force Secretary; in OSD, by the Assistant Secretaries for Comptroller and for Properties & Installations (plus reviews in areas of special interest by other Assistant Secretaries); and by the Bureau of the Budget. Projects surviving this screening are cleared for final design which is accomplished during the review of the military construction program on a line item basis by the House and Senate Armed Services and Appropriations Committees. Design must adhere to OSD (P&I) approval criteria and standards. Thereafter, funds are released as OSD/BOB again review and approve each individual line item in the program. Land acquisition costing over $25,000 requires a third time review by OSD (P&I) and a second approval by the House and Senate Armed Services Committees. All work, except as specifically exempted by OSD (P&I) must be accomplished by the Corps of Engineers or Bureau of Yards and Docks, and funds are accordingly allocated to those offices for construction. Thereafter, the scheduling and accomplishment of construction is outside the control of the Air Force.

It is proposed here that military construction programs in support of ICBM and IRBM #1 be relieved of normal line item and base control to permit maximum flexibility in meeting unforeseen requirements. Accordingly, programs will be presented in terms of a single package for lump sum authorization. For OSD/BOB and Congressional review, the Air Force is prepared to report in detail concerning the actual utilization of bulk lump sum authorizations previously approved for the ICBM and IRBM #1 Programs.

Within the Air Force, it is expected that WDD, with all possible assistance from the Office of the Assistant Chief of Staff for Installations, will submit as an annex to the Development Plan recommendations as to the request for a lump sum bulk authorization; and as the program is definitized, specific requirements and costing thereof. Like other elements of the Air Staff, the Installations Board and the Office of Assistant Chief of Staff for Installations will function to provide the cognizant member of the AF–BMC necessary staffing of this element of the Development Plan, as well as assurance of implementation thereof. The Assistant Chief of Staff, Installations, with recommendations from WDD, will approve the designation of the construction agency and construction period. Funds will be allocated to the designated construction agency direct from Hq. USAF.

Detailed line item scrutiny of the construction program during the apportionment process constitutes a threat of delay that must be eliminated. The exceedingly close ICBM and IRBM #1 schedule of design and construction allows no time for the piece-meal processing of apportionment actions required by memorandum from the Office, Assistant Secretary of Defense, Comptroller, dated 17 February 1954. A waiver of the provisions of this memorandum is required to permit bulk release of construction funds appropriated to the Air Force for support of the ICBM and IRBM #1 Programs.

The facilities to support the ICBM and IRBM #1 Programs are essentially non-standard in the sense that they cannot be constructed or modified from basically repetitive type definitive drawings or standard plans. The functional design requirements must be expressed around missile frames, propulsion units, guidance systems, controls and explosive elements, for which firm data has not been established and must, therefore, be developed during the design stage. Consequently, it will be necessary to keep close and continuing control on design to insure that is is prosecuted with a minimum of lost motion and that the end result achieves the program objective. Furthermore, the problem of engineering and design will frequently not end upon completion of plans, but will carry over into the construction period. The construction agent for highly technical facilities must be cognizant of and responsive to the need for design corrections and be prepared to coordinate these matters effectively so that essential changes are promptly and economically applied. These results cannot be effectively achieved if a third party is placed between the contractor and the user. The Air Force proposes to make maximum use of the established field organizations of the Corps of Engineers and the Bureau of Yards and Docks as design and construction agencies for this program, but a waiver of DOD Directive 4270.5 is required to permit the Air Force promptly to exercise the option of direct Air Force design and construction when such action is considered necessary to the accomplishment of the overall mission.

Design criteria and construction standards developed for the ICBM and IRBM #1 Programs will have no general application for other military construction. The processing of design criteria to the Assistant Secretary of Defense for Properties & Installation for approval as required by memorandum of 2 February 1954 from that office will be detrimental to progress on this project. The Air Force will exert every reasonable effort to provide the most economical design to meet minimum operational needs, but requires final approval authority over design criteria in order to avoid unacceptable delay in the program.

By means of timely programming, careful planning and early initiation of design, it will generally be possible to allow normal periods for actual construction. It is visualized, however, that special circumstances may require completion of facilities in less than the "maximum economy" working period normally prescribed. This condition could easily be aggravated by the necessity to clear this action with the Assistant Secretary of Defense, Comptroller. A delay of 8 weeks or longer in obtaining approval for shortening the construction period on a vital facility, such as was experienced on the ICBM engine test stand at Edwards Air Force Base, would seriously threaten the success of this program. Accordingly, it is necessary that the authority of the Secretary of Defense to establish reasonable completion dates for projects vital to the national defense as prescribed in Sec. 304, PL 219, 84th Congress, be delegated to the Secretary of the Air Force for the ICBM Program.

RECOMMENDATIONS

It is recommended that:

1. ICBM and IRBM #1 construction requirements as included in the appoved Development Plan be programmed for lump sum authorization and appropriation.

2. Air Staff procedures be streamlined to insure prompt approval of the definitive program.

3. The provisions of Assistant Secretary of Defense (Comptroller) memorandum of 17 February 1954 be waived and bulk release secured of all construction funds appropriated for support of ICBM and IRBM #1.

4. Construction funds be allocated promptly to designated construction agencies.

5. The provisions of DOD Directive 4270.5 be waived, and the Air Force be authorized to designate the agency for construction best able to meet the program objectives for the ICBM and IRBM #1 Programs.

6. The provisions of Assistant Secretary of Defense (P&I) memorandum of 2 February 1954 regarding approval of construction criteria and standards be waived and the Air Force be authorized to

proceed immediately with studies and design of facilities required to support these programs.

7. OSD delegate authority to the Air Force to establish completion dates for facilities to meet requirements of the ICBM and IRBM #1 Programs.

8. ARDC (WDD) develop construction requirements and cause them to be included in the Development Plan in compliance with AFR 80-30 (see Planning and Programming, Section II).

SECTION VII

SCIENTIFIC ADVISORY COMMITTEE

It would appear that the Scientific Advisory Committee of the Air Force ICBM Program can, with suitable modifications in its membership and procedure, be made to satisfy not only the needs of the Air Force in its reporting to the Secretary of the Air Force, but also the requirements of the Office of the Secretary of Defense and in addition furnish a similar technical review for the IRBM #1 Program. The Scientific Advisory Committee has served the Air Force well in the past. One of its forerunners was instrumental in securing recognition of the ICBM as a high-priority program, and in re-orienting the program to increase markedly its technical feasibility. In the past it has acted almost as a board of trustees for the effort, though recently its activities have changed more toward the technical advisory type. The membership has served as a scientific nucleus composed of leading scientists and engineers of industry, government, and universities. They have helped not only in giving technical advice but also in the acquisition of some of the leading full-time technical participants in the Program.

In the interest of streamlining and making more efficient the scientific reviews by independent scientists and engineers which are clearly necessary to insure the optimum effort in the ICBM and IRMB #1 Programs, certain membership and procedural changes should be made in the Scientific Advisory Committee.

RECOMMENDATIONS

It is recommended that:

1. The Scientific Advisory Committee, which reports to the Secretary of the Air Force, be considered also as the Scientific Review Committee for the Office of the Secretary of Defense.

2. The Scentific Advisory Committee meet on a quarterly basis and submit technical status reports to the Secretary of the Air Force, who in turn would report to the Secretary of Defense.

3. The members of the Scientific Advisory Commitee spend additional time between quarterly meetings in order to delve more deeply into technical matters which prove of concern to them during the presentations at the quarterly meetings. Such additional time will be used to clear up misunderstandings in presentation and to delineate clearly technical problems before they are reported in detail to the Secretary of the Air Force and the Secretary of Defense.

BALLISTIC MISSILES

THE SECRETARY OF DEFENSE
Washington

8 November 1955

MEMORANDUM FOR ALL ASSISTANT SECRETARIES OF DEFENSE
ALL SERVICE SECRETARIES
CHAIRMAN, JOINT CHIEFS OF STAFF

SUBJECT: Establishment of the OSD Ballistic Missiles
                     Committee (OSD–BMC)

In view of the priority and national importance of the ICBM and IRBM Development Programs I have approved new management procedures designed to achieve maximum acceleration of these two programs.

As part of the process of streamlining organizational alignment, management controls and administrative procedures, it is directed that an OSD Ballistic Missiles Committee (OSD–BMC) be established. This Committee will be Chairmaned by the Deputy Secretary of Defense with the Assistant Secretary of Defense (R&D) as Vice Chairman. The Committee is to review and approve the annual ICBM and IRBM #1 Development Plans as prepared by the Air Force Committee and the IRBM #2 Development Plan as prepared by the Joint Army–Navy Committee. By separate memoranda, copies attached, the Air Force Committee has been assigned full responsibility and authority to carry out the ICBM and IRBM #1 Development Plans and the Joint Army–Navy Committee has been assigned full responsibility and authority to carry out the IRBM #2 Development Plan. The Development Plans for these ballistic missiles are subject to review and approval of the OSD–BMC. The OSD–BMC will be constituted as designated below. Other Assistant Secretaries of Defense can be called in for advice and assistance as required. However, the prime objective is to limit the group to those who are directly concerned, provide the Air Force and Joint Army–Navy Committees with maximum latitude and authority, and utilize every possible means to expedite the approved programs. The personal consideration of Committee members is required in order to preclude the delays inherent in independent staff reviews.

The following are appointed to the OSD Ballistic Missiles Committee:

Deputy Secretary of Defense Chairman
Assistant Secretary of Defense (R&D) Vice Chairman
Assistant Secretary of Defense (AE)
Assistant Secretary of Defense (P&I)
Assistant Secretary of Defense (Comptroller)
An Executive Secretary of the Committee

The Air Force and Joint Army-Navy Committees have been directed to present their annual programs for the ICBM and IRBM #1 and the IRBM #2 to the OSD–Ballistic Missiles Committee for review and approval by 1 October of each year. There is an immediate need for consideration of the financial plans for FY 1956 and the proposed plans for FY 1957. These reviews should be accomplished prior to 1 December 1955.

The Bureau of the Budget has been asked to assign a representative as a member of the Committee to assist in expediting the special financial and budgeting arrangements required by the programs.

I will appreciate receiving progress reports on these Programs following each meeting of the OSD–BMC.

signed/ C. E. WILSON

Attachments: 2

SIGNATURE AUTHENTICATED BY:

signed/Leslie R. Kyle

LESLIE R. KYLE, lst Lt, AGC
Correspondence Control Section
Office of the Administrative Secretary

OFFICE OF THE SECRETARY OF DEFENSE
Washington 25, D.C.

November 8, 1955

MEMORANDUM FOR THE SECRETARY OF THE AIR FORCE

SUBJECT: Management of the ICBM and IRBM Development Programs

The National Security Council has recommended, and the President has approved, the assignment of the highest priority to the Intercontinental Ballistic Missile Program. The attainment of the earliest possible operational capability with this weapon has been defined as being of utmost importance to national security.

The NSC has also recommended, and the President approved, a study by the Department of Defense with the objective of determining the optimum approach for the achievement of a 1500 nautical mile missile capability at the earliest possible date. The DOD has now completed its study and proposes to initiate the IRBM program with a priority equal to the ICBM but with no interference to the valid requirements of the ICBM program. Since the DOD study indicated that an IRBM capability could be achieved at an earlier date than the ICBM capability, the DOD plans to recommend to the NSC that the ICBM and IRBM programs have this priority relationship.

It is the objective of the DOD to carry out these research and development programs at the maximum rate technology will permit. It is therefore necessary for the DOD to devise a specialized management structure to insure that delays inherent in program review and administration are minimized.

In keeping with the above, we have established separate development programs for the ICBM and IRBM. The ICBM program management is assigned to the Air Force. The IRBM program will consist of a land-based development by the Air Force (IRBM #1) and a joint Army–Navy program (IRBM #2) having the dual objective of achieving an early shipboard capability and also providing a land-based alternate to the Air Force program. It is planned that these IRBM programs will enjoy equal priority. The ICBM and the IRBM #1 programs are the development responsibility of the Air Force. The IRBM #2 program is the joint development responsibility of the Army and Navy.

Realization of our early operational capability will demand the utmost in cooperation between these programs. Not only is maximum technical and managerial coordination between the two IRBM programs essential, but maximum coordination among all of the ballistic missile programs is required.

By separate memorandum, I have established the OSD Ballistic Missiles Committee (OSD-BMC) which will serve as the single agency within DOD for all matters requiring OSD attention and for approving ICBM-IRBM Development Programs prepared by the Air Force Committee and the joint Army-Navy Committee. A representative of the Bureau of the Budget has been invited to participate in the actions of this OSD Committee. Subject to approval by the OSD Committee, the Air Force Committee is authorized and directed to carry out all aspects of the ICBM and IRBM #1 programs, employing methods reflecting maximum urgency.

The following additional specific authorizations and general operating concepts are defined for application to the Air Force management of the ICBM and IRBM #1 Development Program

1. The dollar requirements for the ICBM and IRBM #1 Programs are separate from the dollar requirements or limitations applicable to any other Air Force program and will be justified separately.

2. The OSD-Ballistic Missiles Committee will be the sole reviewing agency within OSD for all matters related to the ICBM-IRBM #1 programs, including budget and apportionment requests, facilities, procurement and the composition of the technical programs. Every effort will be made by the Air Force to provide the OSD Ballistic Missiles Committee with information on matters to be considered by the Committee a reasonalbe time in advance of the date decisions or approvals are required. Specifically, the annual program will be submitted to the OSD Ballistic Missiles Committee by 1 October each year. For the current year, the admission of the annual programs will be made prior to 1 December 1955.

3. The Budget Annex of the approved ICBM and IRBM #1 Development Plans will be recognized as the instruments for submission to the OSD Ballistic Missiles Committee of estimates for the President's budget. The approved amounts will be included in the proper Air Force budget activity appropriation accounts as classified "line items." The Bureau of the Budget has been asked to approved bulk apportionments of the amounts in each appropriation.

4. Within the ICBM and IRBM #1 Programs as approved by the OSD Ballistic Missiles Committe, the Secretary of the Air Force is delegated authority to approve all ICBM and IRBM #1 facility

requirements, establish completion dates, designate the agency for construction which is best able to meet the required objectives, and to approve the construction criteria and standards for construction. Funds apportioned by the Bureau of the Budget will be made available in lump sums to the Secretary of the Air Force as justified by the development plan and reflected in the financial plan as approved by the OSD Ballistic Missiles Committee. Meantime, the Secretary of the Air Force is authorized immediately to proceed with studies and the design of facilities required to support the programs.

The current ICBM Scientific Advisory Committee to the Secretary of the Air Force, modified as required, will also serve as the advisory committee to the OSD–BMC and the Air Force ballistic missile programs will be subject to no other outside scientific consultant review. The Secretary of the Air Force will add such additional members as the Secretary of Defense may direct to make the Committee appropriate for that purpose.

The requirements of outstanding directives, instructions and memoranda in conflict with this memorandum are hereby superseded as they relate to the ICBM AND IRBM #1 programs.

The Air Force will report quarterly to the OSD Ballistic Missiles Committee on progress and status of the programs and present any major modifications to the annual program plans for Committee approval. These reports will include appropriate summaries of evaluations prepared by the Air Force Scientific Advisory Group. It is expected that the annual Air Force report will also form an integral part of the annual DOD report to the National Security Council and should include the information requested by the NSC. The OSD Ballistic Missiles Committee will periodically make such audits and inspections as it may deem necessary.

Signed

C. E. WILSON

cc: ASD(R&D)

THE SECRETARY OF DEFENSE
Washington

8 November 1955

MEMORANDUM FOR THE SECRETARY OF THE ARMY
THE SECRETARY OF THE NAVY

SUBJECT: Management of the IRBM #2 Development Program

The National Security Council has recommended, and the President has approved, the assignment of the highest priority to the Intercontinental Ballistic Missile Program. The attainment of the earliest possible operational capability with this weapon has been defined as being of utmost importance to national security.

The NSC has also recommended, and the President approved a study by the Department of Defense with the objective of determining the optimum approach for the achievement of a 1500 nautical mile missile capability at the earliest possible date. The DOD has now completed its study and proposes to initiate the IRBM program with a priority equal to the ICBM but with no interference to the valid requirements of the ICBM program. Since the DOD study indicated that an IRBM capability could be achieved at an earlier date than the ICBM capability, the DOD plans to recommend to the NSC that the ICBM and IRBM programs have this priority relationship.

It is the objective of the DOD to carry out these research and development programs at the maximum rate technology will permit. It is therefore necessary for the DOD to devise a specialized management structure to insure that delays inherent in program review and administration are minimized.

In keeping with the above, we have established separate development programs for the ICBM and IRBM. The ICBM program has been assigned to the Air Force. The IRBM program will consist of a land-based development by the Air Force (IRBM #1) and a joint Army–Navy program (IRBM #2) having the dual objective of achieving an early shipboard capability and also providing a land-based alternate to the Air Force program. It is planned that these IRBM programs will enjoy equal priority. The ICBM and IRBM #1 programs will be directed by the Air Force Committee, with the Secretary of the Air Force as Chairman. The joint Army–Navy program for the IRBM

#2 will be directed by the Joint Army–Navy Committee, with the Secretary of the Navy as Chairman and the Secretary of the Army as Vice Chairman.

Realization of an early operational capability will demand the utmost in cooperation among all three Services and among the ballistic missile programs.

By separate memorandum I have established the OSD Ballistic Missiles Committee (OSD–BMC) which will serve as the single agency within DOD for all matters requiring OSD attention, and for approving ICBM–IRBM development programs prepared by the Air Force Committee and the Joint Army–Navy Committee. A representative of the Bureau of the Budget has been invited to participate in the actions of the OSD Committee. Subject to approval by the OSD–BMC, the Joint Army–Navy Committee is authorized and directed to carry out all aspects of the IRBM #2 program, employing methods reflecting maximum urgency.

The following additional specific authorizations and general operating concepts are defined for application to the IRBM #2 development program:

1. The dollar requirements for the IRBM program are separate from the dollar requirement or limitations applicable to any other Army and Navy program, and will be justified separately.

2. The OSD Ballistic Missiles Committee will be the sole reviewing agency within OSD for all matters related to the ICBM–IRBM programs, including budget and apportionment requests, facilities, procurement and the composition of the technical programs. Every effort will be made by the Joint Army–Navy Committee to provide information to the OSD–Ballistic Missiles Committee on matters which they are to consider, within a reasonable time in advance of the date decisions or approvals are required. Specifically, the annual program will be submitted to the OSD–Ballistic Missiles Committee by 1 October each year. For the current year, the submission of the annual program will be made prior to 1 December 1955.

3. The Budget Annexes of the approved IRBM #2 Development Plans will be recognized as the instrument for submission to the OSD Ballistic Missiles Committee of estimates for the President's budget. The approved amounts will be included in the proper Army and Navy budget activity appropriation accounts as classified "line items." The Bureau of the Budget has been asked to approve bulk apportionments of the amounts in each appropriation.

4. The Army and Navy will streamline to the maximum that part of their organizational structure which is responsible for the IRBM #2 program. The new joint organizational structure will be submitted to the Secretary of Defense for approval.

5. The Redstone Arsenal will be assigned missile system responsibility in the program (as contrasted with the ship-launched weapon responsibility which is assigned to to the Navy), and will be fully responsive to the Navy special requirements for ship launching. Every effort will be made to conduct this program with maximum economy.

6. Within the IRBM #2 Program as approved by the OSD–BMC, the Joint Army–Navy Committee is delegated authority to approve all IRBM #2 facility requirements, will establish completion dates, will designate the agency for construction which is best able to meet the required objectives, and will approve the construction criteria and standards for construction. Funds apportioned by the BOB will be made available in lump sums to the Army and Navy as justified by the development plan and reflected in the financial plan as approved by the OSD–Ballistic Missiles Committee. Meantime, the Joint Army–Navy Committee is authorized immediately to proceed with studies and the design of facilities required to support the program.

The present ICBM Advisory Committee to the Secretary of the Air Force, modified as required, will serve the OSD–Ballistic Missiles Committee. The Joint Army–Navy Committee may use the modified ICBM Advisory Committe, or if desired, may establish a separate advisory committee.

The Joint Army–Navy Committee will report quarterly to the OSD–Ballistic Missiles Committee on progress and status of the program, and present any major modifications to the annual program plan for Committee approval. These reports will include appropriate summaries of evaluations prepared by the Army–Navy Scientific Advisory Group. It is expected that the annual Joint Army–Navy Committee report will also form an integral part of the annual DOD report to the NSC and the OSD–Ballistic Missiles Committee will periodically make such audits and inspections as it may deem necessary.

Signed/C.E. WILSON

cc - ASD(R&D)

Major Offices and Agencies
Having Independent or Separate
Review Responsibility in the ICBM Program

Present System		Proposed System
Congress		Congress
Bureau of the Budget		Bureau of the Budget
National Security Council		National Security Council

Office Secretary of Defense
  Secretary of Defense
  Deputy Secretary
    of Defense

  Armed Forces Policy Council
  Assistant Secretary,
    Comptroller
  Assistant Secretary, R&D
  R&D Policy Council
  Joint Coordinating Committee
    on Guided Missiles
  Technical Advisory Panel
    on Aeronautics
  Committee for Aeronautical
    R&D Facilities
  Assistant Secretary,
    Applications Engineering
  Assistant Secretary, Properties
    and Installations
  Assistant Secretary, Atomic
    Energy

Scientific Advisory Committee*

Secretary of Defense
OSD Ballistic
  Missiles Committee

Office Secretary of the Air Force
  Secretary of the Air Force
  Assistant Secretary, Materiel
  Assistant Secretary, Financial
    Management
  Assistant Secretary,
    Manpower & Personnel
  Assistant Secretary, R&D

Scientific Advisory Committee*

Secretary of the Air Force

Air Force Ballistic
  Missiles Committee

Headquarters USAF
  Chief of Staff
  Air Council
  Deputy Chief of Staff,
    Operations

Chief of Staff

Deputy Chief of Staff,
    Materiel
Deputy Chief of Staff,
    Development
Deputy Chief of Staff,
    Comptroller
Deputy Chief of Staff,
    Personnel
Assistant C/S, Installations
Assistant C/S, Guided Missiles
Program Status Committee
Budget Advisory Committee
Aircraft & Weapons Board
Installations Board
Scientific Advisory Board
Weapon Systems Committee

Air Research and   Air Research and
    Development Command   Development Command

Air Materiel Command

Industrial Facilities Review
    Board

Western Development Division | Scientific Advisory Committee* | Western Development Division

---

* The Scientific Advisory Committee could be consulted by all of the services and OSD.

311

DEPARTMENT OF THE AIR FORCE
Washington

OFFICE OF THE SECRETARY

Nov 14 1955

MEMORANDUM FOR ASSISTANT SECRETARY (RESEARCH AND
DEVELOPMENT)
ASSISTANT SECRETARY (FINANCIAL
MANAGEMENT)
ASSISTANT SECRETARY (MATERIEL)
CHIEF OF STAFF

SUBJECT: Establishment of the Air Force Ballistic Missiles Committee

The Secretary of Defense has established the OSD Ballistic Missiles Committee (OSD–BMC) per the attached memorandum, and the Air Force has been delegated authority and responsibility for implementing the accelerated ICBM and IRBM #1 Development Programs.

Detailed study and analysis of the ways and means to produce maximum acceleration indicates the need for a single agency within my office to exercise management control. This agency will be the Air Force Ballistic Missiles Committee (AF–BMC). This Committee is to review and approve the annual Development Plans as prepared by the Western Development Division and the Air Research and Development Command. Additionally, the Committee is responsible for the review and approval of modifications to the annual programs as they are needed during the operating year. The Committee's responsibilities also include the provision of assistance, advice, and recommendations to the OSD–BMC as required.

In order to avoid the delays inherent in normal staff actions, the review of the Air Force ICBM and IRBM #1 Programs will be the personal responsibility of the Committee members designated below. Other Air Force personnel may be called for advice and assistance as required.

The Air Force Ballistic Missiles Committee:

Secretary of the Air Force, Chairman
Assistant Secretary (Research and Development), Vice Chairman
Assistant Secretary (Materiel)

TAB C

Assistant Secretary (Financial Management)
Assistant Chief of Staff for Guided Missles

The Assistant Secretary (Research and Development) is designated Vice Chairman and will act as the central control point within OSAF for all matters relating to the ICBM and IRBM #1 Programs. The Assistant Chief of Staff for Guided Missiles will be responsible for keeping the Chief of Staff and interested elements of the Air Staff informed of the ICBM and IRBM #1 programs, and the Office of the Assistant Chief of Staff for Guided Missiles will provide the Secretariat for the Committee.

The Assistant Secretary of Defense (Research and Development) will be invited to attend Committee meetings as may be appropriate.

The annual ICBM and IRBM #1 Programs will be presented to the Committee for review and approval by September 1 of each year. As approved by the Air Force Ballistic Missiles Committee, the programs will be presented to the OSD Ballistic Missiles Committee by October 1 of each year for final review and approval. The Air Force Ballistic Missiles Committee will report to the OSD Ballistic Missiles Committee at least quarterly on the progress and status of the programs and present any major modifications to the annual programs for Committee approval. These reports will include appropriate summaries of evaluations prepared by the Air Force Ballistic Missiles Scientific Advisory Committee.

The approved management procedures and concept of operation for the ICBM and IRBM #1 Development Programs are contained in "Air Force Plan for Simplifying Administrative Procedures for the ICBM and IRBM Programs," dated November 10, 1955. A copy of this plan is attached for your information and guidance.

Donald A. Quarles

Att.

BALLISTIC MISSILES

Suggested Draft

TO MAJOR USAF COMMANDS

1. The President has approved National Security Council recommendations directing that the Intercontinental Ballistic Missile (ICBM) research and development program be accorded the highest national priority, above any and all other programs. This priority is subject to modification only by the President. Further recommendations to the National Security Council may result in an Intermediate Range Ballistic Missile (IRBM) program being accorded an equal priority to that of the ICBM.

2. Pending results of the above recommendations, the Secretary of Defense has directed the Department of the Air Force to prosecute these programs with maximum urgency, the IRBM receiving priority second only to the ICBM. All other executive departments and agencies have been directed to assist the programs as required. The Secretary of Defense is required to report promptly to the National Security Council any significant developments or problems having an accelerating or delaying effect on the programs.

3. The IRBM program will consist of a land-based development by the Air Force (IRBM #1) and a joint Army-Navy program (IRBM #2) having the dual objective of achieving an early shipboard capability and also providing a land-based alternate to the Air Force program. It is planned that these IRBM programs will enjoy equal priority. The ICBM and the IRBM #1 programs are the development responsibility of the Air Force. The IRBM #2 program is the joint development responsibility of the Army and Navy. The Secretary of Defense has emphasized that an early operational capability will demand the utmost in cooperation between these programs. He has stated that not only is maximum technical and managerial coordination between the two IRBM programs essential, but maximum coordination among all of the ballistic missile programs is required.

4. Within the Air Force, the Air Research and Development Command has been assigned direct responsibility for accomplishing the ICBM and IRBM Development Programs, subject to review by the Air Force Ballistic Missiles Committee. In support of the Air Force policy outlined in AFR 58-1, this responsibility has been expanded to include matters related to the establishment of the initial ICBM operational capability within the limits of approved USAF operational and logistics concepts for the creation and use of long-range missile systems. Initial operational capability is defined as one which will provide for operational employment of prototype

vehicles. It will include the activation of prototype ICBM operational bases. When established, operational command of these bases will be a responsibility of the Strategic Air Command. Complete command responsibility of such bases will be assumed by the Strategic Air Command at an early date thereafter as determined by Headquarters, United States Air Force.

5. It is a matter of greatest urgency that the plan for the initial capability be evolved and implemented at the earliest possible date. All other commands and Air Force activities are directed to render maximum support and assistance to the Commander, ARDC, in this endeavor. Each Air Force Command and activity having an active or support interest in the ICBM Program will establish a project office directly responsible to the commander for administrative control of ICBM matters. Such special procedures as are required will be established to assure positive actions in keeping with the priority of the program. Specifically, the Strategic Air Command, which will have ultimate command responsibility for operation of the ICBM, will establish closest possible working relationship with ARDC to assure that results are compatible with strategic operational requirements.

6. Matters of initial operational capability and user relationships pertaining to the IRBM program will require further study, the results of which will be announced at a later date. Meanwhile, similar priority, not to interfere with the ICBM program, will be accorded the IRBM, and the same command relationships and administrative procedures relating to the ICBM development will apply to the IRBM.

7. Top precedence and priority will be accorded all actions related to the ICBM and IRBM effort. The Assistant Chief of Staff for Guided Missiles is designated as the single point of contact for all ICBM and IRBM matters that come to Headquarters USAF, and is responsible for central control and direction of all such matters. All personnel coming into this Headquarters on business pertaining to the ICBM and IRBM programs will report to that office, and all ICBM and IRBM correspondence directed to this Headquarters will be forwarded through that office. Any insurmountable situation of a delaying nature will be reported by priority means to the Assistant Chief of Staff for Guided Missiles. Additionally, inability to obtain complete cooperation from other government agencies will be similarly reported.

Sig of Chief of Staff

BALLISTIC MISSILES

Suggested Draft

MEMORANDUM FOR DEPUTIES, DIRECTORS AND CHIEFS OF COMPARABLE OFFICES

SUBJECT: (Uncl) Administration of the ICBM and IRBM Programs

1. The overriding significance and priority of the ICBM and IRBM Programs dictate that special administrative procedures and controls be established. Accordingly, the Assistant Chief of Staff for Guided Missiles has been designated as the single point of contact within Headquarters USAF for all matters related to those programs and is responsible for central control and direction of all such matters.

2. Instructions have been disseminated to command and field activities directing that AFCGM be their single point of contact within headquarters USAF. Additionally, it is required that all actions initiated by Headquarters USAF be coordinated with AFCGM for application of administrative controls. Outgoing correspndence will be forwarded through AFCGM.

3. The Assistant Chief of Staff for Guided Missiles is responsible to the Chief of Staff for maximum acceleration of the programs. Administrative deadlines established by his office will be construed as directive in nature. Only insurmountable causes will be acceptable reason for failure to meet a deadline. In such instances, the matter will be promptly referred to his office.

Sig of Chief of Staff

MEMORANDUM FOR ASSISTANT CHIEF OF STAFF FOR GUIDED MISSILES

SUBJECT: Administration of the ICBM and IRBM Programs

1. The President has approved National Security Council recommendations directing that the Intercontinental Ballistic Missile research and development program be accorded the highest national priority, above any and all other programs. This priority is subject to modification only by the President. Further recommendations to the National Security Council may result in the IRBM program being accorded an equal priority to that of the ICBM. Pending results of the above recommendations, the Secretary of Defense has directed the Department of the Air Force to prosecute these programs with maximum urgency, the IRBM receiving priority second only to the ICBM.

2. Your office will exercise control over all ICBM and IRBM and related affairs requiring Headquarters attention and your office is designated as the single point of contact within Headquarters USAF for all incoming and outgoing ICBM and IRBM matters. All personnel coming in or going out of this Headquarters on business pertaining to the ICBM and IRBM programs will report to your office and all Headquarters correspondence pertaining to these programs will be forwarded through your office.

3. You are hereby delegated authority to act as my representative in all matters relating to these programs. You will establish such controls as are required to prosecute Headquarters actions in keeping with the priority of the program. You will act as the Air Staff representative on the Air Force Ballistic Missiles Committee. Your office will provide the secretariat for this committee. You will insure that the Air Staff takes all necessary action to expedite the handling of ICBM and IRBM matters including rapid processing of the ICBM and IRBM Development Plans, and will keep me informed on these programs. Specifically, you will act for me in all cases where action must be taken to preclude delaying these important programs.

4. It is recognized that assumption of these functions will require resources in excess of those currently allocated to your office. Requests for such additional resources should be promptly prepared and forwarded to the Secretary of the Air Staff for action. It is desired these requirements include relocation of the WDD Liaison Office to become a physical element of your office.

Sig of Chief of Staff

BALLISTIC MISSILES

Suggested Draft

SUBJECT: Initial ICBM Operational Capability

TO: Commander, ARDC

1. The immediate goal of the ICBM effort is the earliest possible attainment of an initial operational capability. To achieve this goal, it is essential that a Programming Plan, specifically encompassing an initial operational capability, be implemented with minimum delay.

2. An initial operational capability is envisaged as one which would provide a capability of operationally employing prototype weapons during the latter phase of the development program. It should include one or two prototype operational bases.

3. Initially, the ICBM will probably incorporate certain marginal technical features. Early systems undoubtedly will undergo a great deal of revision and change as the development progresses. These developmental considerations will have dictatorial influence over many aspects of operations, training, logistics, etc., as related to the initial operational capability. For these reasons, early implementation of the Programming Plan mentioned above will require flexibility of action and singular direction. It is believed this direction can best be provided by your Command.

4. In keeping with the above and in support of Air Force policy outline in AFR 58-1, your responsibility for the ICBM effort is hereby expanded to include all steps in establishing an initial operational capability within the limits of approved USAF operational and logistics concepts for the creation and use of long-range missile systems. In carrying out this responsibility, you will prepare and submit to the Assistance Chief of Staff for Guided Missiles, Headquarters USAF, at the earliest possible date a recommended Programming Plan encompassing this initial operational capability. The requirements of AFR 5-47 are modified in so far as they pertain to this portion of the ICBM Program.

5. All other Commands and Air Force activities have been directed to render you maximum support and assistance in this endeavor. Specifically, the Strategic Air Command has been directed to establish closest possible working relations with your Command to assure maximum compatibility with strategic operational requirements. Evolution and implementation of the directed Programming Plan will be accorded precedence and priority second only to ICBM development efforts. Any insurmountable situation of

a delaying nature will be reported by priority means to the Assistant Chief of Staff for Guided Missiles.

Sig of Chief of Staff

cc: CinC SAC

BALLISTIC MISSILES

OUTLINE OF DETAILED PROCEDURES

a. ARDC (WDD) prepares and maintains current Development Plans on the ICBM and IRBM #1 as described in AFR 80–30. The plans include comprehensive data on composition of the technical programs and requirements for all necessary resources needed for implementation. The Development Plans will be maintained current not less often than monthly. The plans must include all aspects of the program (as described in Section II Planning and Programming).

b. The Development Plans and proposed revisions thereof are forwarded by the Commander, ARDC, to the Assistant Chief of Staff for Guided Missiles who will monitor actions required to obtain approval of the programs.

c. The Office of the Assistant Chief of Staff for Guided Missiles sends copies of the Development Plans and proposed revisions to all interested Air Staff agencies and to the Assistant Secretaries of the Air Force for R&D, Materiel, and Financial Management. This is done at least 30 days in advance of a formal meeting of the Air Force Ballistic Missiles Committee.

d. The Air Staff agencies and the Assistant Secretaries of the Air Force for R&D, Materiel, and Financial Management review the Development Plans and render recommendations to the Air Force Ballistic Missiles Committee.

e. The Air Force Ballistic Missiles Committee reviews the Development Plans, modifies them as necessary and after approval refers them to the OSD Ballistic Missiles Committee for final review. The Secretary of the Air Force will advise the Chief of Staff of his approval and direct the implementation of the programs as approved.

f. The Chief of Staff, through the Office of the Assistant Chief of Staff for Guided Missiles, will direct the implementation of the programs as approved.

g. The approved programs will constitute the basis for the budget estimate for the ICBM and IRBM #1 Programs.

h. The items of the ICBM and IRBM #1 are integrated into the appropriations of the Air Force Budget, but are justified as a separate package. The ICBM and IRBM #1 Budgets would be processed under the proposed procedures through OSD without review.

i. Immediately prior to the beginning of each fiscal year of operations, ARDC will prepare a detailed Financial Plan based upon the then currently approved Development Plans. This is forwarded to the Office of the Assistant Chief of Staff for Guided Missiles.

j. The Assistant Chief of Staff for Guided Missiles arranges for the Assistant Secretaries of the Air Force for R&D, Materiel, and Financial Management and the Air Staff agencies to review the Financial Plan as contained in the then current Development Plan, and schedules a meeting for the Air Force Ballistic Missiles Committee review.

k. The Air Force Ballistic Missiles Committee reviews, approves and directs implementation of the Financial Plan.

l. The Director of the Budget, Headquarters USAF, receives apportionment and allocates funds in accordance with the approved Development Plans to ARDC and AMC for WDD, and construction agencies designated by Headquarters USAF for identified portions of the programs.

m. Major deviation from the approved Development Plans requires approval by the Air Force Ballistic Missiles Committee.

n. During this entire process the Air Force Ballistic Missiles Committee provides status reports as required to the Secretary of Defense.

Appendix 3

Major Officials in
Ballistic Missile Development

Major Officials in
Ballistic Missile Development

Office of the Secretary of Defense

Secretary of Defense

James V. Forrestal	Sep 1947–Mar 1949
Louis Johnson	Mar 1949–Sep 1950
George C. Marshall	Sep 1950–Sep 1951
Robert A. Lovett	Sep 1951–Jan 1953
Charles E. Wilson	Jan 1953–Oct 1957
Neil H. McElroy	Oct 1957–Dec 1959
Thomas S. Gates, Jr.	Dec 1959–Jan 1961
Robert S. McNamara	Jan 1961–Feb 1968

Deputy Secretary of Defense

Stephen T. Early	May 1949–Sep 1950
William C. Foster	Sep 1951–Jan 1953
Roger M. Kyes	Feb 1953–May 1954
Robert B. Anderson	May 1954–Aug 1955
Reuben B. Robertson, Jr.	Aug 1955–Apr 1957
Donald A. Quarles	May 1957–May 1959
Thomas S. Gates, Jr.	Jun 1959–Dec 1959
James H. Douglas, Jr.	Dec 1959–Jan 1961
Roswell L. Gilpatric	Jan 1961–Jan 1964
Cyrus R. Vance	Jan 1964–Jun 1967

Assistant Secretary of Defense (Research and Development)

Donald A. Quarles	Sep 1953–Aug 1955
John B. Macauley (acting)	Aug 1955–Dec 1955
Clifford C. Furnas	Dec 1955–Feb 1957

Assistant Secretary of Defense (Research and Engineering)

Frank D. Newbury	Mar 1957–May 1957
Paul D. Foote	Sep 1957–Oct 1958

Defense Director of Research and Engineering

Herbert F. York	Dec 1958–Apr 1961
Harold Brown	May 1961–Sep 1965

Chiefs of Staff

Chairman, Joint Chiefs of Staff

Gen Omar N. Bradley, USA	Aug 1949–Aug 1953
Adm Arthur W. Radford, USN	Aug 1953–Aug 1957
Gen Nathan F. Twining, USAF	Aug 1957–Sep 1960
Gen Lyman L. Lemnitzer, USA	Oct 1960–Sep 1962
Gen Maxwell D. Taylor, USA	Oct 1962–Jul 1964

Chief of Staff, U.S. Army

Gen Dwight D. Eisenhower	Nov 1945–Feb 1948
Gen Omar N. Bradley	Feb 1948–Aug 1949
Gen J. Lawton Collins	Aug 1949–Aug 1953
Gen Matthew B. Ridgway	Aug 1953–Jun 1955
Gen Maxwell D. Taylor	Jun 1955–Jul 1959
Gen Lyman L. Lemnitzer	Jul 1959–Sep 1960
Gen George H. Decker	Oct 1960–Sep 1962
Gen Earle G. Wheeler	Oct 1962–Jul 1964

Chief of Naval Operations

Adm Chester W. Nimitz	Dec 1945–Dec 1947
Adm Louis E. Denfeld	Dec 1947–Nov 1949
Adm Forrest P. Sherman	Nov 1949–Jul 1951
Adm William M. Fechteler	Aug 1951–Aug 1953
Adm Robert B. Carney	Aug 1953–Aug 1955
Adm Arleigh A. Burke	Aug 1955–Aug 1961
Adm George W. Anderson, Jr.	Aug 1961–Aug 1963

Headquarters, United States Air Force

Secretary of the Air Force

W. Stuart Symington	Sep 1947–Apr 1950
Thomas K. Finletter	Apr 1950–Jan 1953
Harold E. Talbott	Feb 1953–Aug 1955
Donald A. Quarles	Aug 1955–Apr 1957
James H. Douglas, Jr.	May 1957–Dec 1959
Dudley C. Sharp	Dec 1959–Jan 1961
Eugene M. Zuckert	Jan 1961–Sep 1965

Under Secretary of the Air Force

Arthur S. Barrows	Sep 1947–Apr 1950
John A. McCone	Jun 1950–Oct 1951
Roswell L. Gilpatric	Oct 1951–Feb 1953
James H. Douglas, Jr.	Mar 1953–Apr 1957
Malcolm A. McIntyre	Jun 1957–Jul 1959
Dudley C. Sharp	Aug 1959–Dec 1959
Joseph V. Charyk	Jan 1960–Mar 1963
Brockway McMillan	Jun 1963–Sep 1965

Special Assistant for Research and Development

William A. M. Burden	Sep 1950–Jun 1952
Trevor Gardner	Feb 1953–Feb 1955

Assistant Secretary for Research and Development

Trevor Gardner	Mar 1955–Feb 1956
Richard E. Horner (acting)	May 1956–Jun 1957
Richard E. Horner	Jul 1957–May 1959
Joseph V. Charyk	Jun 1959–Jan 1960
Courtland D. Perkins	Apr 1960–Jan 1961
Brockway McMillan	Jun 1961–Jun 1963
Alexander H. Flax	Jul 1963–Mar 1969

Chief of Staff, U.S. Air Force

Gen Carl A. Spaatz	Sep 1947–Apr 1948
Gen Hoyt S. Vandenberg	Apr 1948–Jun 1953
Gen Nathan F. Twining	Jun 1953–Jun 1957
Gen Thomas D. White	Jul 1957–Jun 1961
Gen Curtis E. LeMay	Jun 1961–Jan 1965

Vice Chief of Staff, U.S. Air Force

Gen Hoyt S. Vandenberg	Oct 1947–Apr 1948
Gen Muir S. Fairchild	May 1948–Mar 1950
Gen Lauris Norstad (acting)	May 1950–Oct 1950
Gen Nathan F. Twining	Oct 1950–Jun 1953
Gen Thomas D. White	Jun 1953–Jun 1957
Gen Curtis E. LeMay	Jul 1957–Jun 1961
Gen Frederick H. Smith, Jr.	Jul 1961–Jun 1962
Gen William F. McKee	Jul 1962–Jul 1964

Deputy Chief of Staff, Development

Maj Gen Gordon P. Saville	Jan 1950–May 1951
Maj Gen Donald L. Putt	Jun 1951–Nov 1951
Lt Gen Laurence C. Craigie	Nov 1951–Apr 1954
Lt Gen Donald L. Putt	Apr 1954–Jun 1958
Lt Gen Roscoe C. Wilson	Jul 1958–Nov 1961
Lt Gen James L. Ferguson	Dec 1961–Aug 1966

Assistant Chief of Staff, Guided Missiles

Maj Gen Samuel R. Brentnall	Apr 1954–Sep 1956
Maj Gen Charles M. McCorkle	Oct 1956–Jul 1959

Commander, Air Research and Development Command*

Maj Gen David M. Schlatter	Feb 1950–Jun 1951
Lt Gen Earle E. Partridge	Jun 1951–Jun 1953
Lt Gen Donald L. Putt	Jun 1953–Apr 1954
Lt Gen Thomas S. Power	Apr 1954–Jun 1957
Maj Gen John W. Sessums	Jul 1957–Jul 1957
Lt Gen Samuel E. Anderson	Aug 1957–Mar 1959
Maj Gen John W. Sessums	Mar 1959–Apr 1959
Gen Bernard A. Schriever	Apr 1959–Aug 1966

Commanders, Ballistic Missile Organizations

Western Development Division

Maj Gen Bernard A. Schriever	Jul 1954–Jun 1957

Ballistic Missile Division

Maj Gen Bernard A. Schriever	Jun 1957–Apr 1959
Maj Gen Osmond J. Ritland	Apr 1959–Mar 1961

Air Force Systems Command
Deputy Commander for Aerospace Systems

Lt Gen Howell M. Estes, Jr.	Apr 1961–Oct 1962

Ballistic Systems Division

Maj Gen Thomas P. Gerrity	Apr 1961–Jun 1962

Space Systems Division

Maj Gen Osmond J. Ritland	Apr 1961–May 1962
Lt Gen Howell M. Estes, Jr.	May 1962–Oct 1962
Maj Gen Ben I. Funk	Oct 1962–Aug 1966

---

* Redesignated Air Force Systems Command, April 1, 1961.

Notes

Chapter I

Pilotless Aircraft

1. Paul W. Clark, "Major General George Owen Squier: Military Scientist" (Ph.D. diss., Case Western Reserve University, January 23, 1974), pp 296–306; Charles L. Keller, "The First Guided Missile Program: The Aerial Torpedo," *American Aviation Historical Society Journal* (Winter 1975), pp 268–273. [Reprinted from Sperry Engineering Review, March 1961.]

2. "Summary of Power Driven Weapons Developed by Special Weapons Branch, Equipment Laboratory," Nov 20, 1943, in Doc 1, Robert L. Perry, *Development of the Snark Guided Missile,* (Hist Ofc/WADC, Jan 1956); Henry H. Arnold, *Global Mission* (New York, 1949), p 261.

3. "Summary of Power Driven Weapons Developed by Special Weapons Branch, Equipment Laboratory," Nov 20, 1943, in Doc 1, Robert L. Perry, *Development of the Snark Guided Missile,* (Hist Ofc/WADC, Jan 1956); Henry H. Arnold, *Global Mission* (New York, 1949), p 261; Virginia Baird and Margaret Scriven, *Controlled Missiles Aircraft: Pt. 1—GMA-1* (Historical Div., Wright-Patterson AFB, 1944), passim; Wesley F. Craven and James L. Cate, eds, *The Army Air Forces in World War II,* Vol VI: *Men and Planes,* (Chicago, 1955), pp 254–255 [hereafter Craven and Cate].

4. Intvw, author and Hugh N. Ahmann with Peter R. Murray, Jul 11–12, 1973; "New Developments: Guided Missile," AC&SS Pamphlet No. 54 (Maxwell AFB, Ala., Dec 1948), p 3; Craven and Cate, VI, pp 254–255.

5. Craven and Cate, VI, pp 253, 257–59.

6. Frank Ross, Jr., *Guided Missiles: Rockets & Torpedoes* (New York, 1951), pp 109–110 [hereafter Ross].

7. Craven and Cate, VI, pp 259–260; Mary R. Self, *History of the Development of Guided Missiles,* 1946–1950 (Wright-Patterson AFB, Dec 1951), pp 32–34 [hereafter Self, *1946–1950*]; Ross, pp 101–102.

8. Craven and Cate, VI, pp 259–260; Self, *1946–1950,* pp 32–34; Ross, pp 101–102.

9. Self, *1946–1950,* pp 32–34; Ross, pp 105–107.

10. Ethel M. DeHaven, *Aerospace: The Evolution of USAF Weapons Acquisition Policy, 1945–1961,* Vol VI: *Sup of Hist of DCAS 1961* (Hist Ofc/DCAS, Aug 1962), p 7 [hereafter DeHaven, *Aerospace*].

11. Craven and Cate, VI, pp 256–257; Self, *1946–1950,* p 37; De Haven, *Aerospace,* p 7.

12. Craven and Cate, VI, pp 256–257; Self, *1946–1950,* p 37; DeHaven, *Aerospace,* p 7; memo, Maj Gen Donald Wilson, AC/AS, OCR, to Brig Gen Reuben C. Hood, Jr., DC/AS, subj: Guided Missiles, May 28, 1945, in RG 341, Air Adjutant General File TS, Miscellaneous V and VI Log Sheet Pg 104–120, incl May 11 thru Aug 6, 1945, No. 70, NA.

13. Craven and Cate, VI, pp 256–257; Self, *1946–1950,* p 37; DeHaven, *Aerospace,* p 7; memo, Maj Gen Donald Wilson, AC/AS, OCR, to Brig Gen Reuben C. Hood, Jr., DC/AS, subj: Guided Missiles, May 28, 1945, in RG 341, Air Adjutant General File TS, Miscellaneous V and VI Log Sheet Pg 104–120, incl May 11 thru Aug 6, 1945, No. 70, NA.

14. Ltr, Brig Gen Benjamin W. Chidlaw, Ch Mat Div (AC/AS, MMD), to CG Mat Cmd, subj: Headquarters AAF Project Officer for Controlled Missiles, Oct 14, 1943, in Doc 1, Vol II, Self, *1946–1950*; R&R, Brig Gen William E. Hall, Dep Ch/AS, to Air

Communications Div, subj: Controlled Missiles, Sep 29, 1943, in Doc 7, Vol II, Mary R. Self, *The Development of Guided Missiles* (Hist Div/AMC, Jun 1946) [hereafter Self, *Guided Missiles*]; Edmund Beard, *Developing the ICBM: A Case Study in Bureaucratic Politics* (New York, 1976), pp 17–21 [hereafter Beard].

15. Ltr, Brig Gen Benjamin W. Chidlaw, Ch Mat Div (AC/AS, MMD), to CG Mat Cmd, subj: Headquarters AAF Project Officer for Controlled Missiles, Oct 14, 1943, in Doc 1, Vol II, Self, *1946–1950*; R&R, Brig Gen William E. Hall, Dep Ch/AS, to Air Communications Div, subj: Controlled Missiles, Sep 29, 1943, in Doc 7, Vol II, Self, *Guided Missiles*; Beard, pp 17–21.

16. Memo, Brig Gen Frederic H. Smith, DC/AS, to Management Control, subj: Controlled Missiles, Dec 28, 1944, in Doc 37, Vol II, Self, *Guided Missiles*; HOI 20–79, "Assignment of Guided Missiles Responsibilities within the AAF," HQ AAF, Jan 1, 1945, in Doc 38, Vol II, Self, *Guided Missiles*; Self, *1946–1950*, pp 17–20; ltr, Brig Gen William L. Richardson, Ch Guided Missiles Div, A-4, to AC/AS-3, subj: Office of Primary Interest for Guided Missiles, Feb 8, 1966 in Doc 73, Vol II, Self, *Guided Missiles*; memo, Col James L. Travis, to Brig Gen William L. Richardson, no subj, Mar 19, 1946, in Doc 13, Vol II, Self, *1946–1950*.

17. Max Rosenberg, *The Air Force and the National Guided Missile Program, 1944–1950* (USAF Historical Div Liaison Ofc, Jun 1964), pp 14–17 [hereafter Rosenberg, *National Guided Missile Program*].

18. Craven and Cate, VI, pp 260–261; memo, Lt Col George W. Hill to Lt Col William F. McKee, Actg AC/AS, OCR, subj: Controlled Missiles, Jan 19, 1945, in RG 341, Air Adjutant General Files 325, Ops 5, Post War Planning, Jan 1, 1945, NA.

19. Rosenberg, *National Guided Missile Program*, pp 17, 21.

20. Memo, Lt Gen Joseph T. McNarney, Dep Ch of Staff (WD), to CG AAF, subj: Guided Missiles, Oct 2, 1944, in Spaatz Collection, File 263, R&D 2, LC; Self, *1946–1950*, pp 9–10.

21. Memo, Lt Gen Joseph T. McNarney, Dep Ch of Staff (WD), to CG AAF, subj:

Guided Missiles, Oct 2, 1944, in Spaatz Collection, File 263, R&D 2, LC; Self, *1946–1950*, pp 9–10.

22. Memo, Brig Gen H. I. Hodes, Asst Dep Ch of Staff (WD), to Asst G-3 (WD), subj: Responsibility for Operational Employment of Guided Missiles, Jun 21, 1945, in Doc 52, Vol II, Self, *Guided Missiles*.

23. Rosenberg, *National Guided Missile Program*, pp 28–29.

24. *Ibid.*, pp 29–30.

25. Self, *1946–1950*, p 11; Beard, pp 34–35.

26. Rosenberg, *National Guided Missile Program*, p 31; Memo, LeMay to Asst Sec of War (Air), Sep 3, 1940, cited in Self, *1946–1950*, p 14.

27. Memo, Maj Gen Curtis E. LeMay, DS/AS, R&D to Gen Carl A. Spaatz, CG AAF, Sep 20, 1946, cited in Beard, pp 38–39.

28. Rosenberg, *National Guided Missile Program*, p 45.

29. *Ibid.*, p 46.

30. *Ibid.*, pp 46–47.

31. *Ibid.*, pp 36–37.

32. Memo, Brig Gen H.I. Hodes, Asst Dep Ch of Staff (WD), to CG AAF et al, subj: Guided Missiles, Oct 7, 1946, in Doc 38, Vol II, Self, *1946–1950*; memo, Maj Gen H.S. Aurand, Dir of R&D (USA), to CG AAF et al, subj: Review of Guided Missiles Projects, Oct 10, 1946 in Doc 38, Vol II, Self, *1946–1950*.

33. Rosenberg, *National Guided Missiles Program*, pp 39–40.

34. *Ibid.*, pp 43–45.

35. Self, *1946–1950*; intvw, Maj Paul Clark and Capt Don Beaufort with Lt Gen L. C. Craigie (Ret), Sep 24, 1971, USAF Academy.

36. Ltr, Gen Henry H. Arnold, CG AAF, to Theodore von Kármán, subj: AAF Long Range Development Program, Nov 7, 1944, in SAMSO Basic Documents; ltr, von Kármán, Dir AAF Scientific Advisory Group, to Gen Arnold, no subj, Dec 15, 1945, w/encl: "Toward New Horizons," in SAMSO Basic Documents; Theodore von Kármán with Lee Edson, *The Wind and Beyond: Theodore von Kármán, Pioneer in Aviation and Pathfinder in Space* (Boston, 1967), pp 289, 291–292; Thomas A. Sturm,

The USAF Scientific Advisory Board: Its First Twenty Years, 1944-1964 (Washington, 1967), pp 7-12 [hereafter Sturm, *SAB*]; Ernest G. Schwiebert, *A History of the U.S. Air Force Ballistic Missiles* (New York, 1965), pp 44-45.

37. Self, *1946-1950*, p 110; dir, Joint Committee on New Weapons and Equipment, subj: Formation of a Guided Missiles Committee, Jan 16, 1945, in RG 341, JCS-GMC Program, Box 86, Sec 1, NA.

38. Robert Frank Futrell, *Ideas, Concepts, Doctrine: A History of Basic Thinking in the United States Air Force, 1907-1964* (Maxwell AFB, Ala, 1974), p 105 [hereafter Futrell, *Ideas*]; Sturm, *SAB*, pp 13-16.

39. Sturm, *SAB*, p 22; Alfred Rockefeller, "Brief History: Air Force Missile Development, 1946-1955" (Los Angeles, 1959), p 10, note 2; ltr, Col W.F. McKee, Actg AC/AS, OCR, to Pres AAF Board, subj: Military Characteristics for Guided Missiles, Feb 10, 1945; memo, Brig Gen McKee to AC/AS, M&S, subj: Military Characteristics for Controlled Missiles, Apr 5, 1945; ltr, Maj Gen E.M. Powers, AC/AS-4, to CG ATSC, subj: Goals for Long Term Guided Missiles Program, Sep 10, 1945, w/9 encl, in RG 341, GM Br, Research Program Files, 1943-1951, NA; Self, *1946-1950*, pp 22-23.

40. Self, *Guided Missiles*, p 22; memo, Brig Gen McKee to AC/AS, M&S, subj: Controlled Missile Program, Mar 2, 1945, in RG 341, DCS/M GM Br Research Program Files, 1943-1951, NA; ltr, Maj Gen Hugh J. Knerr, to CG ATSC, subj: AAF Long Term Guided Missiles Program, Nov 26, 1945; ltr,

Col George E. Price, Ch Acft Proj Sec, Engr Div (ATSC), to CG AAF, subj: Progress Report in Current Guided Missiles Program, Dec 5, 1945 (and similar ltrs dated Feb 12, Mar 11, and May 10, 1946); ltr, Col G. F. Smith, Ch Svcs Engr Sbdiv, Engr Div (AMC), to CG AAF, subj: AMC Guided Missile Program, Mar 29, 1946.

41. Rosenberg, *National Guided Missile Program*, pp 77-78.

42. Ltr, Lt Gen Nathan F. Twining, CG AMC, to Gen Spaatz, CG AAF, subj: AAF Guided Missiles Research and Development Program—Where We Stand, Mar 25, 1947, in Doc 67, Vol II, Self, *1946-1950*; ltr, Maj Gen B. W. Chidlaw, Dep CG Engr (T-3) (AMC), to AC/AS-4, subj: AAF Guided Missiles Program, May 6, 1947, in Doc 73, Vol II, Self, *1946-1950*.

43. Memo, Brig Gen Thomas S. Power, to CG AAF, subj: Operational Requirements (Priorities) for Guided Missiles, 1947-1957, June 16, 1947, in Doc 76, Self, *1946-1950*; DeHaven, *Aerospace*, p 11; R&R Sheet, Maj Gen Curtis LeMay, DC/AS, R&D, to AC/AS-3, subj: Operational Requirements (Priorities) for Guided Missiles, 1947-1957, June 19, 1947, in Doc 76, Vol II, Self, *1946-1950*.

44. Memo, Brig Gen Thomas S. Power, to CG AAF, subj: Operational Requirements (Priorities) for Guided Missiles, 1947-1957, June 16, 1947, in Doc 76, Self, *1946-1950*; DeHaven, *Aerospace*, p 11; R&R Sheet, Maj Gen Curtis LeMay, DC/AS, R&D, to AC/AS-3, subj: Operational Requirements (Priorities) for Guided Missiles, 1947-1957, June 19, 1947, in Doc 76, Vol II, Self, *1946-1950*.

Chapter II

Ballistic Missiles

1. Wernher von Braun and Frederick I. Ordway, *History of Rocketry and Space Travel* (New York, 1975), pp 26-36 [hereafter von Braun, *Rocketry*]; Charles H. Gibbs-Smith, *The Aeroplane: An Historical Survey* (London, 1960), pp 163-164.

2. Willy Ley, *Rockets, Missiles and Men in Space* (New York, 1968), p 228 [hereafter Ley, *Rockets*]; Eugene M. Emme, *Aeronau-*

tics and Astronautics: An American Chronology of Science and Technology in the Exploration of Space, 1915-1960 (Washington, DC, 1961) [hereafter Emme, *Aeronautics and Astronautics, 1915-1960*]; G. Edward Pendray, "Pioneer Rocket Development in the United States," in *The History of Rocket Technology*, ed by Eugene M. Emme (Detroit, 1964), pp 19-28; Albert B. Christman,

Sailors, Scientists, and Rockets: Origins of the Navy Rocket Program and of the Naval Ordnance Test Station, Inyokern: History of the Naval Weapons Center, China Lake, California, Vol I (Washington, DC, 1971), pp 36-37 [hereafter Christman, *Sailors, Scientists, and Rockets*].

3. Ley, *Rockets*, p 228; Emme, *Aeronautics and Astronautics, 1915-1960*; G. Edward Pendray, "Pioneer Rocket Development in the United States," in *The History of Rocket Technology*, ed by Eugene M. Emme (Detroit, 1964), pp 19-28; Christman, *Sailors, Scientists, and Rockets*, pp 36-37; Loyd S. Swenson, Jr., James M. Grimwood, and Charles C. Alexander, *This New Ocean: A History of Project Mercury* (Washington, DC, 1966), p 14 [hereafter Swenson, *This New Ocean*].

4. Frank J. Malina, "Origins and First Decade of the Jet Propulsion Laboratory," in *The History of Rocket Technology*, ed by Eugene M. Emme (Detroit, 1964), pp 46-66; Malina, "On the GALCIT Rocket Research Project, 1936-1938," in *First Steps Toward Space*, Smithsonian Annals of Flight No. 10, ed by Frederick C. Durant III and George S. James (Washington, DC, 1974), pp 113-127; Malina, "The U.S. Army Air Corps Jet Propulsion Research Project, GALCIT Project No. 1, 1939-1946," in *Essays on the History of Rocketry and Astronautics*, II, NASA Conference Publication 2014, ed by R. Cargill Hall (Washington, DC, 1977), pp 153-201; Theodore von Kármán with Lee Edson, *The Wind and Beyond: Theodore von Kármán, Pioneer in Aviation and Pathfinder in Space* (Boston, 1967), pp 234-267.

5. Frank J. Malina, "Origins and First Decade of the Jet Propulsion Laboratory," in *The History of Rocket Technology*, ed by Eugene M. Emme (Detroit, 1964), pp 46-66; Malina, "On the GALCIT Rocket Research Project, 1936-1938," in *First Steps Toward Space*, Smithsonian Annals of Flight No. 10, ed by Frederick C. Durant III and George S. James (Washington, DC, 1974), pp 113-127; Malina, "The U.S. Army Air Corps Jet Propulsion Research Project, GALCIT Project No. 1, 1939-1946," in *Essays on the History of Rocketry and Astronautics*, II, NASA Conference Publication 2014, ed by R.

Cargill Hall (Washington, DC, 1977), pp 153-201; Theodore von Kármán with Lee Edson, *The Wind and Beyond: Theodore von Kármán, Pioneer in Aviation and Pathfinder in Space* (Boston, 1967), pp 234-267.

6. Frank J. Malina, "Origins and First Decade of the Jet Propulsion Laboratory," in *The History of Rocket Technology*, ed by Eugene M. Emme (Detroit, 1964), pp 46-66; Malina, "On the GALCIT Rocket Research Project, 1936-1938," in *First Steps Toward Space*, Smithsonian Annals of Flight No. 10, ed by Frederick C. Durant III and George S. James (Washington, DC, 1974), pp 113-127; Malina, "The U.S. Army Air Corps Jet Propulsion Research Project, GALCIT Project No. 1, 1939-1946," in *Essays on the History of Rocketry and Astronautics*, II, NASA Conference Publication 2014, ed by R. Cargill Hall (Washington, DC, 1977), pp 153-201; Theodore von Kármán with Lee Edson, *The Wind and Beyond: Theodore von Kármán, Pioneer in Aviation and Pathfinder in Space* (Boston, 1967), pp 234-267.

7. Frank J. Malina, "Origins and First Decade of the Jet Propulsion Laboratory," in *The History of Rocket Technology*, ed by Eugene M. Emme (Detroit, 1964), pp 46-66; Malina, "On the GALCIT Rocket Research Project, 1936-1938," in *First Steps Toward Space*, Smithsonian Annals of Flight No. 10, ed by Frederick C. Durant III and George S. James (Washington, DC, 1974), pp 113-127; Malina, "The U.S. Army Air Corps Jet Propulsion Research Project, GALCIT Project No. 1, 1939-1946," in *Essays on the History of Rocketry and Astronautics*, II, NASA Conference Publication 2014, ed by R. Cargill Hall (Washington, DC, 1977), pp 153-201; Theodore von Kármán with Lee Edson, *The Wind and Beyond: Theodore von Kármán, Pioneer in Aviation and Pathfinder in Space* (Boston, 1967), pp 234-267.

8. Frank J. Malina, "Origins and First Decade of the Jet Propulsion Laboratory," in *The History of Rocket Technology*, ed by Eugene M. Emme (Detroit, 1964), pp 46-66; Malina, "On the GALCIT Rocket Research Project, 1936-1938," in *First Steps Toward Space*, Smithsonian Annals of Flight No. 10, ed by Frederick C. Durant III and George S. James (Washington, DC, 1974), pp 113-127;

Malina, "The U.S. Army Air Corps Jet Propulsion Research Project, GALCIT Project No. 1, 1939-1946," in *Essays on the History of Rocketry and Astronautics*, II, NASA Conference Publication 2014, ed by R. Cargill Hall (Washington, DC, 1977), pp 153-201; Theodore von Kármán with Lee Edson, *The Wind and Beyond: Theodore von Kármán, Pioneer in Aviation and Pathfinder in Space* (Boston, 1967), pp 234-267; Emme, *Aeronautics and Astronautics, 1915-1960*; Christman, *Sailors, Scientists, and Rockets*, p 103.

9. Frederick I. Ordway and Ronald C. Wakeford, *International Missile and Spacecraft Guide* (New York, 1960), pp 70-72; Walter R. Dornberger, *V-2: The Nazi Rocket Weapon*, trans by James Cleugh and Geoffrey Halliday (New York, 1954), pp 9-10.

10. Frederick I. Ordway and Ronald C. Wakeford, *International Missile and Spacecraft Guide* (New York, 1960), pp 70-72; Walter R. Dornberger, *V-2: The Nazi Rocket Weapon*, trans by James Cleugh and Geoffrey Halliday (New York, 1954), pp 9-10.

11. Dwight D. Eisenhower, *Crusade in Europe* (New York, 1948), pp 258-260; Joseph W. Angell, "Guided Missiles Could Have Won," *Atlantic Monthly* (Dec 1951), pp 29-34, and *Atlantic Monthly* (Jan 1952), pp 57-63.

12. Ltr, Col Gervais W. Trichel, Ch Rocket Development Br (Ord), to Maj Gen Gladion M. Barnes, Ch Army Ordnance, no subj, Jan 15, 1944; Theodore von Kármán with Lee Edson, *The Wind and Beyond: Theodore von Kármán, Pioneer in Aviation and Pathfinder in Space* (Boston, 1967), p 265 [hereafter von Kármán, *The Wind and Beyond*]; Frank J. Malina, "America's First Long-Range Missile and Space Exploration Program: The ORDCIT Project of the Jet Propulsion Laboratory, 1943-1946," in *Essays on the History of Rocketry and Astronautics*, II, NASA Conference Publication 2014, ed by R. Cargill Hall (Washington, DC, 1977), pp 339-83.

13. Ltr, Col Gervais W. Trichel, Ch Rocket Development Br (Ord), to Maj Gen Gladion M. Barnes, Ch Army Ordnance, no subj, Jan 15, 1944; von Kármán, *The Wind and Beyond*, p 265; Malina, "America's First Long-Range Missile and Space Exploration Program: The ORDCIT Project of the Jet Propulsion Laboratory, 1943-1946," in *Essays on the History of Rocketry and Astronautics*, II, NASA Conference Publication 2014, ed by R. Cargill Hall (Washington, DC, 1977), pp 339-83.

14. Hanson Baldwin, "Rocket Program Splits Services; Army Air Forces Seeking Control," *New York Times*, May 12, 1946, p 1.

15. *Ibid.*

16. John B. Medaris with Arthur Gordon, *Countdown for Decision* (New York, 1960), pp 40-42; Clarence G. Lasby, *Project Paperclip: German Scientists and the Cold War* (New York, 1971) pp 5, 32.

17. Clarence G. Lasby, *Project Paperclip: German Scientists and the Cold War* (New York, 1971); Wernher von Braun and Frederick I. Ordway, *History of Rocketry and Space Travel* (New York: Thomas Y. Crowell Co, 1975), pp 118, 140 [hereafter von Braun, *Rocketry*]; Ernest G. Schwiebert, *A History of the U.S. Air Force Ballistic Missiles* (New York, 1964), p 46.

18. John L. Chapman, *Atlas: The Story of a Missile* (New York, 1960), pp 27-28 [hereafter Chapman, *Atlas*]; Ian Pike, "Atlas: Pioneer ICBM and Space-Age Workhorse," *Flight International*, Jan 18, 1962, p 89 [hereafter Pike, *Atlas*]; "Atlas," Convair Rprt, Dec 1, 1949, p 2, in SAMSO Basic Documents; Trevor Gardner, "How We Fell Behind in Guided Missiles," *Air Power Historian*, January 1958, p 7.

19. Chapman, *Atlas*, pp 27-28; Pike, *Atlas*, p 89; "Atlas," Convair Rprt, Dec 1, 1949, p 2, in SAMSO Basic Documents; Trevor Gardner, "How We Fell Behind in Guided Missiles," *Air Power Historian*, January 1958, p 7.

20. Chapman, *Atlas*, pp 28-31.

21. *Ibid.*, pp 31-33.

22. Pike, *Atlas*, p 92; Chapman, *Atlas*, pp 32-33.

23. Pike, *Atlas*, p 92; Chapman, *Atlas*, pp 32-33.

24. Pike, *Atlas*, p 92; Chapman, *Atlas*, pp 32-33.

25. Chapman, *Atlas*, pp 33-34.

26. Pike, *Atlas*, p 92.

27. Chapman, *Atlas*, pp 34–35; Self, *1946–1950*, p 92; Self, *Guided Missiles*, p 42; Chronology, *1956* (SAFOS, 1956), pp 3–6 [hereafter OSAF Chronology].

28. Self, *Guided Missiles*, p. 42.

29. *Ibid*; ltr, Maj Gen B.W. Chidlaw, Dep CG Engr (T–3) (AMC), to AC/AS–4, subj: AAF Guided Missiles Program, May 6, 1947; "Significant Historical Data for Atlas," AFGCM Control No. 575286, Dec 1957.

30. Chapman, *Atlas*, pp 46–48; Pike, *Atlas*, p 93.

31. Chapman, *Atlas*, pp 46–48; Pike, *Atlas*, p 93.

32. Chapman, *Atlas*, pp 46–48; Pike, *Atlas*, p 93.

33. Max Rosenberg, *Plans and Policies for the Ballistic Missile Initial Operational Capability Program* (Hist Div Liaison Ofc/ HQ USAF, Feb 1960), pp 2–3 [hereafter Rosenberg, *IOC*]; ltr, Lt Gen H.A. Craig, DCS/M, to CG AMC, subj: Procurement of Guided Missiles from Project 180 Supplemental FY 1948 Funds, Sep 20, 1948; Minutes of the 15th GMC Mtg, Feb 10, 1949; R&R, Col J.H. Carter, Ch GM Sect, Engr Div, to Electronics Div (AMC), subj: MX–774 Missiles to be Used in Upper Air Research Program, Feb 28, 1949; R&R, Col Carter to Power Plant Lab (AMC), subj: Discontinuance of Project MX–774, Apr 7, 1949, Minutes of GMC Mtg, Apr 14, 1949; OSAF Chronology, *1956*, p 6.

34. Self, *1946–1950*, p 109.

35. *Ibid*, p 110; JNWE Dir 3210, subj: Formation of A Guided Missiles Committee, Jan 16, 1945, in RG 341 NA, JCS–GMC Program, Box 8G, Sec 1.

36. JCS 1620, Feb 5, 1946; JCS 1620/1, Mar 5, 1946; JCS 1620/3, Apr 1, 1946.

37. Rosenberg, *National Guided Missile Program*, pp 63–65.

38. PL 253, 80th Cong, *The National Security Act of 1947*, Jul 26, 1947.

39. Army–Air Force Agreements as to the Initial Implementation of the National Security Act of 1947, Sep 15, 1947; memo, James V. Forrestal, SECDEF, to Secy Army and SAF, no subj, Oct 14, 1947.

40. Annual Rprt of Exec Secy RDB, Sep 17, 1948; Stmt, Vannevar Bush, Chmn RDB, to Presidential Air Policy Commission, Oct 28, 1947.

41. Annual Rprt of Exec Secy RDB, Sep 17, 1948; Stmt, Vannevar Bush, Chmn RDB, to Presidential Air Policy Commission, Oct 28, 1947; memo, E.F. Sweetser, Dir/Panels (RDB), to L.R. Hafstad, Chmn GMC, subj: Air Force Practices Affecting the Guided Missiles Program, Apr 5, 1948.

42. Memo, Gordon Gray, Actg Secy Army, to SECDEF, subj: Assignment of Responsibility for Guided Missiles Operations and Development, May 16, 1949; memo, Louis A. Johnson, SECDEF, to JCS, same subj, May 25, 1949; memo, Secy Navy to JSPG, same subj, May 30, 1949; memo, Maj Gen Samuel E. Anderson, Dir/P&O, to SAF, subj: DOD Policy Governing Assignment of Operational and Development Responsibilities for New Weapons, Sep 6, 1949; rprt, Ad Hoc Sbcmte on Assignment of Responsibility for Research and Development in the Field of Guided Missiles, Mar 31, 1950; memo, Thomas O. Lanphier, Spec Consultant, to SAF, subj: Analysis of JCS 1620/17 on Guided Missiles, Mar 22, 1950, RG 341 NA, 310.1 GM Policy within USAF.

43. Memo, Fred W. Darwin, Exec Dir/ GMC, to RDB, subj: Assignment of Responsibilities for Research and Development in the Field of Guided Missiles, Dec 5, 1949; rprt, Ad Hoc Sbcmte on Assignment of Responsibility for Research and Development in the Field of Guided Missiles, Mar 31, 1950; memo, SECDEF to Chmn RDB, same subj, Jul 27, 1950; memo, Chmn RDB to SECDEF, same subj, Aug 9, 1950.

44. Memo, Lt Col W. C.. Addeman, Asst Exec (Dir/P&O), to DCS/M, subj: Significant Actions of the AFPC at its Meeting of December 20, ca. Dec 1949; memo, Brig Gen D.T. Spivey, Ch WPD, to Maj Gen S.E. Anderson, Dir/P&O, no subj, Jan 9, 1950; memo, H. C. Stuart, Air Force assistant, to SAF, subj: Comments on Study of National Guided Missile Program, Jan 24, 1950; memo, Col M.C. Young, SIGMB Recorder, to Stuart, subj: Navy Remarks at Eighth Meeting of SIB and Comments Thereon, Jan 30, 1950; MR, Maj James R. Dempsey, GM Br (Dir/R&D), subj: Sequence of Events Concerning SIB, Feb 20, 1950; memo, SAF to

JCS, subj: Guided Missiles Report Submitted to SOD, Feb 11, 1950, RG 341 NA, JCS–GMC Box 87.

45. Rprt, Rprt of the Special Interdepartmental Guided Missiles Board, Feb 1950; memo, R.F. Rinehart, Exec Secy RDB to JCS, subj: Guided Missiles Inquisition, Feb 28, 1950; MR, Maj J.R. Dempsey, GM Br (Dir/R&D), subj: Sequence of Events Concerning SIB, Feb 20, 1950; memo, JCS to SECDEF, subj: DOD Guided Missiles Program, Feb 24, 1950.

46. Rprt, Technical Evaluation Group, Cmte on Guided Missiles (RDB), May 20, 1949; ltr, W. Webster, Chmn RDB, to JCS, subj: Establishment of a Military Basis for Guided Missile Program Planning, Jul 21, 1949; memo, Maj Gen S.E. Anderson, Dir/P&O, to DCS/O, same subj, Oct 30, 1949; R&R, Gen Anderson to Asst for GM and Dir/R&D, subj: Priority on Guided Missiles, Nov 4, 1949; R&R-2, Maj Gen Donald L. Putt, Dir/R&D, to Dir/P&O, same subj, Dec 6, 1949.

47. Rosenberg, *National Guided Missile Program*, pp 113–119.

48. *Ibid.*

49. *Ibid.*; De Haven, *Aerospace*, pp 11–12.

50. Futrell, *Ideas*, pp 115–118.

51. Minutes, Board of Senior Officers, Dec 29–31, 1948; Jan 3–6, 1949.

52. Rosenberg, *National Guided Missile Program*, p 150.

53. Memo, Lt Col V. A. Stace, Ch Spec Wpns Sect, to Lt Col L.T. Bradbury, Actg Ch Engr Br (AC/AS-4), subj: New Explosives and Propulsion for Guided Missiles, Aug 8, 1945; memo, Bradbury to Stace, same subj, Aug 10, 1945; memo, Col Millard C. Young, Ch GM Br, to Maj Gen L. C. Craigie,

Dir/R&D, subj: Delays in Obtaining Information from Atomic Energy Commission, Sep 12, 1947; MR, V.S. Roddy, GM Br, Dir/R&D, subj: Atomic Warheads for Guided Missiles, Jan 26, 1947; MR, Roddy to Lt Col Charles H. Terhune, Dep Ch GM Br (Dir/R&D), same subj, Mar 4, 1949; memo, Gen Omar H. Bradley, CSA, to JCS, subj: Research and Development for Weapons for Support of Land Operations, May 24, 1949; memo, CNO to JCS, same subj, Jun 28, 1949; memo, CSAF to JCS, same subj, Jul 12, 1949; memo, JCS to RDB, same subj, Jul 14, 1949; ltr, Maj Gen L. C. Craigie, Dir/R&D, to CG AMC, subj: Military Characteristics for Surface-to-Surface and Surface-to-Air Guided Missiles, Dec 3, 1947.

54. Memo, SECDEF to Lt Gen John E. Hull, Dir/WSEG, subj: Development of Guided Missiles with Atomic Warheads, Jan 21, 1949; memo, Hull to CSA, CNO, and CSAF, same subj, Jun 24, 1949.

55. Memo, Lt Gen John E. Hull, Dir/WSEG, to W. Webster, Dep SECDEF for Atomic Energy Matters, subj: Guided Missiles with Atomic Warheads, Sep 14, 1949.

56. Memo, SECDEF to JCS, subj: Guided Missiles with Atomic Warheads, Sep 29, 1949; Rosenberg, *National Guided Missile Program*, p 163.

57. Memo, CSAF to JCS, subj: Atomic Warheads for Guided Missiles, Nov 22, 1949.

58. Memo, Maj Gen Joseph Smith, AF Member JSPC, to CSAF, subj: Atomic Warheads for Guided Missiles, Dec 27, 1949; memo, JCS to SECDEF, subj: Guided Missiles with Atomic Warheads, Dec 30, 1949; memo, SECDEF to RDB, same subj, Jan 16, 1950; Rosenberg, *National Guided Missile Program*, pp 165–166.

Chapter III

Contest for Control

1. Ltr, DCS/D to K. T. Keller, Dir/GM (OSD), subj: ATLAS Program, Aug 8, 1952, in AFCHO; ltr, DCS/D to CG AMC, subj: Long Range Rocket, Jan 16, 1951; AMC Technical Instruction (TI) 2003-116, subj: Long Range Rocket, Jan 31, 1951; Lee Bowen, *An Air Force History of Space Activities, 1945-1959* (Washington, DC: USAF Historical Division Liaison Office, 1964), p 39.

2. Ltr, DCS/D to K. T. Keller, Dir/GM (OSD), subj: ATLAS Program, Aug 8, 1952, in AFCHO; ltr, DCS/D to CG AMC, subj: Long Range Rocket, Jan 16, 1951; AMC Technical Instruction (TI) 2003-116, subj: Long Range Rocket, Jan 31, 1951; Lee Bowen, *An Air Force History of Space Activities, 1945-1959* (Washington, DC: USAF Historical Division Liaison Office, 1964), p 39.

3. RAND, *A Comparison of Long Range Surface-to-Surface Rocket and Ramjet Missiles* (R-174, Santa Monica, May 1950), and continuing reports through R-182; briefing, J. E. Lipp, RAND, to Cmte on Guided Missiles (RDB), no subj, Jan 26, 1951; memo, Brig Gen P. H. Robey, ARDRD-AC-2/C, Exec Dir/Cmte on Guided Missiles (RDB), subj: Long-Range Rocket Study, Jan 26, 1951; Martin Caidin, *Countdown for Tomorrow* (New York: E. P. Dutton & Co, Inc, 1958), pp 243 ff. [hereafter Caidin, *Countdown for Tomorrow*].

4. Caidin, *Countdown for Tomorrow*, pp 243 ff.

5. Progress rprt on Project Atlas, MX-1593, Hotel Lord Baltimore, Baltimore, Md., Sep 10, 1951, in Basic Documents Collection, SAMSO Hist. Ofc.

6. *Ibid*; ltr, Brig Gen John W. Sessums, Dep for Dev (ARDC), to AFDRD-AC-2/R (HQ USAF), subj: Approval of Long-Range Rocket Missile Program ATLAS (MX-1593), Sep 25, 1951.

7. Ltr, Brig Gen Donald N. Yates, Dir/R&D, to CG ARDC, subj: Program Guidance for Long-Range Strategic Rocket—ATLAS (MX-1593), Nov 16, 1951 in Basic Docs.

8. Ltr, Gen Sessums, Dep for Dev (ARDC), to Asst for Dev Prog (HQ USAF), subj: Additional Funds for Project ATLAS During Fiscal Year 1952, Oct 25, 1951; memo, Col H. J. Halberstadt, Ch GM Div, to Col H. C. Nelson, Asst for Dev Prog (ARDC), subj: Application of $300,000 FY 52 Funds to Project ATLAS (MX-1593), Dec 21, 1951; msg, Col H. C. Nelson to Col Halberstadt, same subj, Dec 26, 1951, in Basic Docs.

9. Trip rprt, Maj Robert T. Franzel, Asst Strategic Combat Systems (ARDC), from Wright Patterson, Jul 22, 1952; ARDC Intel Memo, No. 52-17, subj: Soviet Guided Missiles, Oct 2, 1952, AFSC Hist Files. In June 1952 Col John L. Zoeckler, USAF, testified before a congressional committee that the Soviets were making spectacular progress in guided missiles. He predicted that they would spend about $1 billion during 1953 on missiles (Congressional Chronology).

10. Memo, Brig Gen Alfred R. Maxwell, Spec Asst to CG ARDC, to Maj Gen John W. Sessums, Commander, ARDC, subj: Project ATLAS, Mar 5, 1952, w/atch: draft memo, Lt. Gen Earle E. Partridge, CG ARDC, to Lt Gen L. C. Craigie, DCS/D, subj: USAF Continental Capabilities, Feb 21, 1952.

11. Ltr, Maj Gen John W. Sessums, Commander, ARDC, to DCS/D, subj: Long Range Rocket Pilotless Aircraft Program, ATLAS (MX-1593), Mar 20, 1952; memo, Sessums to Col H. J. Halberstadt, Ch GM Div (ARDC), subj: Project ATLAS, Apr 7, 1952.

12. Memo, Brig Gen Alfred R. Maxwell, Spec Asst to CG ARDC, to Maj Gen John W. Sessums, Commander, ARDC, no subj, Mar 5, 1952, w/atch; memo, Col H. J. Halberstadt, Ch GM Div (ARDC), to Gen Sessums, subj: Project ATLAS, Mar 20, 1952.

13. Ltr, Col R. L. Johnson, Ch WS Div (WADC), to CG ARDC, subj: MX-1593, Contract AF 33 (038)-19956, Apr 3, 1952; ltr, Col B. K. Holloway, Dep Dir/R&D (HQ USAF), to CG ARDC, subj: ATLAS Presentation, Nov 21, 1951; briefing, Col. R. L. Johnson, Ch WS Div (WADC), Initial Presentation of ATLAS at 40th Meeting of the Committee on Guided Missiles (RDB), May 21-22, 1952, in Basic Docs.

14. Ltr, Brig Gen Donald N. Yates, Director R&D, DCS/Development, to CG ARDC, no subj, Jun 18, 1952; ltr, DCS/D (HQ USAF), to K. T. Keller, Dir/GM (OSD), subj: ATLAS Project, Aug 8, 1952 in AFCHO.

15. Ltr, Maj Robert T. Franzel, Asst Dep for Dev, to Maj Gen John W. Sessums, Dep for Dev, ARDC, subj: Report of Visit to Project ATLAS, Jul 22, 1952, in Basic Docs.

16. 1st Ind, Lt Col Wayne H. McCandless, Asst Ch Dev Opns Div (WADC), to Dep for Dev (ARDC), Aug 25, 1952, w/atch: Proposed Military Characteristics Project

MX–1593, Aug 22, 1952; ltr, Col Thomas S. Jeffrey, Asst Dep for Dev (ARDC), to CG WADC, same subj, Aug 5, 1952, in Basic Docs.

17. Ltr, Col T. S. Jeffrey to Dir/R&D (HQ USAF), subj: Military Characteristics for Project ATLAS, Oct 1, 1952, w/atch: Proposed Military Characteristics ATLAS Project MX–1593, n.d., in Basic Docs.

18. Ltr, N. Rosenbaum, Proj Engr (Convair), to R. B. Swanson, Wash Rep (Convair), no subj, Nov 24, 1952, in Basic Docs.

19. Ltr, Dr. Clark B. Millikan, Head of GAL, to Lt Gen L. C. Craigie, DCS/D, no subj, Dec 30, 1952, w/atch: "Report on the USAF Scientific Advisory Board's Ad Hoc Committee on Project ATLAS," Dec 30, 1952, in RG 341, Box 18, File 334.5, NA.

20. Draft, "Comments of MX–1593 Project Office on SAB Committee's Report on Project ATLAS," Jan 16, 1953; ltr, Gen Yates, Dir/R&D (HQ USAF), to CG ARDC, subj: ATLAS, Jan 12, 1953, in SAMSO Hist Ofc Files; 1st Ind, Col Arthur A. Fickel, Asst Dep for Dev (ARDC), to Dir/R&D, subj: ATLAS, Jan 22, 1953, w/atch: "ARDC Comments on the SAB Ad Hoc Committee's Report Concerning Project ATLAS," n.d., in Basic Docs; ltr, Col T. S. Jeffrey, Asst Dep for Dev (ARDC), to CG WADC, subj: ATLAS, Jan 28, 1953.

21. Ltr, Brig Gen Floyd B. Wood, Dep for Dev (ARDC), to Dir/R&D, subj: ATLAS, Mar 12, 1953, w/atch: "ARDC Recommended Program for the Development of the ATLAS Weapon System," n.d., in SAMSO Hist Ofc Files; 1st Ind, Col Victor R. Haughen, Dep for Opns (WADC), subj: ATLAS, Mar 9, 1953, to ltr, Col T. S. Jeffrey, Asst for Dev (ARDC), to CG WADC, subj: ATLAS, Jan 28, 1953, in SAMSO Hist Ofc Files; MR, Lt Gen L. C. Craigie, DCS/D (HQ USAF), no subj, Mar 17, 1953, in SAMSO Hist Ofc Files.

22. Ltr, Brig Gen Floyd B. Wood, Dep for Dev (ARDC), to Dir/R&D, subj: ATLAS, Mar 12, 1953, w/atch: "ARDC Recommended Program for the Development of the ATLAS Weapon System," n.d., in SAMSO Hist Ofc Files; 1st Ind, Col Victor R. Haughen, Dep for Opns (WADC), subj: ATLAS, Mar 9, 1953, to ltr, Col T. S. Jeffrey,

Asst for Dev (ARDC), to CG WADC, subj: ATLAS, Jan 28, 1953, in SAMSO Hist Ofc Files; MR, Lt Gen L.C. Craigie, DCS/D (HQ USAF), no subj, Mar 17, 1953, in SAMSO Hist Ofc Files.

23. Sup, to Report of the USAF SAB Ad Hoc Committee on Project ATLAS of Dec 30, 1952, Apr 13, 1953, in SAMSO Hist Ofc Files; ltr, Lt Gen L. C. Craigie, DCS/D, to Dr. C. B. Millikan, Head of GAL, no subj, May 18, 1953; ltr, Millikan to Craigie, no subj, Jun 1, 1953, in SAMSO Hist Ofc Files.

24. Ltr, Brig Gen Donald N. Yates, Director R&D, DCS/Development, to CG ARDC, subj: Realistic Evaluation of Snark, Navaho, Atlas, Apr 2, 1953; 1st Ind, Col A. A. Fickel, Asst Dep for Dev (ARDC), to Gen Yates, same subj, May 13, 1953, in Doc 31, Ethel De Haven, *Aerospace*, Vol II; ltr, Col T. S. Jeffrey, Asst Dep for Dev (ARDC), to CG WADC, same subj, Apr 2, 1953, in Doc 125, Robert L. Perry, *The Development of the Snark Guided Missile, 1945–1953*, 2 vols. (Wright-Patterson AFB, Historical Branch, Wright Air Development Center, AFSC, 1956) [hereafter Perry, *History of Snark*].

25. Ltr, Gen Yates to CG ARDC, subj: ATLAS, Jun 22, 1953, in SAMSO Hist Ofc Files.

26. Ltr, Col T. S. Jeffrey, Asst Dep for Dev (ARDC), to CG WADC, subj: ATLAS, Jul 9, 1953; 1st Ind, Col Otto R. Haney, Asst Ch WS Div (WADC), to Dep for Dev (ARDC), same subj, Aug 17, 1953; 2nd Ind, Col Leo W. Killen, Asst Dep for Dev (ARDC), to CG WADC, same subj, Sep 9, 1953; Dev Dir, ARDC No. 3082, subj: Development of the Atlas (MX–1593), Jul 31, 1953, in SAMSO Hist Ofc Files; WADC Development Plan, for the Strategic Rocket Weapon System (ATLAS), Oct 15, 1953, in Basic Docs; rprt, RDB Project Card, "G/M Progress Report," ARDC, Oct 1, 1953, in Dr. Rockefeller File, 1951–1954, AFSC Hist Ofc.

27. Development Plan, for the Strategic Rocket Weapon System (ATLAS), WADC, Oct 15, 1953, in Basic Docs, Vol 1A; Standard Missile Characteristics, AMC, "MX–1593 ATLAS," Nov 1, 1953, in SAMSO Hist Ofc Files.

28. Development Plan, for the Strategic Rocket Weapon System (ATLAS), WADC,

Oct 15, 1953, in Basic Docs, Vol 1A; Standard Missile Characteristics, AMC, "MX-1593 ATLAS," Nov 1, 1953, in SAMSO Hist Ofc Files.

29. Memo, Col J. R. Sutherland, Dep Asst DCS/O (GM), to Dir/Plans, subj: History of GMIORG and GMIORG Actions, Jun 23, 1952, in OSAF Files.

30. Memos, John A. McCone, Under SAF, to Thomas K. Finletter, SAF, no subj, Aug 10, 1950 and Aug 15, 1950, in Hist, OSAF, Jul 1, 1950–Mar 31, 1951, Tabs 27 and 28.

31. Rprt, K. T. Keller, Dir/GM (OSD), to Staff, subj: National Guided Missiles Program, Sep 17, 1953; speech, Keller to National War College, Feb 10, 1953; speech, Maj Gen K. D. Nichols (USA), Dep Dir/GM (OSD), to Armed Forces Staff College, subj: Current Status of Developments and Production of Guided Missiles, May 5, 1952, in OSAF Files, ASD (R&E) 209.5.

32. Rosenberg, *Guided Missiles*, p 167.

33. Minutes, Munitions Board Meeting No. 141, subj: Planning and Production Responsibilities, Feb 1, 1951, in OSAF RG 033, MB 506/1.

34. Memo, Joseph S. Imirie, Dep Asst SAF (Materiel Programs), to Roswell L. Gilpatric, Under SAF, subj: Guided Missiles, Nov 20, 1951; memo, Gilpatric to Chmn Munitions Board, no subj, May 13, 1952, in OSAF Files RG 033, Folder 557 (58).

35. File, "Guided Missiles Production and Procurement, 1951–1952," AFCHO; memo, Lt. Gen. C. P. Cabell (USAF), Dir/Joint Staff, to Chmn Munitions Board, subj: Assignment of Procurement and Programming Responsibilities for Guided Missiles, Oct 7, 1952, in OSAF Files, RG 520, A 56–9, File 557 (50), Jan–Dec 1952, Vol 4; memo, Gilpatric to Lt Gen O. Cook, DCS/M, subj: Guided Missiles Program, Nov 24, 1952, in OSAF Files, RG 033, 54–266.

36. Rprt, "Changes in Organization of Guided Missile Functions," n.d., *passim*, AFCHO.

37. *Ibid.*

38. *Ibid.*

39. Hist, Deputy Chief of Staff, Operations (DCS/O), Jan–Jun 1952, pp 1–3; draft memo, Col J. R. Sutherland, Dep Asst DCS/O (GM), to Lt Gen Thomas D. White, DCS/O, subj: Progress Report, Office of Asst DCS/O (Guided Missiles), Jun 30, 1953, in Notes, Max Rosenberg, AFCHO; memo, Brig Gen P. H. Robey, Asst DCS/O (GM), to Gen White, subj: Office of the Assistant Deputy Chief of Staff, Operations (Guided Missiles), ca Jul 1953.

40. Memo, Col E. P. Mechling, Ch Special Weapons Team, DCS/O, to Dir/Plans, subj: Introduction of New Weapons, Oct 8, 1951; memo, Col J. R. Sutherland, Ch Special Weapons Team, DCS/O, to Dir/Plans, subj: Expansion of Special Weapons Team, War Plans Division, Directorate of Plans, Feb 2, 1952, in AFCHO.

41. Memo, Col David A. Burchinal, Sec AF Council, to DCS's and IG, May 15, 1951, in OSAF Files; ltr, Brig Gen Sessums, Dir/Opns (ARDC), to CG ARDC, subj: Nomenclature of Guided Missiles, Jul 11, 1951, in OSAF Files.

42. 1st Ind, to ltr, Brig Gen John W. Sessums, Dep for Ops (ARDC), to CG ARDC, Jul 11, 1951, Aug 2, 1951, in OSAF Files.

43. JCSM 1620/42, CSAF to JCS, subj: Policy Guidance for the Guided Missiles Interdepartmental Requirements Group, Oct 29, 1951, in RG 218, 334 Guided Missiles Committee, NA.

44. *Ibid.*

45. *Ibid.*

46. *Ibid.*

47. *Ibid.*

48. Note passed by Brig Gen Mickelsen (USA) to Rear Adm G. B. Hall at the GMIORG Meeting of Oct 29, 1951, in Max Rosenberg Missile Notes, AFCHO.

49. Ltr, SAF to Chmn RDB, subj: White Sands–Holloman Complex, ca May 1952, in OSAF Files.

50. Memo, Col John R. Sutherland, Deputy Assistant DCS/O, to Col Richard D. Curtin, no subj, Aug 4, 1952, in OSAF Files.

51. Draft agreement, Jun 28, 1952; briefing, Ad Hoc Committee to Resolve Army-USAF Differences of View, s/Lt Gen Charles L. Bolte (USA), DCS/Plans and Research, and Lt Gen Thomas D. White (USAF), DCS/O, Jul 26, 1952, in OSAF Files, OPD 472, Sec 20.

52. Ltr, Brig Gen John W. Sessums, Dep for Dev (ARDC), to DCS/D, no subj, Jul 1, 1952, in OSAF Files, RG 525, A56-39/360.4 Guided Missiles; memo, Lt Gen Charles L. Bolte (USA), DCS/Plans and Research, and Lt Gen Thomas D. White (USAF), DCS/O, to Cols P. J. Black (USA), L. V. Hightower (USA), Harry T. Alness (USAF), and E. O. McComas (USAF), subj: Ad Hoc Committee to Resolve Army–USAF Differences of View, Jul 26, 1952, in OSAF Files, OPD 472, Sec 20.

53. ASSS, Col H. T. Alness, Sep 2, 1952, w/atch: study, Ad Hoc Committee to Resolve Army–USAF Differences of View, presented to Lt Gen L. L. Lemnitzer (USA), DCS/ Plans and Res, and Lt Gen T. D. White (USAF), DCS/O, Aug 27, 1952, in OSAF Files, OPD 472, Sec 20.

54. *Ibid.*

55. Memo, Maj Gen R. M. Lee, Dir/ Plans, to Gen Thomas White, DCS/O, subj: Special Ad Hoc Committee Report on Division of Army–Air Force Responsibilities for Guided Missiles, Dec 15, 1952; memo, Gen Lee to Ch War Plans Div, subj: Guided Missile Responsibilities, Mar 19, 1953; R&R, Col R. D. Curtin, same subj: Mar 30, 1953, in OSAF Files, OPD 472, Sec 20.

56. Ltr, Col K. E. Thieubaud, AAG, to CGs and COs of Major Air Commands, et al, AFODC 452.1, subj: Air Force Policy—

Guided Missiles," Sep 16, 1952; AF ltr, No. 136-3, subj: Guided Missiles in the United States Air Force, Sep 18, 1952, in OSAF Files; draft memo, Col J. R. Sutherland, Dep Asst DCS/O (GM), to Lt Gen T. D. White, DCS/O, subj: Guided Missile Policy— Development and Background, Feb 1953, in Gen White Papers, LC.

57. Draft memo, Col J. R. Sutherland, Dep Asst DCS/O (GM), to Lt Gen T. D. White, DCS/O, subj: Guided Missile Policy— Development and Background, Feb 1953, in Gen White Papers, LC.

58. Ltr, Lt Gen E. E. Partridge, CG ARDC, to Lt Gen T. D. White, DCS/O, no subj, Jan 8, 1953, in OSAF Files 452.1 GM (AFODC GM) E.

59. Ltr, Lt Gen T. D. White, DCS/O, to Lt Gen Earl E. Partridge, Commander, ARDC, no subj, Feb 2, 1953, in OSAF Files.

60. Presentation, Col J. R. Sutherland, Dep Asst DCS/O (GM), to Hq AMC Staff, Jul 22, 1953, in OSAF Files; MR, Asst DCS/ O (GM), subj: Implications of the Guided Missile Program with Report to the Dept of Air Force, ca Sep 1953, in AFCHO.

61. Rprt, K. T. Keller, Dir/GM (OSD), to Staff, subj: National Guided Missiles Program, Sep 17, 1953, in OSAF Files; ltr, Ralph O. Moore, Secy Armed Forces Policy Council, to SAF, Sec Army, and Sec Navy, subj: Guided Missiles, Jun 16, 1953, in RG 340, 341.6, 557-50, Vol 5, NA.

Chapter IV

A Radical Reorganization

1. Alice C. Cole, et al, *The Department of Defense: Documents on Establishment and Organization, 1944–1978*, OSDHO (Washington: GPO, 1978), pp 123–24, 157–59 [hereafter Cole, *DOD Documents*]; DOD Dir. 5105.1, subj: Reorganization of the Office of Secretary of Defense, June 30, 1953; DOD Dir. 5128, subj: Responsibilities of the Assistant Secretary of Defense (Research and Development), Nov 12, 1953.

2. Ltr, Ralph O. Moore, Sec Armed Forces Policy Council (DOD), to Sec's Army, Navy, and Air Force, subj: Guided Missiles,

Jun 16, 1953; memo, H. E. Talbott, SAF, to Sec Army and Sec Navy, no subj, Jun 19, 1953, in RG 340, 471.6, 557-50, Vol 5, NA.

3. Hearings before the Committee on Armed Services, Senate, *Nomination of Trevor Gardner*, 84th Cong, 1st Sess (Washington, 1955), *passim*; intv, Gen James H. Doolittle, Chairman of the Board, TRW, with Eugene M. Emme and William D. Putnam, Apr 1969, p 46; Beard, p 166.

4. Memo, Trevor Gardner, Special Assistant for R&D, to Donald A. Quarles, Assistant Secretary of Defense, subj: Summary

Report of the Special Study Group on Guided Missiles, Oct 1, 1953; MR, Lt Col P. J. Schenck, Sec Ad Hoc Cmte on Guided Missiles, Jul and Aug 1953, in RG 340, 471.6, 557-50, Vol 5 and RG 341, 360.4.1, Box 19, NA.

5. Memo, C. E. Wilson, SECDEF, to Sec's AF, Army and Navy, subj: Administration of Guided Missiles Program, Nov. 12, 1953, in OSAF Files, AFODC (GM), Mar 25, 1952-Jan 1954, Suitland NFRC; memo, H. E. Talbott to Wilson, no subj, Oct 24, 1953, in RG 340, 471.6, 557-50, Vol 5, NA; DOD Dir 5128.15, subj: Coordination of Research and Development on Guided Missiles, Jan 6, 1954, in AFCHO.

6. Eugene M. Emme, *Aeronautics and Astronautics: An American Chronology of Science and Technology in the Exploration of Space, 1915-1960* (NASA, 1961), p 70.

7. *Ibid.*

8. Ltr, Lt Gen J. H. Doolittle, Spec Asst to CSAF, to Gen Hoyt S. Vandenberg, subj: S.A.B. Nuclear Weapons Panel, Feb 10, 1953, in RG 341, Special Asst to the C of S, Box 18, NA; Sturm, *SAB*, p 48.

9. Ltr, Gen T. D. White, AF Vice Chief of Staff, to Dr. Theodore von Kármán, no subj, Jun 8, 1953.

10. Technical Note SWC 53-12, "A Preliminary Study of Nuclear Warheads for High Performance Missiles," AFSWC, Sep 15, 1953, in BAS Papers.

11. Ltr, Trevor Gardner, Special Assistant for R&D, to Dr. John von Neumann (and identical ltrs to other members of the Teapot Committee), no subj, Oct 31, 1953, in RG 340, 471.6, 557-50, Vol 6, NA; memo, Lt Col P. J. Schenck to Gardner, subj: Atlas Program, Sep 8, 1953; *Who's Who in America,* 29th ed, 1956 (Chicago, Marquis, p 266); Beard, p 157.

12. Ltr, Simon Ramo to Trevor Gardner, no subj, Feb 10, 1954, w/atch: Recommendation of the Strategic Missiles Evaluation Committee, Feb 10, 1954, in AFSC/HO, Alfred Rockefeller Documents, 1951-1954.

13. *Ibid.*

14. *Ibid.*

15. *Ibid.*

16. *Ibid.*

17. Memo, Gardner to Quarles, no subj, Feb 16, 1954, in SAMSO/HO, Basic Documents. The main contribution of the Rand studies was their confirmation of the ICBM's technical feasibility using lightweight, high-yield thermonuclear warheads. See Rand RM-1191, "Revised Development Program for Ballistic Missiles of Intercontinental Range," Feb 8, 1954 in SAMSO/HO.

18. Ltr, Brig Gen Floyd B. Wood, ARDC Vice Comdr, to Gen Bernard A. Schriever, WDD Commander, no subj, Mar 30, 1954; ARDC Staff Summary Sheet, Maj R.T. Franzel, subj: Rand Recommendations on Atlas (T-4-101, and T-4-89), ARDC Strategic Systems Div, Mar 30, 1954.

19. Memo, Col D. E. Hooks, AFSWC C of S, to ARDC Comdr, subj: Status Report of the Guided Missiles Atomic Warhead Marriage Program in AFSWC, Apr 16, 1953, Doc 81 in De Haven Collection; hist, AFSWC, 1953, Vol I, p 256.

20. Memo, Col Leo W. Killen, Asst Dep for Dev (ARDC) to Brig Gen F. B. Wood, Dep for Dev (ARDC), subj: Atlas Development Program, Feb 5, 1954, in SAMSO/HO Basic Documents; ltr, Brig Gen Wood to Dir/R&D, subj: Proposed Warhead Military Characteristics for XB-65 (Atlas), Mar 18, 1954, in AFSC/HO.

21. Memo, Trevor Gardner, Special Assistant for R&D, to Gen Nathan F. Twining, AF Chief of Staff, no subj, Jan 27, 1954, in Twining Papers, Box 42, SAF (2), LC (also in BAS Papers); intvw, Maj Gen O. J. Ritland, BMD Commander, with Lt Col L. R. Officer, Mar 19-21, 1974, pp 145 and 227-28.

22. Memo, Maj Gen James McCormack, ARDC Vice Comdr, to Lt Gen Donald L. Putt, ARDC Comdr, subj: Mr. Gardner's Conference on IBMS, February 26 and Mar 8, 1954, in Basic Documents; memo, Trevor Gardner, Special Assistant for R&D, to Gen Nathan F. Twining, AF Chief of Staff, and Harold E. Talbott, AF Secretary, subj: Intercontinental Ballistic Missile System Acceleration Plan, Mar 11, 1954, in Basic Documents.

23. *Ibid.*

24. Memo, Gen T. D. White, AF Vice Chief of Staff, to CSAF, subj: USAF Strategic Missile Program, Mar 23, 1954, in Basic Documents. (General Twining's approval was annotated to this memo, same date.)

25. Memo, Harold E. Talbott, AF Secretary, to Gen Nathan F. Twining, AF Chief of Staff, subj: Acceleration of the Intercontinental Ballistic Missile Program, Mar 19, 1954, in De Haven Collection; memo, Harold E. Talbott, AF Secretary, to Trevor Gardner, Special Assistant for R&D, subj: Intercontinental Ballistic Missile System Acceleration Plan, Mar 19, 1954, in BAS Papers.

26. Memo, Gen T. D. White, AF Vice Chief of Staff, to CSAF, subj: USAF Strategic Missile Program, Mar 23, 1954 (annotated by Twining).

27. Memo, Trevor Gardner, Assistant Secretary for R&D, to DCS/D, subj: Security of the Acceleration of the IBMS, Apr 14, 1954; memo, Gardner to Gen Nathan F. Twining, AF Chief of Staff, subj: USAF Strategic Missile Program, Apr 14, 1954.

28. Memo, Gen T. D. White, AF Vice Chief of Staff, to Air Staff, subj: Project Atlas, May 14, 1954, in Basic Documents; memo, atch to ltr, Harry C. Jordan, BSD Historian, to Col Ray E. Soper, Vice Comdr BSD, subj: Interview, Nov 28, 1966, in AFCHO K 105.5-141; Gardner's testimony Jun 14, 1956 in Hearings Before the Subcommittee on the Armed Services, Senate, *Study of Airpower*, 84th Congress, 2d Sess (Washington, 1957), p 1113 [hereafter Symington, *Airpower Hearing*].

29. HQ USAF HOI 21-2, subj: Office of the Assistant for Guided Missiles, Feb. 18, 1954.

30. Memo, Maj Gen S. R. Brentnall, Asst DCS/O (GM), to VCSAF, subj: Proposal for the Establishment of a Central Office of USAF Guided Missile Program, Dec 14, 1953, in OSAF, AFCGM Organizational Files, Suitland NFRC; memo, Col John R. Sutherland, Deputy Assistant DCS/O, to Maj Gen Samuel R. Brentnall, no subj, Dec 23, 1953.

31. HQ USAF HOI 21-2, subj: Assistant Chief of Staff for Guided Missiles, Apr 8, 1954.

32. Ltr, Lt Gen Putt, DCS/D, to Comdr ARDC, subj: Project Atlas, Jun 21, 1954, in BAS Papers.

33. General Order No 42 (ARDC), Jul 15, 1954, in AFSC/HO (this order confirmed the verbal order by Lt Gen Thomas S. Power, ARDC Commander, of Jul 1, 1954), in BAS Papers; memo, Maj Gen Bernard A. Schriever, WDD Commander, to Maj Gen James McCormack, ARDC Vice Comdr, subj: Back-Up Project Atlas Directives, Jul 19, 1954, in Krudener Documents.

34. Jacob Neufeld, "Bernard Schriever: Challenging the Unknown," in John L. Frisbee, ed, *Makers of the United States Air Force* (Washington: Office of Air Force History, 1987), Chapter 12.

35. "Man in the News," *New York Times*, Dec 1957 (copy in AFCHO).

36. Ltr, Gen Bernard A. Schriever, WDD Commander, to Lt Gen Thomas S. Power, ARDC Commander, no subj, Aug 6, 1954, in BAS Papers; intv, author with Dr. Alfred Rockefeller, WDD Historian, Aug 16, 1977.

37. Ltr, Gen E. W. Rawlings, Comdr AMC, to Lt Gen Power, Comdr ARDC, subj: Military Operations Order for Project Atlas, Jun 11, 1954; memo, Maj Gen S.R. Brentnall, Asst Ch of Staff (GMs), to Lt Gen B. L. Boatner, DCS/M, Lt Gen D. L. Putt, DCS/D, and Brig Gen Schriever, CG Proj Atlas, subj: Decision on Procurement Authority with Respect to IBMS, Jun 10, 1954; ltr, Gen Boatner to Comdr ARDC, same subj, Jun 21, 1954.

38. Agreement, AMC/ARDC, Project Atlas, s/Maj Gen William F. McKee, Commander AFLC, and Lt Gen Thomas S. Power, Commander ARDC, Jul 28, 1954, in Doc 49, De Haven Collection; AMC Letter 20-12, subj: Establishment of Special Aircraft Project Office AMC (MCPT), Aug 6, 1954, in BAS Papers. (SAPO was officially established Aug 15, 1954.)

39. Chron, *SAMSO: A Chronology, 1954–1976*, Thomas S. Snyder, et al, 1978.

40. Minutes of Scientific Advisory Committee Meeting July 20 and 21, 1954, s/Lt Col B. L. Boatman, approved by the committee at January 1955 meeting, in BAS Papers.

41. Msg, Lt Gen Thomas S. Power, Commander ARDC, to Gen Bernard A. Schriever, Commander WDD, 30/2000Z Jul 1954, in AFSC/HO.

42. Ltr, Gen Bernard A. Schriever, Commander WDD, to Lt Gen Thomas S. Power, Commander ARDC, no subj, Aug 24, 1954; rprt, A Study of the Development Manage-

ment Organization for the Atlas Program, WDD, Aug 18, 1954, in BAS Papers.

43. MR, Roger Lewis, Asst SAF (Materiel), subj: Summary of Discussion re Intercontinental Ballistic Missile Program, Sep 8, 1954, in Doc 55, De Haven Collection.

44. Memo, Gen Bernard A. Schriever, Commander WDD, to Lt Gen Thomas S. Power, Commander ARDC, subj: Policy and Procedure for R-W Study Contracts, Oct 2, 1954, in Doc 57, De Haven Collection; Minutes of ICBM Scientific Advisory Committee Meeting, Oct 15, 1954, s/Lt Col Boatman, in BAS Papers.

45. Ltr, F. R. Collbohm, Dir Rand Corp, to Gen Bernard A. Schriever, Commander WDD, no subj, Oct 14, 1954; ltr, F. R. Collbohm, Dir Rand Corp, to Dr. John von Neumann, no subj, Oct 14, 1954, in AFSC/HO.

46. MR, Gen Bernard A. Schriever, Commander WDD, subj: Selection of Initial Air Frame Contractor, Oct 25, 1954; msg, Gen Bernard A. Schriever, Commander WDD, to Lt Gen Thomas S. Power, Commander ARDC, 26/0515Z Oct 1954, in AFSC/HO; ltr, Power to Schriever, no subj, Nov 4, 1954, in AFSC/HO.

47. Memo, Gen Bernard A. Schriever, Commander WDD, to Maj Gen John W. Sessums, Vice Comdr ARDC, subj: Memorandum for record, Oct 29, 1954, in AFSC/HO; MR, Schriever, subj: Discussion of the Convair and Ramo-Wooldridge Work Statements, Oct 29, 1954, in BAS Papers.

48. Memo, Gen Bernard A. Schriever, Cmdr WDD, to Trevor Gardner, Special Assistant for R&D, subj: Briefing for Mr. Anderson and the Collbohm Panel, Nov 24, 1954; memo, Gen Schriever, to Col B. L. Boatman, subj: Friday, 3 December Panel Meeting, Nov 30, 1954, in AFSC/HO.

49. Memo, George B. Kistiakowsky, Harvard Univ, et al, to Trevor Gardner, Special Assistant for R&D, subj: Management Structure for ICBM Development, Dec 3, 1954, w/atch: Report of the Atlas Scientific Advisory Committee Panel Meeting of December 3, 1954, s/Col Boatman.

50. MR, Gen Bernard A. Schriever, Cmdr WDD, subj: Interaction of TBMS with ICBM, Dec 20, 1954; msg, Schriever to Lt Gen Thomas S. Power, Cmdr ARDC, 20/2350Z Dec 1954, in BAS Papers; memo, Donald A. Quarles, Assistant Secretary of Defense, R&D, to Charles E. Wilson, Secretary of Defense, subj; Collaboration with the British on Long Range Ballistic Missile Development, Jun 3, 1954; ltr, Lt Gen D. L. Putt, DCS/D, to Lt Gen Thomas S. Power, subj: Tactical Ballistic Missile, Aug 16, 1954 and 1st Ind, in BAS Papers.

51. Chron, Thor (SM-75), ca Oct 1959, in AFCHO; memo, Col R. A. Ballweg, OSAF, to Trevor Gardner, Special Assistant for R&D, subj: Tactical Ballistic Missile, Dec 17, 1954; ltr, Garrison Norton, OSAF consultant, to Gen Bernard A. Schriever, Cmdr WDD, no subj, Dec 20, 1954; GOR No 50, HQ USAF Dir/Reqts, Tactical Ballistic Missile Weapon System, Dec 2, 1954, in BAS Papers.

52. Memo, Trevor Gardner, Special Assistant for R&D, to Maj Gen Samuel R. Brentnall, no subj, Oct 1, 1954.

53. Ltr, Gen Bernard A. Schriever, Cmdr WDD, to Trevor Gardner, Special Assistant for R&D, no subj, Nov 30, 1954, in AFSC/HO.

54. Memo, Harold E. Talbott, AF Secretary, to Lyle S. Garlock, Secretary of Defense, no subj, Jan 24, 1955.

55. Ltr, Gen Bernard A. Schriever, Cmdr WDD, to Joseph T. McNarney, President Convair, no subj, Nov 3, 1954, in AFSC/HO.

56. Ltr, Joseph T. McNarney, President Convair, to Gen Bernard A. Schriever, Cmdr WDD, Nov 12, 1954, in AFSC/HO.

57. Ltr, Gen Bernard A. Schriever, Cmdr WDD, to Joseph T. McNarney, President Convair, no subj, Nov 22, 1954, in AFSC/HO.

58. Ltr, Trevor Gardner, Special Assistant for R&D, to Gen Bernard A. Schriever, Cmdr WDD, no subj, Nov 13, 1954; ltr, Joseph T. McNarney, President, Convair, to Gen Bernard A. Schriever, no subj, Dec 6, 1954; ltr, Frank Pace, Jr., Exec VP Gen Dynamics, to Trevor Gardner, no subj, Dec 13, 1954; ltr, Roger Lewis, Assistant Secretary AF for Materiel, to Frank Pace, Jr., Exec VP Gen Dynamics, no subj, Dec 20, 1954, in AFSC/HO.

59. MR, Gen Bernard A. Schriever, Cmdr WDD, subj: AFSWC-WDD Relation-

ship, Sep 21, 1954; MR, Gen Bernard A. Schriever, no subj, Sep 22, 1954, in BAS Papers; Blue Cover Study.

60. Blue Cover Study; hearings before Military Applications Committee, Senate, testimony by Trevor Gardner, Special Assis-

tant for R&D, on May 25, 1955; Jacob Neufeld, "Atlas: The Race for Missile Supremacy," paper presented at Missouri Valley Historical Conference, Omaha, Nebraska, Mar 1979.

Chapter V

A Family of Missiles

1. Intvw, Maj Gen Osmond J. Ritland, former Commander BMD, with Lt Col Lyn R. Officer, Mar 19–21, 1974, p 177.

2. Msg, Gen Bernard A. Schriever, Cmdr WDD, to Lt Gen Thomas S. Power, Cmdr ARDC, WDG 15-E, Oct 26, 1954; msg, Power to Schriever, RDGB, 11-9-E, Nov 4, 1954.

3. MR, Simon Ramo, Ramo-Wooldridge Corp., subj: Background Facts on Convair in the ICBM Program, Apr 24, 1956, in BAS Papers; Chronology, OSAF, Feb 1956.

4. Msg, Gen Bernard A. Schriever, Cmdr WDD, to Lt Gen Thomas S. Power, Cmdr ARDC, WDG 1-4-E, 12/1701Z Jan 1955, in Basic Documents.

5. De Haven, *Aerospace*, p 38; ltr, Gen Bernard A. Schriever, Cmdr WDD, to Lt Gen Thomas S. Power, Cmdr ARDC, subj: Contractors Selection Procedure for the ICBM Program, Jan 28, 1955, in Basic Documents.

6. Ltr, Col. C. H. Terhune, Dep Comdr for Tech Opns (WDD), to Convair and AFPR, subj: Configuration Decision for the Atlas ICBM Program, Jan 12, 1955, in Basic Documents.

7. Ltr, Gen Bernard A. Schriever, Cmdr WDD, to Maj. Robert Franzel, Asst to Lt Gen Thomas S. Power, Cmdr ARDC, subj: Test Philosophy for Guided Missiles, Feb 7, 1955, w/atch: draft ltr, Power to CSAF, no subj, nd, in Doc 82, De Haven, *Aerospace*; minutes, ICBM Scientific Advisory Committee Meeting, Oct 17–18, 1955, in Basic Documents.

8. Memo, Gen Bernard A. Schriever, Cmdr WDD, to Lt Gen Thomas S. Power, Cmdr ARDC, subj: Atlas Test Facilities, Apr 7, 1955, in Doc 89, De Haven, *Aerospace*;

MR, Simon Ramo, Ramo-Wooldridge Corp., subj: Background Facts on Convair in the ICBM Program, Apr 24, 1956.

9. "A Report on the Ramo-Wooldridge Corporation," Jan 5, 1956, atch to memo, Col James T. Stewart, Dep Asst for Devt Prog, DCS/D, to Gen Donald L. Putt, DCS/D, same subj, Jan 18, 1956, in AFCHO K168.041-6, pt 1.

10. Memo, Trevor Gardner, Special Assistant for R&D, to Asst SECDEF (R&D), et al, no subj, Apr 11, 1955, w/atch: ATLAS SUMMARY, nd, in OSAF 471.6, File 13–55, "Guided Missiles 10/8/76," Suitland FRC.

11. Ltr, Trevor Gardner, Special Assistant for R&D, to John B. Macauley, Actg Asst SECDEF for R&D, no subj, Aug 15, 1955; ltr, Macauley to Trevor Gardner, no subj, Sep 9, 1955.

12. Memo, Col Harold T. Morris, Chief SAPO (AMC), to Gen Bernard A. Schriever, Cmdr WDD, subj: Mr. Gardner's Query as to the Value of Competition, Mar 15, 1955, w/atch: draft ltr, Schriever to Trevor Gardner, Special Assistant for R&D, subj: Delays Due to Utilization of Competition in Placing ICBM Procurements, nd, in Doc 86, De Haven, *Aerospace*; memo, Schriever to Col Vincent Ford, Spec Asst to Gen Bernard A. Schriever, Cmdr WDD, subj: General Dynamics–Convair Propaganda Campaign, Mar 18, 1955.

13. Memo, Gen Bernard A. Schriever, Cmdr WDD, to Lt Gen Thomas S. Power, Cmdr ARDC, subj: Airframe Industries vs Air Force ICBM Management, Feb 24, 1955, in Basic Documents.

14. MR, Simon Ramo, subj: Background Facts on Convair in the ICBM Pro-

gram, Apr 24, 1956; ltr, Roger Lewis, Assistant Secretary AF for Materiel, to Gen Bernard A. Schriever, Cmdr WDD, no subj, Apr 29, 1955; ltr, Schriever to Lt Gen Thomas S. Power, Cmdr ARDC, no subj, Jun 8, 1955, all in BAS Papers.

15. Msg, Lt Gen Thomas S. Power, Cmdr ARDC, to HQ USAF/DDC, 03/1600Z Mar 1955, in BAS Papers; memo, Trevor Gardner, Special Assistant for R&D, to Harold E. Talbott, AF Secretary, subj: ICBM Airframe Alternate Source, Apr 1, 1955, in OSAF 471.6 File 13–55 (TS), "Guided Missile 10/8/76," Suitland FRC.

16. Memo, Harold E. Talbott, AF Secretary, to Trevor Gardner, Special Assistant for R&D, subj: ICBM Airframe Alternate Source, Apr 2, 1955; memo, Maj. Robert T. Franzel, Asst to Lt Gen Thomas S. Power, Cmdr ARDC, to Gen Bernard A. Schriever, Cmdr WDD, subj: General Power's Conversation with Secretary Talbott Concerning Directives Conflict on Atlas, Apr 8, 1955, in Basic Documents.

17. Memo, Gen Bernard A. Schriever, Cmdr WDD, to Lt Gen Thomas S. Power, Cmdr ARDC, subj: Atlas Test Facilities, Apr 7, 1955, in Doc 89, De Haven, *Aerospace*.

18. Chronology, OSAF, Feb 1956.

19. MR, Roger Lewis, Assistant Secretary AF for Materiel, subj: Agreements with Respect to Air Force IBM [sic] Program, Apr 27, 1955, in Basic Documents; msg, HQ USAF/DDC to Comdr ARDC, #58849, May 2, 1955, in BAS Papers; memo, Trevor Gardner, Special Assistant for R&D, to Donald A. Quarles, Secretary AF, no subj, Aug 30, 1955, in OSAF 471.6 File 13–55 (TS), "Guided Missiles 10/8/76," in Suitland FRC.

20. HQ USAF Development Directive No. 76, Jul 27, 1955.

21. Memo, Donald A. Quarles, Secretary AF, to CSAF, subj: Application of the Dispersal Policy to the ICBM Development Program, Oct 8, 1955, in Basic Documents.

22. Msg, Gen Bernard A. Schriever to Lt Gen Thomas S. Power, Cmdr ARDC, and Gen Edwin W. Rawlings, Cmdr, AMC, no subj, Sep 15, 1955 and 1st Ind, nd; MR, Gen Bernard A. Schriever, subj: Sole Source Procurement vs Competition for Alternate WD

[sic] 107A Airframe, ca Aug 13, 1955, in Basic Documents.

23. John T. Greenwood, "The Air Force Ballistic Missile and Space Program (1954–1974)," *Aerospace Historian*, Vol. 21 No. 4, Winter/December 1974, p 194.

24. "Brief of the Report to the President by the Technological Capabilities Panel of the Science Advisory Committee," Feb 14, 1955, in Basic Documents [hereafter Killian Report]; memo, Trevor Gardner, Special Assistant for R&D, to Harold E. Talbott, Secretary AF, no subj, May 5, 1955; Hearings before Committee on Armed Services, Subcommittee on the Air Force, Senate, *Study of Airpower*, 84th Cong, 2d Sess (Washington, April–July 1956) [hereafter Symington, *Airpower Hearings*].

25. Memo, Trevor Gardner, Special Assistant for R&D, to Harold E. Talbott, Secretary AF, no subj, May 5, 1955; Symington, *Airpower Hearings*.

26. Memo, Trevor Gardner, Special Assistant for R&D, to Harold E. Talbott, Secretary AF, no subj, Jun 28, 1955, in Doc 99, De Haven, *Aerospace*.

27. *Ibid.*

28. Ltr, Sen Clinton P. Anderson, Chmn Jt Cmte on Atomic Energy, and Sen Henry M. Jackson, Chmn Sbcmte on Military Applications, to President Eisenhower, no subj, Jun 30, 1955, in Basic Documents.

29. Memo, Col A. J. Goodpaster (USA), Gen Thomas D. White House Staff Secy, to SECDEF, no subj, Jul 1, 1955, in Basic Documents; ltr, President Eisenhower to Sens Clinton P. Anderson and Henry M. Jackson, no subj, Jul 27, 1955, in Basic Documents.

30. Memo, Trevor Gardner, Special Assistant for R&D, to Gen Nathan F. Twining, AF Chief of Staff, no subj, Aug 1, 1955.

31. Diary, Office of the Commander WDD, Addendum to Weekly Report July 25–31, 1955, s/Lt Col Beryl L. Boatman, Exec Ofcr WDD, in Basic Documents; Ernest G. Schiebert, "A Look Back—A Look Ahead," *Air Force and Space Digest*, May 1964, p 43.

32. *A Chronological Brief of Selected Guided Missile Projects, OSAF*, Feb 1956, in AFCHO K168.041-3 [hereafter *OSAF Chronology*, Feb 1956].

33. *Ibid;* NSC 1433, Aug 1955.

34. Memo, Reuben B. Robertson, Jr, Dep SECDEF, to SAF, et al, subj: Intercontinental Ballistic Missiles Program, Sep 17, 1955; memo, Trevor Gardner, Special Assistant for R&D, to Hyde Gillette, Dep for Budget and Prog Mgmt, OSAF (Fin Mgmt), no subj, Sep 14, 1955, in Basic Documents; memo atch to ltr, Harry C. Jordan, BSD Historian, to Col. R. E. Roper, Vice Comdr BSD, subj: Interview, Nov 28, 1966, in AF-CHO K105.5-141; Rosenberg, *IOC*, p 20n.

35. Ltr, Donald A. Quarles, Secretary AF, to Reuben B. Robertson, Deputy SEC-DEF, subj: ICBM Procedure, Oct 15, 1955, w/atch: Air Force Plan for Simplifying Administrative Procedures for the ICBM and IRBM Programs, nd, in Twining Papers, Box 53, "SECDEF," LC Manuscript Division.

36. *Ibid*.

37. Memo, Charles E. Wilson, SECDEF, to Donald A. Quarles, Secretary AF, subj: Management of the ICBM and IRBM Development Programs, Nov 8, 1955, in Basic Documents; Symington, *Airpower Hearings*, pp 350-353.

38. Memo, Donald A. Quarles, Secretary AF, to Trevor Gardner, Special Assistant for R&D, et al, subj: Establishment of the Air Force Ballistic Missiles Committee, Nov 14, 1955, in *Air Force Plan for Simplifying Administrative Procedures for the ICBM and IRBM Programs*, revised Nov 10, 1955, in AFCHO K168.041-6, pt. 5.

39. *Ibid*, Tab D, "Suggested Directives from Chief of Staff, USAF."

40. *OSAF Chronology*, Feb 1956.

41. Memo, Col William A. Sheppard, Dep for Plans (WDD), to Gen Bernard A. Schriever, Cmdr WDD, subj: Accelerating the Atlas Operational System, Jul 18, 1955, in Doc 101, De Haven, *Aerospace*.

42. Rosenberg, *IOC*, pp 28-29.

43. Ltr, Gen Thomas D. White, VCSAF, to Lt Gen Thomas S. Power, Comdr ARDC, subj: Initial ICBM Operational Capability, Nov 18, 1955, in BAS Papers; ltr, White to CINCSAC, subj: Priority of the ICBM and IRBM Programs, Nov 18, 1955, in Basic Documents.

44. Ltr, Gen Curtis LeMay, CINCSAC, to CSAF, subj: SAC Position on Missiles, Nov 26, 1955, in Twining Papers, Box 47, "Commander, SAC" LC Manuscript Division.

45. "Minutes of the ICBM Scientific Advisory Committee Meeting 17-18 Oct 1955," nd, in Basic Documents; AFR 58-1, Guided Missiles, Aug 15, 1955.

46. Ltr, Lt Gen Thomas S. Power, Cmdr ARDC, to Gen Bernard A. Schriever, Cmdr WDD, subj: Authority for ICBM and IRBM Programs, Dec 14, 1955, in BAS Papers; ARDC Operations Order 4-55, Dec 9, 1955, in SAMSO Hist Office; ltr, White to Power, subj: Initial Operational Capability, SM-65, Dec 29, 1955; 1st Ind, Power to Schriever, Dec 29, 1955, in AFSC Hist Office.

47. Ltr, Trevor Gardner, Special Assistant for R&D, to Gen Donald L. Putt, Cmdr ARDC, subj: Minutes of Meeting ICBM Scientific Advisory Committee, Jan 3-4, 1955, in BAS Papers.

48. Ltr, Trevor Gardner, Special Assistant for R&D, to Sir Steuart Mitchell, Comptroller of Guided Missiles and Electronics (Min of Supply, UK), no subj, Feb 25, 1955; memo, Gardner to Harold E. Talbott, Secretary AF, and James H. Douglas, Undersecretary AF, subj: Visit to England re: Mutual Assistance in Guided Missile Programs, Apr 15, 1955; memo, H. B. Loper, Asst SECDEF (Atomic Energy), to Gardner, no subj, Sep 16, 1955; memo, Gardner to Loper, subj: Implementation of Exchange Agreements, Dec 27, 1955, w/atch: Draft Agreement, ca. Nov 1955, all in OSAF 471.6, File 5168-55 (TS), "U.S.-U.K. Guided Missiles, 10/8/76"; MR, Vincent S. Roddy, Dep Techl Exec (HQ USAF Dir/R&D), subj: British Guided Missile Team, Aug 5, 1955, in BAS Papers.

49. Brief of the Report to the President by the Technological Capabilities Panel of the Science Advisory Committee, [Killian Report] 14 Feb 1955, pp 198-200, in Basic Documents.

50. Memo, Gen Bernard A. Schriever, Cmdr WDD, to Lt Gen Thomas S. Power, Cmdr ARDC, subj: Redstone-Scientific Satellite, Mar 30, 1955, in BAS Papers.

51. *Ibid*.

52. HQ USAF GOR (SA-2C), subj: Strategic Reconnaissance Satellite Weapon System, Maj Gen George E. Price, Dir/Rqts,

Mar 16, 1955, in Basic Documents; ltr, Maj Gen Albert Boyd, Dep Comdr/Weapon Systems (ARDC), no subj, Nov 7, 1955, in Basic Documents.

53. Memo, Gen Bernard A. Schriever to Maj Gen Donald P. Yates, DCS/Devel, et al, no subj, Sep 8, 1955, w/atch: General Officer Board study on the Establishment of a Guided Missile Center, Sep 8, 1955.

54. Ltr, Maj Gen Herbert G. Thatcher, Asst DCS/Dev, to Comdr ARDC, subj: Tactical Ballistic Missile, May 9, 1955 and 1st Ind, same subj, May 25, 1955, in BAS Papers.

55. Symington, *Airpower Hearings*, p 730.

56. Ltr, Gen Bernard A. Schriever, Cmdr WDD, to Simon Ramo, Ramo-Wooldridge Corp., subj: TBM Evaluation, Aug 4, 1955, in BAS Papers.

57. Memo, Charles E. Wilson, Secretary of Defense, to Military Departments and

JCS, Nov 8, 1955, in Basic Documents; Rosenberg, *IOC*, pp 23–24.

58. *OSAF Chronology*, Feb 1956; draft MOU, Dec 6, 1955, in OSAF File 13–55, Vol I, Suitland FRC.

59. Draft MOU, Dec 6, 1955, in OSAF File 13–55, Vol I, Suitland FRC.

60. *Ibid*.

61. Memo, Lt Gen Thomas S. Power, Cmdr ARDC, to Gen Bernard A. Schriever, Cmdr WDD, subj: Authority for ICBM and IRBM Programs, Dec 14, 1955, in BAS Papers; memo, Schriever to Col Charles H. Terhune, Chairman, Source Selection Board, subj: Recommendation of IRBM Contractor to USAF, Nov 30, 1955, in BAS Papers; memo, Terhune to Col Harold T. Morris, Gillette Committee, subj: Approval of IRBM Contractor, Dec 23, 1955, in Basic Documents.

62. SAMSO Chronology.

Chapter VI

The Poor Man's Approach

1. MR, Gen Bernard A. Schriever, Cmdr WDD, subj: Coordination of Missile Programs with Army and Navy, Jan 3, 1956, in Basic Documents; MOU, subj: Allocation of IRBM Engines for Calendar Year 1956, s/ Schriever, Maj Gen John B. Medaris, CG Army Balllistic Missile Agency (Redstone Arsenal), Rear Adm William F. Raborn, Dir BuOrd, Spec Proj Ofc, Jan 12, 1956; msg, Lt Gen Thomas S. Power, Cmdr ARDC, to Gen Bernard A. Schriever, Cmdr WDD, RDGB-1-19-E, 30/2228Z Jan 1956, in Basic Documents; memo, Gen Nathan F. Twining, AF Chief of Staff, to Donald A. Quarles, Secretary AF, subj: priority of ICBM and IRBM Programs, Feb 6, 1956, in BAS Papers; memo, Gen Nathan F. Twining to Lt Gen Thomas S. Power, Cmdr ARDC, no subj, Feb 6, 1956, in BAS Papers.

2. Memo, Trevor Gardner, Special Assistant for R&D, to Donald A. Quarles, Secretary AF, no subj, Jan 16, 1956; memo, Donald A. Quarles, Secretary AF to Trevor Gardner, Special Assistant for R&D, no subj,

Jan 28, 1956; memo, Trevor Gardner, Special Assistant for R&D, to Donald A. Quarles, Secretary AF, no subj, Feb 10, 1956 [all in Symington, *Airpower Hearings*]; DOD Dir No. 5105.10, subj: Establishment of a Special Assistant to the Secretary of Defense for Guided Missiles, Mar 27, 1956, in AFCHO Melden Smith Documents; memo atch to ltr, Harry C. Jordan, BSD Historian, to Col. Ray E. Soper, BSD Vice Comdr, Nov 28, 1966, in AFCHO K105.5-141; Anthony Leviero, "An Aide Resigns on Missile Rift," *The New York Times*, Feb 8, 1956, p 1; Leviero, "President Disputes Aide on Missile Lag," *New York Times*, Feb 9, 1956, p 1; Robert Hotz, "Gardner Quits, Starts USAF R&D Fight," *Aviation Week*, Feb 13, 1956, pp 28–29.

3. *American Aviation*, May 7, 1956, p 42.

4. Ltr, Lt Gen Thomas S. Power, Cmdr ARDC, to Gen Bernard A. Schriever, Cmdr WDD, subj: Authority for ICBM and IRBM Programs, Dec 14, 1955; Hist, WDD, Jul-Dec 1955, pp 3, 114.

5. ASSS, Col. C. O. Easly, Dep DCS/O, to VCSAF, subj: Initial Operational Capability, ICBM and IRBM, May 31, 1956; memo, Gen Maj Gen Samuel R. Brentnall, Assistant Chief of Staff, Guided Missiles, to VCSAF, subj: ICBM/IRBM Initial Operational Capability (IOC) Plans, Jul 6, 1956; ltr, Gen Thomas D. White to Lt Gen Thomas S. Power, Cmdr ARDC, subj: Initial Operational Capability, SM-65, Dec 28, 1955, in Doris E. Krudener, *Site Activation: Plans, Policies, and Decisions, 1954-1961* (Norton AFB, Calif., Historical Division, Office of Information (BSD), 1963; revised 1964), Doc. 92.

6. Ltr, Gen Thomas D. White, Vice Chief of Staff, to Lt Gen Thomas S. Power, Cmdr ARDC, no subj, Dec 28, 1955; draft, Preliminary Operational Concept for SM-65 (Atlas), Jan 18, 1956, revised Feb 27, 1956.

7. WDD (ARDC) Development Plan, Nov 18, 1955, in Basic Documents; minutes, 1st AF-BMC Mtg, Nov 23, 1955, in Basic Documents.

8. WDD (ARDC) Development Plan, Vol II, Mar 15, 1956, in Basic Documents; ltr, Gen Bernard A. Schriever to CSAF, subj: Western Development Division (ARDC), Development Plan, Mar 19, 1956; MR, Maj Gen W. G. Wells, Dep Asst CSAF (GM), subj: Operational Planning for ICBM, Mar 28, 1956; minutes, 3rd AF-BMC Mtg, Mar 29, 1956.

9. ASSS, Brig Gen R. E. Koon, Dep Dir/Opns, to CSAF, subj: Initial Operational Capability for the ICBM, Apr 30, 1956; ltr, Gen Thomas D. White, Vice Chief of Staff, to Lt Gen Thomas S. Power, Cmdr ARDC, subj: Initial Operational Capability for the ICBM, May 4, 1956, in Basic Documents.

10. Msg, Lt Gen Thomas S. Power, Cmdr ARDC, to Maj Gen Samuel R. Brentnall, Assistant Chief of Staff, Guided Missiles, RDGB 5-7-E, 09/1300Z May 1956, in Basic Documents.

11. Ltr, Gen Curtis LeMay, CINCSAC, to CSAF, subj: IRBM/ICBM Conference Between SAC and ARDC, May 17, 1956.

12. Memo, Col William A. Sheppard to Gen Bernard A. Schriever, Cmdr WDD, subj: IOC for ICBM, May 24, 1956; msg, Gen Thomas D. White to ARDC, WDD, and SAC, AFCVC 51340, 25/1952Z May 1956, in BAS Papers.

13. Ltr, Gen Bernard A. Schriever, Cmdr WDD, to CSAF, subj: Transmittal of Revision to WDD (ARDC) Ballistic Missile Development Plan, Jun 14, 1956; memo, Maj Gen Samuel R. Brentnall, Assistant Chief of Staff, Guided Missiles, to Air Staff, subj: Review of the ICBM/IRBM Operational Program, Jun 19, 1956; memo, Brentnall to VCSAF, no subj, Jul 6, 1956.

14. Minutes, 4th AF-BMC Mtg, Jul 3, 1956; handwritten notes, Col Ray E. Soper, BSD Vice Comdr, Jul 3, 1956, in BAS Papers; memo, Maj Gen Samuel R. Brentnall, Assistant Chief of Staff, Guided Missiles, to VCSAF, no subj, Jul 6, 1956; memo, Donald A. Quarles, Secretary AF, SAF, to James H. Douglas, Secretary AF, Under SAF, subj: ICBM Operational Sites, Jul 24, 1956; MR, Lt Col Vernon L. Hastings, subj: Asst for IOC (WDD), Jul 9, 1956, in BAS Papers; MR, Gen Bernard A. Schriever, no subj, Sep 18, 1956, in BAS Papers; MR, Col William A. Sheppard, subj: Comments of Secretary Quarles Relative to IOC Siting, Jul 17, 1956, in BAS Papers; memo, Quarles to Douglas, subj: ICBM Operational Sites, Jul 24, 1956, in BAS Papers.

15. Symington, *Airpower Hearings*, pp 1540, 1544 ff.

16. Memo, Maj Gen Samuel R. Brentnall, Assistant Chief of Staff, Guided Missiles, to VCSAF, Jul 6, 1956; memo, Maj Gen Jacob B. Smart, Asst VCSAF, to DCS/Opns, subj: ICBM Capability, Jul 19, 1956; ASSS, Brig Gen Charles M. McCorkle, Dep Asst VCSAF (GM), to CSAF, subj: ICBM/IRBM Initial Operational Capability (IOC) Plans, Aug 19, 1956; memo, Gen Thomas D. White to McCorkle, no subj, Aug 20, 1956.

17. Staff Study, Col Ray E. Soper, BSD Vice Comdr, subj: Annual Review of Ballistic Missile Program, Sep 19, 1956; minutes, 5th AF-BMC Mtg, Sep 27, 1956.

18. Staff Study, Col Ray E. Soper, BSD Vice Comdr, subj: Annual Review of Ballistic Missile Program, Sep 19, 1956; minutes, 5th AF-BMC Mtg, Sep 27, 1956; memo, Gen Thomas D. White to CSAF, subj: Annual Review of the Ballistic Missile Program, Sep 26, 1956, w/ Twining's approval attached;

notes, Soper, Sep 24, 1956; MR, Gen Bernard A. Schriever, subj: Secretary Quarles Request for WDD Study of an Alternate IOC Program for Ballistic Missiles Representing a "Poor Man's Approach," Sep 18, 1956, in Basic Documents.

19. Minutes, 5th AF–BMC Mtg, Sep 27, 1956; notes on mtg by Col Ray E. Soper, Secy AF–BMC, Sep 27, 1956.

20. Staff Study, Col Ray E. Soper, BSD Vice Comdr, Sep 19, 1956; memo, Maj Gen Jacob B. Smart, Asst CSAF, to Brig Gen Charles M. McCorkle, Asst CSAF (GM), subj: Ballistic Missile Program, Nov 9, 1956; MR, Soper, subj: AFC Review of WS–107/ 315 Programs, Nov 9, 1956; minutes, 6th AF–BMC Mtg, Nov 10, 1956; msg, CSAF to WDD, 48676, Nov 16, 1956.

21. Memo, Richard E. Horner, Actg Asst SAF (RD), to OSD–BMC, subj: Air Force Ballistic Missile Program, Nov 23, 1956; memo, Col Ray E. Soper, BSD Vice Comdr, to SAF and Air Staff, subj: OSD–BMC Review of the Air Force Revised Ballistic Missile Program, Dec 6, 1956; memo, Charles E. Wilson, SECDEF, to Mil Depts and JCS, subj: Ballistic Missile Program, ca Jan 11, 1957.

22. Memo, Donald A. Quarles, Secretary AF, to Charles E. Wilson, Secretary of Defense, subj: Ballistic Missile Operational Capability, Jan 12, 1957; memo, Dr. Eger V. Murphree, OSD Director, Guided Missiles, to Charles E. Wilson, Secretary of Defense, no subj, Mar 21, 1957; ltr, Wilson to President Eisenhower, no subj, Mar 23, 1957; memo, R. B. Robertson, Dep SECDEF, to Mil Depts and JCS, subj: Ballistic Missiles Program, Apr 5, 1957.

23. Ltr, Maj Gen Jacob B. Smart, Asst VCSAF, to Comdr ARDC, subject: Initial Operational Capability, ICBM, Mar 5, 1957, in AFSC Hist Ofc.

24. Ibid.

25. Ibid.

26. Msg, HQ USAF/GCM 56310, Feb 17, 1956; msg, Lt Gen Thomas S. Power, Cmdr ARDC, to Gen Bernard A. Schriever, Cmdr WDD, RDGB–T–6–88, 24/1600Z Mar 1956, in Basic Documents.

27. Memo, Lt Col David K. Lyster, Ch WS–315 Oper Readiness Gp, to Dep Comdr Plans (WDD), subj: SAC/ARDC Joint Agreement for IRBM IOC Responsibilities, May 4, 1956, in Basic Documents; Agreement, SAC/ARDC, Joint Agreement for IRBM IOC Responsibilities, May 7, 1956, in Basic Documents.

28. Ltr, Gen Curtis LeMay to CSAF, subj: IRBM/ICBM Conference between SAC and ARDC, May 17, 1956; msg, Gen Bernard A. Schriever, Cmdr WDD, to CSAF, WDO 5–7–E, May 24, 1956; msg, CSAF to ARDC, 40470, Jun 1, 1956.

29. Ltr, Gen Bernard A. Schriever to CSAF, subj: Transmittal of Revision to WDD (ARDC) Ballistic Missile Development Plan, Jun 14, 1956; WDD Development Plan, Jun 15, 1956, in Basic Documents.

30. Memo, Maj Gen Samuel R. Brentnall, Assistant Chief of Staff, Guided Missiles, to Air Staff, subj: Review of the ICBM/ IRBM Operational Program, Jun 19, 1956; minutes, 4th AF–BMC Mtg, Jul 3, 1956; notes by Col Ray E. Soper, Secy AF–BMC, Jul 3, 1956; memo, Brentnall to Gen Thomas D. White, VCSAF, subj: ICBM/IRBM Initial Operational Capability Plans, Jul 6, 1956.

31. Minutes, 4th AF–BMC Mtg, Jul 3, 1956; ASSS (draft), Maj Gen Samuel R. Brentnall, Assistant Chief of Staff, Guided Missiles, to Gen Nathan F. Twining, AF Chief of Staff, subj: ICBM/IRBM Initial Operational Capability Plans (IOC), ca Jul 10, 1956; WDD Development Plan, Vol II, Sep 1, 1956, in Basic Documents; memo, Gen Thomas D. White, VCSAF, to Twining, subj: Annual Review of the Ballistic Missile Program, Sep 26, 1956; notes by Col Ray E. Soper, BSD Vice Comdr, Sep 24, 1956.

32. Minutes, 5th AF–BMC Mtg, Sep 27, 1956; notes by Col Ray E. Soper, BSD Vice Comdr, Sep 27, 1956; memo, Col J. J. Huddleston, Dep Asst CSAF(GM), to Gen Thomas D. White, VCSAF, subj: Presentation Schedule of Ballistic Missile Program, Oct 29, 1956; Stf study by Soper, subj: Annual Review of Ballistic Missile Program, Nov 2, 1956; memo, Maj Gen Jacob B. Smart, Asst VCSAF, to Brig Gen Charles M. McCorkle, Asst CSAF (GM), subj: Ballistic Missile Program, Nov 9, 1956; minutes, 6th AF–BMC Mtg, Nov 10, 1956; msg, CSAF to WDD, 48676, Nov 16, 1956.

33. Memo, Richard E. Horner, Actg Asst SAF (RD), to OSD–BMC, subj: Air Force Ballistic Missile Program, Nov 23, 1956; memo, Col Ray E. Soper, BSD Vice Comdr, to SAF and Air Staff, subj: OSD–BMC Review of the Air Force Ballistic Missile Program, Dec 6, 1956; memo, Charles E. Wilson, Secretary of Defense, to Mil Depts and JCS, subj: Ballistic Missile Program, ca Jan 11, 1957; memo, Donald A. Quarles, Secretary AF, to Charles E. Wilson, Secretary of Defense, subj: Ballistic Missile Operational Capability, Jan 12, 1957; memo, Dep SECDEF to Mil depts and JCS, subj: Ballistic Missile Program, Apr 5, 1957.

34. Ltr, Maj Gen Jacob B. Smart, Asst VCSAF, to Lt Gen Thomas S. Power, Cmdr ARDC, subj: Initial Operational Capability, IRBM, Mar 5, 1957, in Basic Documents.

35. Memo, Donald A. Quarles, Secretary AF, to Charles E. Wilson, Secretary of Defense, subj: Operational Employment of the Land-Based Intermediate Range Ballistic Missile (IRBM), Mar 31, 1956, in OSAF Files 1063-56, Suitland NFRC; memo, Gen Nathan F. Twining, AF Chief of Staff, to Quarles, same subj, Mar 28, 1956; memo, Wilson to Armed Forces Policy Council, subj: Clarification of Roles and Missions to Improve the Effectiveness of Operation of the Department of Defense, Nov 26, 1956, in Hearings before the Subcommittee of the Committee on Government Operations, *Organization and Management of Missile Programs*, House of Representatives, 86th Cong, 1st Sess (Washington, 1956), pt 6, p 748; Michael H. Armacost, *The Politics of Weapons Innovation: The Thor-Jupiter Controversy* (New York, 1969), pp 117–120; intvw, Maj Gen O. J. Ritland, former BMD Commander, with Lt Col L. R. Officer, Mar 19–21, 1974.

36. Minutes, 6th AF–BMC Mtg, Nov 10, 1956; ltr, 1st Ind, Lt Gen Thomas S. Power, Cmdr ARDC, to CSAF, subj: IRBM Emergency Capability Plan, Dec 28, 1956.

37. Ltr, Gen Bernard A. Schriever, Cmdr WDD, to CSAF, subj: IRBM Emergency Capability Plan, Dec 24, 1956.

38. Memo, Brig Gen Charles M. McCorkle, Dep Asst VCSAF (GM), to Asst DCS/O, subj: IRBM Emergency Capability, Nov 29, 1956; memo, McCorkle to Dir/Plans, subj: IRBM Emergency Capability Study, Jan 7, 1957; memo, Col Ray E. Soper, BSD Vice Comdr, to Dir/Plans, subj: IRBM Capability Plan, Jan 7, 1957; memo, Col F. O. Easly, Dep Dir/Opns, to Dir/Plans, same subj, Jan 10, 1957.

39. Memo, Gen Thomas D. White, VC-SAF, to Donald A. Quarles, Secretary AF, subj: IRBM Emergency Capability Plan, Jan 9, 1957; ASSS, Maj Gen R. C. Lindsay, Dir/Plans, to Quarles, subj: Provision of the SM–75 (THOR) Weapon System to the British and IRBM Emergency Capability Plan, Jan 17, 1957; memo, Dr. Eger V. Murphree, OSD Director, Guided Missiles, to Charles E. Wilson, Secretary of Defense, subj: IRBM Discussions with United Kingdom Representatives, Jan 24, 1957; memo, Quarles to Wilson, subj: Provision of the SM–75 (THOR) Weapon System to the British and IRBM Emergency Plan, Jan 25, 1957; memo, Murphree to Wilson, no subj, Jan 28, 1957; ltr, Wilson to President Dwight D. Eisenhower, no subj, Jan 28, 1957.

40. Memo, Richard E. Horner, Actg Asst SAF (RD), to Asst SECDEF (ISA), subj: US–UK Talks, January 28–February 1, 1957, Mar 7, 1957.

41. Memo, Gen Thomas D. White, VC-SAF, to AF–BMC, subj: IRBM Emergency Capability Plan, Mar 29, 1957; minutes, 9th AF–BMC Mtg, Mar 29, 1957; memo, Donald A. Quarles, Secretary AF, to White, subj: IRBM Emergency Capability Plan, April 5, 1957; ltr, Charles E. Wilson, Secretary of Defense, to Duncan Sandys, Min of Defence (UK), no subj, Apr 18, 1957; msg, CSAF to SAC, ARDC, and WDD, 55351, Apr 26, 1957.

42. Minutes, 3d AF–BMC Mtg, Mar 29, 1956; memo, Col J. E. Dougherty, Dep Ch Opns Control Div, to Dir/Opns, subj: IRBM Overseas Facility Requirements, Aug 21, 1956.

43. Minutes, 6th AF–BMC Mtg, Nov 10, 1956.

44. Presn by Gen Bernard A. Schriever, Cmdr WDD, to NSC, subj: Progress of the USAF Ballistic Missile Program During Calendar Year 1956, Jan 11, 1957; SAC Strategic Missile Monthly Progress Report, Jan 1957.

45. Memo, Dr. Eger V. Murphree, OSD Director, Guided Missiles, to Charles E. Wilson, Secretary of Defense, Jan 28, 1957; ltr, Wilson to President Eisenhower, no subj, Jan 28, 1957; memo, Richard E. Horner, Acting Asst Sec for R&D, to Asst SECDEF (ISA), Mar 7, 1957; memo, Donald A. Quarles, Secretary AF, to Wilson, subj: IRBM Deployment in UK, Mar 26, 1957; ASSS, Maj Gen K. P. Bergquist, Dir/Opns, to DCS/O, subj: Initial Operational Capability, IRBM, Apr 26, 1957.

46. Minutes, 9th AF–BMC Mtg, Mar 29, 1957, Apr 8, 1957; minutes, 10th AF–BMC Mtg, May 27, 1957, Jun 10, 1957; ltr, Brig Gen Charles M. McCorkle, Dep Asst VCSAF (GM), to Gen Bernard A. Schriever, Cmdr WDD, subj: Reduction of Second Source Contract Efforts ICBM/IRBM Programs, Jun 10, 1957, in Basic Documents.

47. AFPC Advice of Action, May 22, 1957; minutes, 10th AF–BMC Mtg, May 27, 1957, Jun 10, 1957; DOD Directive 4105.48, Jun 19, 1957; memo, William Holaday, Spec Asst for GM (OSD), to Chmn AF–BMC, subj: Overtime Requirements of ICBM and IRBM Programs, Jul 16, 1957, in Basic Documents.

48. Memo, Gen Thomas D. White to SAF, subj: Defense Against Possible Guided Missile Program Reductions, Aug 6, 1957.

49. Memo, Charles E. Wilson, Secretary of Defense, to President Eisenhower, no subj, Jul 31, 1957; NSC Action 1765, Aug 1, 1957.

50. Presn by Gen Bernard A. Schriever, Cmdr WDD, to Air Staff, Sep 11, 1957.

51. Memo, Gen Thomas D. White, CSAF, to SAF, Aug 6, 1957.

52. Ibid.

53. MR, Col Ray E. Soper, BSD Vice Comdr, subj: OSD Review of ICBM/IRBM Program, Aug 10, 1957; msg, WDG 8–4–E, BMD to ARDC, 09/0010Z Aug 1957; memo, Charles E. Wilson, Secretary of Defense, to SAF, subj: Revision of ICBM/IRBM Program, Aug 16, 1957, w/atch, in Basic Documents.

54. Memo, Gen Bernard A. Schriever, Cmdr WDD, to Brig Gen Bernard I. Funk, Head, AMC Ballistic Missile Office, and Col Charles H. Terhune, Chairman, Source Selection Board, subj: Instructions for Briefing Prime Weapon System Contractors in the Ballistic Missile Program, Aug 14, 1957, in Basic Documents; msg, Schriever to J. A. Anderson, Gen Mgr, AC Spark Plug, and to major missile contractors, WDTD–8–1, Aug 15, 1957, in Basic Documents.

55. Msg, BMD to ARDC, WDG 8–4–E, Aug 10, 1957; minutes, 12th AF–BMC Mtg, Sep 11, 1957; notes, Col Ray E. Soper, BSD Vice Comdr, same subj, Sep 12, 1957; MR, Soper, subj: Revised Missile Program, Sep 16, 1957; memo, Soper to Under SAF, subj: Additional Funding, Sep 16, 1957, in Basic Documents.

56. Memo, Col Ray E. Soper, BSD Vice Comdr, to Under SAF, subj: Additional Funding, Sep 16, 1957, in Basic Documents.

57. Notes, Col Ray E. Soper, BSD Vice Comdr, subj: Revised Ballistic Missile Program, Sep 12, 1957.

58. Memo, James H. Douglas, Secretary AF, to Charles E. Wilson, Secretary of Defense, subj: Requested ICBM Program Appropriations and Expenditures for FY 1958–FY 1959, Sep 17, 1957; memo, Wilson to Douglas, subj: ICBM Appropriations and Expenditures, Sep 19, 1957; MR, Col Ray E. Soper, BSD Vice Comdr, no subj, Oct 2, 1957; MR, Lt Col Charles W. Getz, Prog Mgmt and Presn Div (BMD), no subj, Jun 21, 1957, in Basic Documents.

59. Memo, Charles E. Wilson, Secretary of Defense, to James H. Douglas, Secretary AF, subj: ICBM Program, Oct 5, 1957, in Basic Documents; Ltr, Lt Gen Donald L. Putt, DCS/D, to Lt Gen Samuel E. Anderson, Comdr ARDC, no subj, Oct 17, 1957 in Basic Documents; ltr, Neil H. McElroy, SECDEF, to President Eisenhower, no subj, Dec 3, 1957.

60. Intvw, author with Joseph Alsop, columnist, Washington, DC, Sep 7, 1977. Stewart Alsop, "Matter of Fact," New York Herald Tribune, Aug 30, Sept 8, Sept 16, Oct 9, 1957; Joseph Alsop, "Matter of Fact," New York Herald Tribune, Oct 14, Oct 16, 1957.

61. Msg, Gen Thomas D. White, CSAF, to Gen Bernard A. Schriever, Cmdr WDD, 51210, Oct 8, 1957; msg, Schriever to White, WDG 10–3–E, 09/1109Z Oct 1957, in Basic Documents; memo, Maj Gen Jacob B.

Smart, Asst VCSAF(GM), to DCS/Plans and Programs, no subj, Oct 8, 1957; memo, Brig Gen Charles M. McCorkle, Dep Asst VCSAF(GM) to White, subj: Proposed Possible Acceleration of IRBM, ICBM, and WS-117L Programs, Oct 10, 1957; MR, Col J. J. Courtney, Dep Ch, Ball Msl Div, subj: Meeting with General White, Oct 17, 1957; ltr, Brig Gen O. J. Ritland, Vice Comdr BMD, to McCorkle, subj: Acceleration of the Ballistic Missile Programs, Oct 25, 1957, in Basic Documents; memo, SAF to SECDEF, subj: FY 1958 Supplemental and FY 1959 Package Augmentation, Nov 14, 1957; memo, McCorkle to White, subj: Material for Statement on "Immediate requirements," Dec 27, 1957.

62. NSC Action 18000, Oct 10, 1957; memo, William Holaday, Spec Asst for GM (OSD), to Charles E. Wilson, Secretary of Defense, subj: Report of the Thor–Jupiter IRBM Review Committee, Oct 8, 1956, in Basic Documents.

63. Memo, Neil McElroy, Secretary of Defense, to James H. Douglas, Secretary AF, subj: IRBM Program, Oct 31, 1957.

64. Msg, Gen Bernard A. Schriever, Cmdr WDD, to Gen Thomas D. White, AF Chief of Staff, WDG 11-4-E, Nov 9, 1957; ltr, Schriever to White, subj: IRBM Program, Nov 13, 1957; memo, Brig Gen Charles M. McCorkle, Dep Asst VCSAF(GM), to White, subj: IRBM Program, Nov 22, 1957, in White Papers, Box 5, LC.

65. Memo, James H. Douglas, Secretary AF, to William Holaday, Spec Asst for GM (OSD), subj: Ballistic Missile Weekly Progress Report, Nov 1, 1957; memo, Douglas to Neil McElroy, Secretary of Defense, no subj, Nov 8, 1957; memo, Holaday to Douglas, subj: Use of Overtime in ATLAS and TITAN Ballistic Missile Programs, Nov 22, 1957, in Basic Documents.

66. Memo, James H. Douglas, Secretary AF, to Neil McElroy, Secretary of Defense, no subj, Nov 14, 1957; memo, Douglas to William Holaday, Spec Asst for GM(OSD), subj: Ballistic Missile Weekly Progress Report, Nov 15, 1957.

67. Ltr, Gen Bernard A. Schriever, Cmdr WDD, to Gen Thomas D. White, AF Chief of Staff, no subj, Nov 13, 1957.

68. Memo, James H. Douglas, Secretary AF, to Neil McElroy, Secretary of Defense, subj: IRBM Program, Nov 18, 1957.

69. Msgs, Gen Thomas D. White, AF Chief of Staff, to Gen Samuel E. Anderson, Gen Bernard A. Schriever, and Gen Ben I. Funk, 52878, Nov 15, 1957, and Nov 22, 1957.

70. Memo, Neil McElroy, Secretary of Defense, to James H. Douglas, Secretary AF, no subj, Nov 25, 1957; DOD Press Release, Nov 27, 1957.

71. Memo, William Holaday, Spec Asst for GM (OSD), to SAF and Sec Army, subj: IRBM Program, Nov 25, 1957; memo, Holaday to SAF and SEC Army, subj: THOR–JUPITER Missile Systems, Nov 27, 1957; MR, Col Ray E. Soper, BSD Vice Comdr, subj: IRBM Program, Nov 27, 1957.

72. Memo, James H. Douglas, Secretary AF, to Neil McElroy, Secretary of Defense, no subj, Nov 18, 1957; MR, Col Ray E. Soper, BSD Vice Comdr, subj: IRBM Program, Nov 27, 1957; ltr, Gen Bernard A. Schriever, Cmdr WDD, to Gen Thomas D. White, AF Chief of Staff, subj: Production of Thor and Jupiter IRBM's for Operational Use, Dec 2, 1957; memo, White to Douglas, subj: THOR–JUPITER Decision, Dec 3, 1957; ASSS, Soper to Douglas, subj: IRBM Program, Dec 4, 1957; MR, Soper, subj: IRBM Program, Dec 11, 1957; memo, White to Douglas, no subj, Dec 19, 1957; memo, William Holaday, Spec Asst for GM (OSD) to JCS, subj: Deployment of IRBM Missile, Dec 20, 1957.

73. History, 7th Air Division (SAC), Jan 1–Jun 30, 1958, pp 62–86.

74. Memo, James H. Douglas, Secretary AF, to Gen Thomas D. White, AF Chief of Staff, no subj, Oct 8, 1957; memo, William Holaday, Spec Asst for GM (OSD), to Douglas, subj: Use of Overtime in ATLAS and TITAN Ballistic Missile Programs, Nov 22, 1957; memo, Holaday to AF-BMC, subj: Reinstatement of ICBM Launch Complex #20, Patrick AFB, Nov 27, 1957.

75. Msg, Gen Bernard A. Schriever, Cmdr WDD, to Gen Thomas D. White, AF Chief of Staff, WDG 10-3-E, Oct 9, 1957; ltr, Maj Gen Osmond J. Ritland, Cmdr BMD, to Brig Gen Charles M. McCorkle, Dep Asst VCSAF(GM), no subj, Oct 25,

1957; memo, James H. Douglas, Secretary AF, to Neil McElroy, Secretary of Defense, no subj, Nov 14, 1957.

76. Memo, James H. Douglas, Secretary AF, to Neil McElroy, Secretary of Defense, no subj, Nov 14, 1957; memo, Brig Gen Charles M. McCorkle, Dep Asst VCSAF(GM), to Spec Asst to CSAF, no subj, Dec 27, 1957.

77. Memo, Brig Gen Charles M. McCorkle, Dep Asst VCSAF(GM), to Spec Asst to CSAF, no subj, Dec 27, 1957.

78. Memo, William Holaday, Spec Asst for GM (OSD), to AF–BMC, subj: Acceleration of ATLAS ICBM Program, Dec 12, 1957; ltr, Maj Gen Osmond J. Ritland, Cmdr BMD to Brig Gen Charles M. McCorkle, Dep Asst VCSAF(GM), subj: Ballistic Missile Program Acceleration, Dec 21, 1957, in Basic Documents; memo, McCorkle to Spec Asst to CSAF, no subj, Dec 27, 1957; ltr, Ritland to Gen Thomas D. White, AF Chief of Staff, subj: Atlas Program Acceleration, Dec 31, 1957; MR, Col Ray E. Soper, BSD Vice Comdr, subj: ICBM Program, Jan 7, 1958; msg, White to Gen Bernard A. Schriever, Cmdr WDD, 54975, Jan 10, 1958.

79. Presn, William Holaday, Spec Asst for GM (OSD) to NSC, subj: The U.S. Ballistic Missiles Program, Jan 30, 1958; memo, Neil McElroy, Secretary of Defense, to JCS, Dir/ GMs (OSD), and Mil Depts, subj: Ballistic Missile Programs, Feb 10, 1958.

80. Monthly Status Report, BMD, Mar 1958, in Basic Documents.

81. Ltr, Maj Gen Donald L. Putt, Vice Cmdr ARDC, to Comdr ARDC, subj: Project ATLAS, Jun 21, 1954; memo, Maj Roy L. Ferguson, Asst for Plans (WDD), to Col Charles H. Terhune, Dep Comdr for Technical Opns (WDD), subj: Outline of Weapons System Planning, Jan 13, 1955; ltr, Gen Bernard A. Schriever, Cmdr WDD, to CSAF, subj: SM–65 Operational Concepts, Feb 18, 1955, in Basic Documents.

82. Memo, Maj Roy L. Ferguson, Asst for Plans (WDD), to Col Charles H. Terhune, Dep Comdr for Technical Opns (WDD), subj: Training Philosophy for ICBM Programs, Feb 8, 1955, in Basic Documents.

83. "Recommended Operational Concepts for the SM–65 Intercontinental Ballistic Missile," WDO, Mar 1955, in Basic Documents; "Outline of Actions Accomplished Prior to 1 Aug 1955," Maj Roy L. Ferguson, Aug 11, 1955, in Basic Documents.

84. Weapon System 107A Development Plan, Apr 15, 1955, in Basic Documents.

85. Ltr, Col William Sheppard , Dep Cmdr, Plans & Ops (WDD), to CINCSAC, subj: Preliminary SM–65 Operational Considerations, ca Jul 1955, in Basic Documents; ltr, Gen Bernard A. Schriever, Cmdr WDD, to CSAF, subj: Operational Concepts for SM–65, Oct 3, 1955; ltr, Lt Gen Thomas S. Power, Cmdr ARDC, to Schriever, subj: Authority for ICBM and IRBM Programs, Dec 14, 1955; Trip Rprt, Lt Col R. J. Lynch and Maj R. L. Ferguson, Asst for Plans (WDD), subj: Visit to Headquarters SAC on Feb 7, 1956, nd.

86. Memo, James H. Douglas, Secretary AF, to Donald A. Quarles, Secretary AF, subj: ICBM Operational Sites, Jul 19, 1956; MR, Lt Col Vernon L. Hastings, Dir/ Installations (WDD), subj: Site Selection Briefing for Secretary Quarles, Aug 20, 1956, in BAS Papers; MR, Maj Gen Osmond J. Ritland, Cmdr BMD, subj: IRBM Training and IOC Planning, Aug 16, 1956; MR, Maj C. B. Alexander, Planning and Site Selection Branch (WDD), subj: Briefing Supporting Operational Requirement for Camp Cooke, Aug 31, 1956; hist, WDD, Jan 1–Dec 31, 1956, pp 58–71; memo, Quarles to CSAF, subj: ICBM Site Planning, Sep 1, 1956; memo, Charles E. Wilson, Secretary of Defense, to Sec Army, subj: Camp Cooke, California, Nov 16, 1956; Monthly Status Report, BMD, Sep 1957.

87. Hist, WDD, Jan 1–Dec 31, 1956, pp 66–69; minutes, 10th AF–BMC Mtg, May 27, 1957; Monthly Status Reports, BMD, Sep and Oct 1957.

88. "Atlas: Intercontinental Ballistic Missile," *Convair/ Astronautics*, Sep 1959, in Basic Documents; Chronology, *Atlas* (Asst CSAF (GM), nd), in AFCHO K416.516–6.

89. Chronology, *Atlas* (Asst CSAF (GM), nd), in AFCHO K416.516–6.

90. *Ibid.*

91. Ltr, Lt Gen Thomas S. Power, Cmdr ARDC, to CSAF, subj: Ballistic Missile Weapon Systems, Aug 14, 1956; ASSS, Dir/

M&O to CSAF, subj: Ballistic Missile Weapon systems, Aug 24, 1956; ltr, Maj Gen G. A. Blake, Asst DCS/O to Power, subj: Ballistic Missile Weapon Systems, Aug 28, 1956; ltr, Col R. M. Grek, Dir/M&O (ARDC), to Dir/M&O (Hq USAF), subj: Manpower Requirements for IOC, Nov 21, 1956; ltr, Maj Gen T. C. Musgrove, Dir/ M&O, to Power, subj: Manpower Requirements for IOC, Nov 30, 1956.

92. Ltr, Col J. A. McKerley, Asst Dep Comdr for Resources (ARDC), to Dir/M&O (Hq USAF), subj: Manpower Requirements for Ballistic Missile IOC Program, Jan 14, 1957; msg, Gen Bernard A. Schriever, Cmdr WDD, to CSAF, RDS001-21-E, Jan 15, 1957; MR, Maj W. G. Wells, Dep Spec Asst CSAF (GM), subj: Summary of Current Manpower and Organization Status, Jan 29, 1957; ltr, Maj Gen John W. Sessums, Vice Comdr ARDC, to CSAF, subj: Manpower Requirements for the Ballistic Missile IOC Program, Feb 14, 1957.

93. Ltr, Maj Gen T. C. Musgrove, Actg Asst DCS/O, to Lt Gen Thomas S. Power, Cmdr ARDC, subj: Manpower Requirements for the Ballistic Missile Initial Operational Program, Mar 13, 1957; BMD Monthly Status Report, BMD, Jul 1957; ARDC GO 7, Mar 27, 1957; 1st Missile Div GO 1, Apr 15, 1957, in Basic Documents.

94. BMD Monthly Status Reports, Dec 1957 and Jan 1958.

95. Hearings before the Committee on Post Office and Civil Service, House of Representatives, 86th Cong, 1st Sess (Washington, 1957).

96. Ltr, Gen Bernard A. Schriever, Cmdr WDD, to Comdr ARDC, subj: Management of Air Force Ballistic Missiles Program, May 23, 1957, in Basic Documents.

97. Memo, Col Charles H. Terhune, Chairman, Source Selection Board, to WDD Staff, subject; Reorganization of WDT, Feb 6, 1956; ltr, Maj William C. Bumm, Adjutant, to WDD Staff, subj: Reorganization and Realignment of Functions of Technical Operations (WDT), Feb 23, 1956; memo, Col Charles E. Norton, Asst Dep Cmdr, Tech Ops (WDD), to Col Osmond J. Ritland, subj: Report of the Committee Appointed to Study WDD Organizational Problems, Jul 31, 1956;

MR, Terhune, subj: Engineering Management as Associated with the R–W Contract, Aug 24, 1956; ltr, Gen Bernard A. Schriever, Cmdr WDD, to Comdr AFMTC, subj: Management Requirements, Nov 6, 1956, w/atch: Integration of WDD into Normal Structure of ARDC, in Basic Documents; memo, Schriever to Terhune and Simon Ramo, subj: Development–Management Organization Role of R–W, Nov 19, 1956, in BAS Papers.

98. Memo, Gen Bernard A. Schriever, Cmdr WDD, to Col Charles H. Terhune and Simon Ramo, subj: Development–Management Organization Role of R–W, Nov 19, 1956, in BAS Papers; ARDC GO 19, May 21, 1957, in AFSC Hist Ofc; memo, Maj Gen John S. Mills, Asst DCS/D, to DCS/D, subj: Policy Regarding the Ballistic Missile Program, Jun 3, 1957, in Basic Documents.

99. MOUs, s/ Gen Bernard A. Schriever, Cmdr WDD, and Brig Gen Howell M. Estes, Dir of WS (ARDC Det 1), subj: Transfer of Functional Responsibility for ARS Program, Jan 13, 1956, in BAS Papers; excerpt from ARDC Guided Missiles and Space Vehicle Working Group, Report of Meetings held Dec 2–11, 1957 and Dec 17–19, 1957, Mar 21, 1958, in Basic Documents.

100. Rprt, The Scientific Advisory Committee's First Report on Ballistic Missiles to the Secretary of Defense, OSD, Feb 11, 1956, in Basic Documents.

101. Ltr, Gen Donald L. Putt, Cmdr ARDC, to Lt Gen Thomas S. Power, Cmdr ARDC, subj: IRBM Weapon Systems, Mar 20, 1957; GOR No. 161, Hq USAF, subj: Short-Range Ballistic Missile Weapon System, Jul 19, 1957; ltr, Maj Gen John W. Sessums, ARDC, to Gen Bernard A. Schriever, Cmdr WDD, no subj, Aug 16, 1957; ltr, Schriever to Sessums, no subj, Sep 20, 1957; memo, Col Charles H. Terhune, Chairman, Source Selection Board, to Col Charles E. Norton, Asst Dep Cmdr, Tech Ops (WDD), subj: Creation of a Solids WS Office, Sep 27, 1957; ltr, Gen Samuel E. Anderson, AMC Cmdr, to Gen Thomas D. White, AF Chief of Staff, no subj, Oct 4, 1957, in Basic Documents; ltr, Schriever to Anderson, subj: Proposal for Future Air Force Ballistic Missile and Space Technology Development, Dec 18, 1957, in Basic Documents.

102. Msg, Cmdrs AMC, ARDC and SAC to CSAF, MCG–3627, Nov 27, 1957; "Gen. White, USAF Chief of Staff, Discusses Space Age Missions of All Three Services," *Army-Navy-Air Force Journal*, Dec 7, 1957; msg, Gen Bernard A. Schriever, Cmdr WDD, to Cmdrs ARDC, SAC, AMC, and Asst CSAF (GM), WDG 11–16–E, Nov 29, 1957; msg, CSAF to Cmdrs ARDC, SAC, AMC, BMD, 53440, Dec 1, 1957; msg, CSAF to AMC, 53891, Dec 12, 1957; msg, CSAF to Cmdrs SAC, ARDC, and ATC, 54251, Dec 20, 1957; MOU, SAC and BMD, subj: Ballistic Missiles IOC Responsibilities, Dec 31, 1957, in Basic Documents.

103. MOU, SAC and BMD, subj: Ballistic Missiles IOC Responsibilities, Dec 31, 1957, in Basic Documents; SAC GO 1, Jan 2, 1958.

104. Intvws, Max Rosenberg, AFCHO, with Maj Gen Charles M. McCorkle, Dep Asst VCSAF(GM), Col L. C. Brooks, Ch Msl Br (Dir/Opns), and Lt Col E. J. Istvan, Bal Div Asst CSAF (GM), cited in IOC monograph, AFCHO.

105. Presn, William Holaday, Spec Asst for GM (OSD) to NSC, subj: The U.S. Ballistic Missile Program, Jan 30, 1958; msg, CINCSAC to CSAF and Comdr ATC, C9159, Dec 24, 1957; Development Plan (BMD), May 1958.

Chapter VII

The Operational Force

1. AFPC Advice of Action, subj: Evaluation of Offensive and Defensive Weapon Systems, Jan 30, 1958; Minutes, 14th AFBMC Meeting, Feb 6, 1958, in BAS Papers.

2. Memo, SAF to SECDEF, subj: Air Force Ballistic Missile Objectives, Feb 10, 1958; MR, Col R.E. Soper, Asst CS (GM), subj: Secretary of Defense Review of Ballistic Missile Proposals, Feb 10, 1958; AFC 10/301, subj: Ballistic Missile Programs, Feb 24, 1958.

3. Memo, Neil McElroy, Secretary of Defense, to JCS, subj: Air Force Ballistic Missile Objective, Feb 14, 1958; JCS 2101/295, no subj, Feb 24, 1958; memo, SECDEF to JCS, subj: Report to the President, Feb 24, 1958; memo, SECDEF to JCS, subj: Augmentation of the Present ICBM and Polaris Submarine Weapons Systems, Apr 9, 1958.

4. AF BMD Development Plan, May 20, 1958; Minutes, 19th AF–BMC Meeting, Jun 11, 1958; memo, James H. Douglas, Secretary AF to OSD–BMC, subj: Submission of the May 20, 1958 BMD Development Plan, Jun 24, 1958; Rough Draft, "Atlas History," nd, in SAMSO/Hist Ofc; Atlas Programming Actions, BMD, ca. Jan 1961, in AFSC/Hist Ofc.

5. Atlas Programming Actions, BMD, ca. Jan 1961, in AFSC/Hist Ofc.

6. Minutes, 21st AF–BMC Meeting, Jul 18, 1958; memo, James H. Douglas, Secretary AF, to SECDEF, subj: ICBM Programs, Aug 5, 1958; memo, William Holaday, Spec Asst for GM (OSD) to Douglas, subj: Atlas and Titan Programs, Aug 14, 1958; memo, Holaday to Douglas, subj: Air Force Planning and Programming for a Ballistic Missile Force Build-up, Sep 10, 1958; The USAF Ballistic Missile Program, WDGP–60–25, 7 vols (Los Angeles: Ballistic Missile Division, 1960), Vol II, IV–64 (124) [hereafter LeMay Report].

7. Minutes, 26th AF–BMC Meeting, Nov 13, 1958.

8. Memo, Lt Gen C. S. Irvine, DCS/M, to Asst CS(GM), subj: Atlas, Titan, and Minuteman Programs, Aug 21, 1958.

9. Minutes, 26th AF–BMC Meeting, Nov 13, 1958; JCS 1800/275, no subj, Dec 6, 1958; memo, William Holaday, Spec Asst for GM (OSD), to AF–BMC, subj: Fund Reservations for FY 1959 and Prior Air Force Ballistic Missile Programs, Jan 8, 1959; President's Budget Message to Congress, Jan 19, 1959.

10. Memo, JCS to SECDEF, subj: Weapon Systems for Strategic Delivery, Jan 20, 1959; Hearings before the Subcommittee of the Committee on Appropriations, *DOD*

Appropriations for 1960, House of Representatives, 86th Cong, 1st Sess (Washington, 1960), Pt I and Pt VI, *passim* [hereafter Mahon Hearings]; Hearings before the Subcommittee of the Committee on Appropriations, Senate, *DOD Appropriations for 1960*, 86th Cong, 1st Sess (Washington, 1960), *passim* [hereafter Chavez Hearings].

11. Chavez Hearings.

12. *Ibid.*

13. Memo, SAF to SECDEF, subj: Basic Factors Concerning Atlas Deployment Concepts, Feb 17, 1959; minutes, 29th AF-BMC Meeting, Feb 25, 1959; MR, Maj E. J. Istvan, Asst CS(GM), subj: Series of Meetings Relating to Atlas MAX-MAX Program, Feb 28, 1959.

14. Msg, SAC to VCSAF, C2233, Mar 3, 1959; memo, VCSAF to DCS/Plans and Progs, et al, subj: Ballistic Missile Force Structure, Mar 5, 1959; ASSS, Dir/Plans to SAF, subj: Ballistic Missile Force Structure, Mar 5, 1959; ASSS, Dir/Plans to SAF, subj: Strategic Force Considerations, Mar 13, 1959; memo, James H. Douglas, Secretary AF, to SECDEF, subj: Strategic Force Considerations, Apr 14, 1959.

15. Mahon Hearings, Pt IV, p 43; ltr, William Holaday, Spec Asst for GM (OSD), to House Amd Svcs Cmte, no subj, May 6, 1959; AFC 13/3, subj: USAF Tasks and Objective Force Structure (1959-1970), May 15, 1959; memo, SAF to Holaday, subj: Tooling for Higher Atlas Production, May 19, 1959; Memo, Holaday to Under SAF, same subj, May 21, 1959; memo, Asst SAF (FM) to SECDEF, subj: Atlas "E" Program Jun 5, 1959; Chavez Hearings, pp 1424, 1489.

16. JCS 1620/215, no subj, Jan 14, 1959; JCS 1800/288, no subj, May 25, 1959; memo, Lt Gen J.K. Gerhart, DCS/Plans and Progs, to CSAF, subj: JCS position on ICBM Quantity, Jan 8, 1960; Chavez Hearings, pp 189 and 195-196; Mahon Hearings, pp 330-331.

17. Minutes, 28th AF-BMC Meeting, Feb 4, 1959; memo, SAF to SECDEF, no subj, Feb 12, 1959.

18. Msg, CSAF to AFBMD, 58945, Apr 15, 1959; msg, CSAF to AFBMD and SAC, 59085, Apr 16, 1959; memo, Asst CS(GM) to Dist, subj: Review of AFBMD Ballistic Missile Development Plans, May 21, 1959.

19. Memo, Asst CS(GM) to Dist, subj: Review of AFBMD Ballistic Missile Development Plans, May 21, 1959.

20. Rprt, Ad Hoc Group of the Scientific Advisory Committee to the Secretary of Defense for Ballistic Missiles, Jun 17-18, 1959; memo, SAF, to SECDEF, subj: Status of Atlas IOC, Jun 24, 1959.

21. Minutes, 21st AF-BMC Meeting, Jul 18, 1958; memo, James H. Douglas, Secretary AF to SECDEF, no subj, Apr 14, 1959; memo, Asst CS(GM) to Dist, subj: Review of AF-BMD Atlas, Titan and Thor Ballistic Missile Development Plans, May 6, 1959.

22. Minutes, 35th AF-BMC Meeting, Jul 1, 1959.

23. Msg, CSAF to AFBMD, No. 64250, Aug 14, 1959; msgs, AFBMD to CSAF, Nos. 21704, 22345, and 67332, dated Aug 22, 23, and 25, 1959.

24. Max Rosenberg, *USAF Ballistic Missiles, 1958-1959* (Washington: USAF Historical Division Liaison Office, 1960), p 26.

25. *Ibid*, pp 29, 31.

26. Atlas Development Plan, AFBMD, Dec 15, 1959, in Basic Documents.

27. Titan Development Plan, AFBMD, Nov 30, 1959, in Basic Documents.

28. Jacob Van Staaveren, *USAF Intercontinental Ballistic Missiles, Fiscal Years 1960-1961*, pp 9-18.

29. "Atlas History" (Draft), in SAMSO/Hist Ofc; Atlas Programming Actions, AFBMD, ca. 1961, in SAMSO/Hist Ofc.

30. Memo, Thomas S. Gates, Secretary of Defense, to Spec Asst to the President (NSC), subj: Scope of Operational Capability of the Atlas and Titan ICBM Programs and Polaris FBM Program, Jan 4, 1960; memo, Gates to SAF et al, no subj, Jan 25, 1960.

31. Ltr, Gen Bernard A. Schriever, Cmdr WDD, to Gen Thomas D. White, AF Chief of Staff, subj: Titan ICBM Program, Dec 19, 1959, in OSAF Files 6-59; memo, SAF to AF-BMC, subj: Cost of ICBM Operational Force, Feb 19, 1960; Mahon Hearings, Pt III, pp 778-779; "Martin Will Consolidate Its Titan Plan," *Baltimore Sun*, Dec 24, 1959.

32. Mahon Hearings, Pt II, pp 330-338, and Pt VI, pp 84-93; Chavez Hearings, pp 1824-1825; Gen Bernard A. Schriever, Cmdr WDD, is said to have coined the term "aero-

space" (see Futrell, *Ideas*, p 295, citing 86th Cong, 1st Sess, *Investigation of Governmental Organization for Space Activities*, p 396).

33. Memo, SAF to SECDEF, subj: Cost of ICBM Operational Forces, Mar 15, 1960; memo, Asst CS(GM), to Asst SAF (FM), subj: Adapting Atlas to Titan Facilities, Jan 20, 1960, in OSAF Files, pp 23–60.

34. Mahon Hearings, Pt I, pp 59 and 159; Pt II, pp 211 and 330–338; Pt III, pp 778–779; Chavez Hearings, Pt II, pp 611–612.

35. Minutes, 45th and 46th AF-BMC Meetings, Feb 10 and 17, 1960, in OSAF files, pp 23–60; rprt, AFBMD, subj: Summary Report on USAF Ballistic Missile Program, Feb 21, 1960; msg, CSAF to AFBMD and SAC, Feb 25, 1960; "Atlas History" (Draft), SAMSO/HO, nd; msg, SAF to AFBM No. MPP–W–2 68301, Jul 11, 1960.

36. Memo, Dep SECDEF to Chmn AF-BMC, subj: Atlas FY 1960 Dev & Fiscal Plans, Mar 14, 1960; memo, Under SAF to OSD–BMC, same subj: Mar 30, 1960; memo, Chmn OSD–BMC to Chmn, AF–BMC, same subj, Jun 22, 1960.

37. Minutes, 45th, 46th, and 47th AF-BMC Meetings, Feb 10, Feb 17, and Apr 14, 1960.

38. Minutes, 50th AF-BMC Meeting, Jun 3, 1960; msg, CSAF to AFBMD, No. 99900, Jun 7, 1960.

39. Ltr, Dr. Charles E. Lauritsen, ICBM Committee, to Gen Bernard A. Schriever, Cmdr WDD, subj: Ad Hoc Evaluation of ICBM Program, May 31, 1960, w/atch.

40. Memo, Chmn OSD-BMC to Chmn AF-BMC, subj: Atlas, Titan, and Minuteman Fiscal & Dev Plans, Aug 15, 1960, in OSAF Files, pp. 23–60; msg, CSAF to ARDC and AMC, Sep 28, 1960; msg, ARDC to CSAF, Aug 27, 1960.

41. Memo, Chmn OSD-BMC to Chmn AF-BMC, subj: Atlas, Titan, and Minuteman Fiscal and Dev Plans, Dec 13, 1960; msg, James H. Douglas, Secretary AF, to Chmn AF-BMC, same subj, Dec 30, 1960.

42. "Who Leads in Race of Atoms, Space?" *Philadelphia Inquirer*, Sep 4, 1959, p 1; Louis Kraar, "President Expected to Name Gates Defense Chief This Week, Succeeding McElroy," *Wall Street Journal*, Dec

1, 1959, p 1; James E. Warner, "Bombers Defend Until the Missiles Are Ready," *New York Herald Tribune*, Dec 6, 1959, p 1; Maxwell Taylor, *The Uncertain Trumpet* (New York, 1960), p 131; Emme, *Aeronautics and Astronautics, 1915–1960*.

43. Hearings before the Preparedness Investigating Subcommittee, *Missiles, Space and Other Defense Matters*, Senate, 86th Cong, 2d sess (Washington, 1959), pp 456–480 [hereafter Johnson Hearings].

44. State of the Union Message, Jan 7, 1960, in Public Papers of the Presidents of the United States: Dwight D. Eisenhower, 1960–61 (Office of the Federal Register, National Archives and Records Service, 1961), pp 3–10; Hanson W. Baldwin, "Straight Shooting Atlas," *New York Times*, Jan 8, 1960, p 1; rprt, "The Budget of the United States Government, Fiscal Year Ending June 30, 1961" pp 20–21; Chavez Hearings, Pt I, pp 192 and 213; Mahon Hearings, Pt I, p 8, and Pt II, p 202.

45. Mahon Hearings, Pt I, pp 3, 4, and 28; Hanson W. Baldwin, "Straight Shooting Atlas," *New York Times*, Jan 8, 1960, p 1.

46. Chavez Hearings, pp 1363–1369; Johnson Hearings, pp 441–463, 476.

47. Chavez Hearings, pp 1363–1369; Johnson Hearings, pp 441–463, 476.

48. Rprt, Site Activation of the 564th SMS—Aug 1960, nd; draft rprt, 566th SMS (SAC), nd, in SAMSO/Hist Ofc.

49. Draft rprt, 566th SMS (SAC), nd, in SAMSO/Hist Ofc.

50. *Ibid*.

51. *Ibid*.

52. *Ibid*.

53. *Ibid*.

54. *Ibid*.

55. Hist, SAC, Jul–Dec 1963, II, pp 187–189 and 191–192.

56. Hist, SAC, Jan–Jun 1962, I, pp 170–171; Jul 1962-June 1963, II, pp 223–224.

57. Marven R. Whipple, comp, *Index of Missile Launchings by Missile Program: July 1950–June 1960, First Ten Years of Effort by the Atlantic Missile Range* (Patrick AFB, Fla, AFMTC, ARDC, 1960); chronology, SAMSO, 1954–1976.

58. Chronology, SAMSO, 1954–1976.

59. *Ibid*; ltr, Roy W. Johnson, Dir/

ARPA, to Gen Bernard A. Schriever, Cmdr WDD, no subj, Jan 5, 1959, in BAS Papers.

60. Marven R. Whipple, comp, *Index of Missile Launchings by Missile Program: July 1950-June 1960, First Ten Years of Effort by the Atlantic Missile Range* (Patrick AFB, Fla, AFMTC, ARDC, 1960); chronology, SAMSO, 1954-1976.

61. Chronology, SAMSO, 1954-1976.

62. Hist, 1st Missile Div, Jul-Dec 1959, pp 77-84; memo, Gen Curtis LeMay to SAF, subj: Status of Atlas IOC, Jun 19, 1959; Hearings before Committee on Science and Astronautics, House of Representatives, *Progress of Atlas and Polaris Missiles*, 86th Cong, 1st sess (Washington, 1959), p 21; Gladwin Hill, "Atlas Declared Operational Now," *New York Times*, Sep 2, 1959, in Current News.

63. Minutes, 40th AF-BMC Meeting, Nov 18, 1959.

64. Hist, 1st Missile Divison, Jan-Jun 1960, pp 39-41; msg, CSAF to SAC, No. 89041, Apr 26, 1960.

65. Msg, SAC to CSAF, No. C-3624, Apr 28, 1960; msg, Gen Bernard A. Schriever, Cmdr WDD, to Maj Gen Osmond J. Ritland, Cmdr BMD, Jun 13, 1960; *The USAF Ballistic Missile Program*, WDGP-60-25, 7 vols (Los Angeles: Ballistic Missile Division, 1960), Vol I, p 3.

66. Minutes, 48th AF-BMC Meeting, May 4, 1960; msg, CSAF to SAC, No. 61256, Jun 13, 1960; msg, CSAF to ARDC and AMC, Jun 16, 1960; memo, Brig Gen M. B. Adams, Asst CS(GM), to Gen Thomas D. White, AF Chief of Staff, subj: New Operational Dates for the Atlas Program, Jul 20, 1960, in OSAF Files; memo, Brig Gen R. D. Curtin, Dep Dir/Sys Dev, to Gen Curtis LeMay, CINCSAC, subj: Site Activation for the SM-65, Jul 5, 1960; minutes, 53d AF-BMC Meeting, Jul 7, 1960.

67. Ltr, Gen Curtis LeMay, CINCSAC, to Gen Samuel E. Anderson, AMC Cmdr, subj: Installation and Checkout of ICBM Squadrons, Mar 22, 1960; ltr, Anderson to LeMay, same subj, Apr 25, 1960; msg, CSAF to ARDC and AMC, No. 87431, Apr 27, 1960; msg, CSAF to SAC, No. 68258, Jul 9, 1960.

68. Memo, Hugh M. Milton, Actg Sec-Army, to SAF, subj: Construction of Air Force Ballistic Missile Facilities, Jul 14, 1960; MR, C. P. Benedict, Dep Asst SECDEF (P&I), subj: Site Activation Program, Jul 27, 1960; Brig Gen Alvin C. Welling, "Constructing Missile Bases," *Army Information Digest*, Apr 1961, pp 40-46; DOD Press Release, Sep 23, 1960; Mark Watson, "Contractors—Being Called in by Gates," *Baltimore Sun*, Jul 27, 1960, p 1.

69. DOD Press Release, Sep 15, 1960; Atlas Program Summary, Jan 25, 1961, in Basic Documents.

70. Ltr, Gen Bernard A. Schriever, Cmdr WDD, to Chmn AF-BMC, subj: AFBMD/BMO/SAC-Mike/STL(R-W), Apr 1, 1958, in BAS Papers.

71. Msg, CSAF to ARDC, No. 55965, Jun 31, 1958; ltr, Gen Bernard A. Schriever, Cmdr WDD, to Gen Samuel E. Anderson, Cmdr AMC, no subj, May 21, 1958; ltr, Anderson to Schriever, no subj, Jun 3, 1958; msg, ARDC to AFBMD, 04/2130Z Apr 1958, in Basic Documents; ltr, Schriever to Roy W. Johnson, Dir/ARPA, no subj, Jun 27, 1958.

72. Report by the Committee on Government Operations, House of Representatives, *Organization and Management of Missile Programs*, 86th Cong, 1st sess (Washington, Sep 2, 1959), pp 81-101 [hereafter Eleventh Report].

73. *Ibid.*

74. *Ibid.*

75. *Ibid.*

76. *The Aerospace Corporation: Its Work 1960-1980* (Los Angeles, 1980), p 18.

77. Jacob van Staaveren, *USAF Intercontinental Ballistic Missiles, Fiscal Years 1960-1961*, pp 53-57.

78. John C. Norris, "McNamara Names 4 to Study Arms," *The Washington Post*, Jan 31, 1961; MR, Maj Gen R. D. Curtin, Dep Dir/Sys Dev, no subj, Jan 30, 1961; minutes, 68th AF-BMC Meeting, Feb 15, 1961.

79. Memo, SECDEF to SAF, et al, subj: Assignment of Projects Within DOD, Mar 8, 1961; memo, Under SAF to SECDEF, subj: Appraisal of Titan II and Minuteman Alternatives, Apr 24, 1961; Jack Raymond, "President Urges Missile Build-Up; Budget is Raised," *New York Times*, Mar 29, 1961;

Jacob van Staaveren, *USAF Intercontinental Ballistic Missiles, Fiscal Years 1960–1961*, p 38.

80. Mahon Hearings, 1962, Pt II, p 847; Pt III, pp 439–442; Chavez Hearings, 1962, pp 5–13.

81. Memo, SAF to SECDEF, subj: Assignment of Projects Within the DOD, Mar 27, 1961, w/atch; memo, SAF to SECDEF, subj: B-52 Procurements and Force Requirements, Jun 3, 1961.

82. Mahon Hearings, 1962, Pt III, p 397; memo, Eugene M. Zuckert, AF Secretary, to Gen Thomas D. White, AF Chief of Staff, no subj, Apr 20, 1961; memo, Zuckert to White, subj: ICBM Flight Test Demonstration Results, May 17, 1961, in OSAF Files.

83. Hist, 1st Missile Div, Jul–Dec 1959, pp 77–84, Jan–Jun 1960, Chap II, and Jul–Dec 1960, pp 18–22.

84. Msg, SAC to CSAF, No. 4534, Jul 29, 1960; msg, CSAF to SAC and ARDC, No. 73789, Jul 30, 1960; DDR&E Report, Operational Status of Ballistic Missiles, May 29, 1961.

85. Hist, 1st Missile Div, Jul–Dec 1960, pp 23–34; msg, SAC to CSAF, No. C-2044, Sep 3, 1960; memo, Lt Gen Thomas S. Power, Cmdr ARDC, to Gen Thomas D. White, AF Chief of Staff, no subj, Oct 16, 1960.

86. Msg, CSAF to SAC and ARDC, No. 89208, Sep 28, 1960; ltr, Lt Gen Thomas S. Power, Cmdr ARDC, to Gen Thomas D. White, AF Chief of Staff, no subj, Oct 6, 1960; msg, SAC to CSAF, No. 93162, Oct 13, 1960; msg, SAC to CSAF, No. 26439, Oct 19, 1960.

87. Hist, SAC, Jul–Dec 1960, p 153; msg, SAC to CSAF, Oct 19, 1960.

88. Msg, CSAF to SAC and ARDC, No. 89208, Sep 28, 1960; msg, CSAF to ARDC, No. 93104, Oct 12, 1960.

89. Memo, Maj Gen Marvin C. Demler, Dir/Sys Dev, to DCS/D, HQ USAF, subj: Atlas ICBM Reliability, Oct 18, 1960; minutes, 63d AFBMC Meeting, Dec 19, 1960.

90. Minutes, 66th AF–BMC Meeting, Jan 30, 1961; MR, Maj Gen M. C. Demler, Dir Systems Development to DCS/D, HQ USAF, subj: Explosion of Titan Missile, Dec 7, 1960.

91. Memo, Brig Gen George S. Brown, Mil Asst to SECDEF, to Dir/Jt Staff, subj: Effectiveness of Ballistic Missiles, Dec 5, 1960; memo, Dir/Plans, to Dir/Opns, HQ USAF, subj: Joint Staff Evaluation of Operational Effectiveness of Ballistic Missiles, Mar 30, 1961.

92. Memo, Eugene M. Zuckert, Secretary AF, to Robert S. McNamara, Secretary of Defense, subj: Recent Atlas E and Titan I R&D Difficulties, Jan 31, 1961; Mahon Hearings, 1962, Pt III, p 397; memo, Zuckert to Gen Thomas D. White, AF Chief of Staff, no subj, Apr 20, 1961; memo, Zuckert to White, subj: ICBM Flight Demonstration Results, May 17, 1961.

93. DDR&E Report, Operational Testing of Ballistic Missiles, May 29, 1961.

94. *Ibid*; hist, 1st Missile Div, Jan–Jun 1961, pp 26–35.

95. Msg, CSAF to ARDC, No. 94555, Mar 15, 1961; msg, ARDC to CSAF, No. 50848, Mar 18, 1961; minutes, 78th AF–BMC Meeting, Jun 29, 1961.

96. Hist, 1st Missile Div, Jan–Jun 1961, pp 78–99; minutes, 77th AF–BMC Meeting, Jun 8, 1961.

97. Trip rprt, J. R. Brower, L&L, subj: Trip Report, Preparedness Subcommittee, Senate Committee on Armed Services, Jul 6, 1961; MR, Lt Col E. Linhof, L&L, subj: Visit of Stennis Investigators with General Schriever, Jun 20, 1961.

98. "Excerpts from Task Force's Report to Kennedy on U.S. Position in Space Race," *New York Times*, Jan 12, 1961.

99. Report No. 51, Committee on Appropriations, 87th Cong, 1st sess, *Air Force Intercontinental Ballistic Missile Construction Program* (Washington, 1961), *passim*; ltr, T. D. Morris, Asst SECDEF (I&L), to Rep. Harry R. Sheppard, no subj, Jun 29, 1961.

100. Hearings before Permanent Subcommittee on Investigations, Senate, *Work Stoppages at Military Bases*, 87th Cong, 1st sess (Washington, 1961), Pt I, *passim*.

101. DOD Press Release, Mar 3 and Mar 17, 1961; msg, CSAF to ARDC and AMC, No. 9477, Mar 17, 1961; Clyde R. Littlefield, *The Site Program, 1961*, AFSC/HO, pp 10–11; Hearings before Preparedness Investigating

Subcommittee, Senate, *Construction of the Air Force Atlas and Titan Missile Sites*, 87th Cong, 2d sess (Washington, 1961), passim; Margaret C. Bagwell, *Buying the USAF Aerospace Force*, in *The History of AFSC* (Andrews AFB, Maryland, Office of History, Air Force Systems Command, ca. 1962; reissued 1980 as "Procurement of Air Force Systems, 1945–1961: AMC/ARDC Interface").

102. Intvw, Gen Bernard A. Schriever, Cmdr WDD, with Lt Col Lyn R. Officer and James C. Hasdorff, Washington, DC, June 20, 1973; Futrell, *Ideas*, p 401.

103. Futrell, *Ideas*, p 401.

104. Clyde R. Littlefield, *The Site Program*, 1961, AFSC/HO, pp 22–23; Executive Order No. 10946, Establishing a Program for Resolving Labor Disputes and Missile and Space Sites, May 26, 1961.

105. Hist, SAC, Jul 1962–Jun 1963, pp 248–256.

106. Memo, JCS to SECDEF, subj: FY 1959 Budget, Nov 17, 1957; ASSS, Maj Gen J.C. Donnelly, Asst DCS/P&P, subj: Air Staff Position on IRBM Deployment, Jan 30, 1958; memo, SAF to SECDEF, subj: IRMB Program, Feb 25, 1958; memo, JCS to SECDEF, subj: IRBM Operational Status, Mar 28, 1958.

107. Memo, James H. Douglas, Secretary AF, to Neil McElroy, Secretary of Defense, subj: Deployment of the Jupiter, Apr 12, 1958, in Basic Documents; msg, AFSC to AFBMD, 04-24-01 Apr 24, 1958, in Basic Documents; memo, William Holaday, Spec Asst for GM (OSD), to Sec Army, subj: Jupiter Program, Apr 25, 1958; memo, Holaday, subj: Thor Program, Apr 25, 1958; JCS 2101/314, Apr 29, 1958.

108. Dept of State Press Release No. 82, Feb 24, 1958, w/tests, in Basic Documents; hist, 7th Air Div (SAC), Jan–Jun 1958, pp 62–86; ltr, Col Ernest C. Hadin, Dep Dir/Plans, HQ USAF, to Gen Bernard A. Schriever, Cmdr WDD, subj: IRBM Technical Agreement, Jul 18, 1958, w/atch, in Basic Documents.

109. Memo, James H. Douglas, Secretary AF, to SECDEF, subj: Deployment of the Jupiter, Apr 12, 1958; MR, C. L.Waggoner, Asst for Resources (ARDC), no subj, Apr 23, 1958; msg, CSAF to AF-BMD, No.

50070, Apr 26, 1958; minutes, 19th AF-BMC Meeting, Jun 11, 1958.

110. Memo, James H. Douglas, Secretary AF, to Chmn OSD-BMC, subj: Submission of the May 20, 1958 BMD Development Plan, Jun 24, 1958; memo, Lt Gen Hewitt T. Wheless, DCS for Programs and Requirements, HQ USAF, to Dir/Plans, subj: Status of IRBM Deployments and Negotiations, Jul 15, 1958; memo, Donald A. Quarles, Secretary AF, to SAF, subj: Thor Deployment Schedule, Aug 28, 1958; memo, J. M. Sprague, Dep Asst SECDEF (Compt), to SECDEF, subj: Status of IRBM Negotiations, Italy, Sep 9, 1958; memo, Quarles to JCS, subj: IRBM Deployments, Oct 20, 1958; JCS 2277/47/1, Oct 24, 1958; memo, JCS to SECDEF, subj: IRBM Deployment, Oct 31, 1958; DOD Minutes of Press Conference, Nov 13, 1958; Missiles and Rockets, Nov 24, 1958, p 41; msg, VCSAF to SAC, No. 3363, Dec 22, 1958.

111. Juliam Hartt, *The Mighty Thor: Missile in Readiness* (New York: Duell, Sloan and Pearce, 1961), pp 170–187; memo, William Holaday, Spec Asst for GM (OSD) to SAF and Sec Army, subj: Thor-Jupiter Missile Systems, Nov 27, 1957; memo, Brig Gen Charles M. McCorkle, Dep Asst VC-SAF(GM), to CSAF, subj: Weekly Summary of Significant Events, Sep 24, 1958; ltr, Gen Bernard A. Schriever, Cmdr WDD, to CSAF, subj: Status of First Thor Squadron, Mar 13, 1959; MR, Col H. W. Gainer, Asst CS(GM), subj: Discussion by Colonel Cavner, AFMPP-WS at 1500, Mar 31, 1959, Apr 1, 1959; Monthly Status Report, AFBMD, May 1959.

112. DOD News Release, Apr 30, 1959; Chavez Hearings, pp 713–714.

113. Rprt, Monthly Status Report, AFBMD, Dec 1958, in Basic Documents; rprt, USAF Ballistic Missile Program, Comptr, HQ USAF, Jul 24, 1959.

114. Rprt, USAF Ballistic Missile Program, Comptr, HQ USAF, Jul 24, 1959; hist, SAC, Jan–Dec 1959, pp 94–96.

115. Memo, William Holaday, Spec Asst for GM (OSD), to SAF and Sec Army, no subj, Nov 27, 1957; memo, Col Ray E. Soper, BSD Vice Comdr, to Distr, no subj, May 1, 1958, in Basic Documents; ltr, Maj Gen J.C.

Donnelly, Asst DCS/P&P, to Depl Comdr USAFE, no subj, Jun 19, 1958; memo, Lt Gen Hewitt T. Wheless, DCS for Programs and Requirements, HQ USAF, to Dir/Plans, no subj, Jul 3, 1958; memo, J. M. Sprague, Dep Asst SECDEF (Compt), to SECDEF, no subj, Sep 9, 1958; minutes, 30th AFBMC Meeting, Mar 29, 1959; MR, Lt Col J. R. Smith, Asst CS(GM), subj: Jupiter Deployment, Jun 8, 1959.

116. Hist, Dir/Opns, HQ USAF, Jul–Dec 1959, pp 77–78, in AFCHO K 143.507; minutes, Thor/Jupiter Working Group, January–April 1960, in OSAF Files. The SAC history (January–June 1962, Vol I, p 208) erroneously states that the NATO II squadron was turned over to the Turks on May 25, 1962.

117. Minutes, Thor/Jupiter Working Group, Aug 12, Sep 12, Oct 10, and Nov 10, 1960, in OSAF Files.

118. Ltr, Dir/Opns to CSAF, subj: Status of Thor/Jupiter/Bomarc Weapon Systems, Feb 10, 1961; MR, Dir/Opns, HQ USAF, subject: Jupiter, Apr 26, 1961, in OSAF Files; hist, Dir/Opns, Jul–Dec 1961, p 121, in AFCHO K143.507.

119. Ltr, Dir/Opns to CSAF, subj: Status of Thor/Jupiter/Bomarc Weapon Systems, Feb 10, 1961; MR, Dir/Opns, HQ USAF, subject: Jupiter, Apr 26, 1961, in OSAF Files; hist, Dir/Opns, Jul–Dec 1961, p 121, in AFCHO K143.507; rprt, Dir/Opns, HQ USAF, subj: Project 92A, Apr 2, 1962, in AFSC/HO.

120. MR, Col Ray E. Soper, BSD Vice Comdr, Feb 10, 1958; memo, Brig Gen Charles M. McCorkle, Dep Asst VC-SAF(GM), to William Holaday, Spec Asst for GM(OSD), no subj, Feb 21, 1958; AFC 10/301, subj: Ballistic Missile Program, Feb 24, 1958; memo, Holaday to SAF, subj: Air Force Ballistic Missile Objecives, Feb 27, 1958; memo, Dudley C. Sharp, Actg SAF, to OSD-BMC, subj: Facility Expansion Projects for Solid Propellant Rocket Motors, May 23, 1958; memo, Holaday to AF-BMC, same subj, Jun 19, 1958; memo, Sharp to Asst SECDEF (S&L), subj: Master Urgency List, Jun 26, 1958.

121. Minutes, 21st AF-BMC Meeting, Jul 21, 1958; Minuteman Development Plan, AFBMD, Jun 8, 1958; ltr, Dr. Clark B. Millikan, Head of GAL, to William Holaday, Spec Asst for GM(OSD), no subj, Jul 24, 1958; Final Report No. 30, WSEG, Aug 13, 1958; memo, James H. Douglas, Secretary AF, to Holaday, subj: Minuteman Development Plan and Fiscal Year 1959 Program, Aug 11, 1958.

122. Memo, James H. Douglas, Secretary AF, to William Holaday, Spec Asst for GM(OSD), subj: Minuteman Development Plan and Fiscal Year 1959 Program, Aug 11, 1958; memo, Holaday to JCS, subj: Minuteman Program, Aug 7, 1958.

123. Memo, Lt Gen Hewitt T. Wheless, DCS for Programs and Requirements, HQ USAF, to CSAF, subj: Minuteman Program, Nov 6, 1958.

124. Memo, Lt Gen C. S. Irvine, DCS/M, to Asst CS(GM), no subj, Aug 21, 1958; memo, Maj Gen J.C. Donnelly, Asst DCS/P&P, to DCS/P&P, no subj, Aug 27, 1958; memo, Lyle S. Garlock, Assistant Secretary for Financial Management, to Asst SECDEF (Compt), subj: Release of Industrial Facilities Funds for Minuteman Propulsion Program, Sept 15, 1958; memo, William Holaday, Spec Asst for GM (OSD), to SAF, subj: Minuteman Program, Sep 17, 1958.

125. Memo, James H. Douglas, Secretary AF, to SECDEF, subj: Industrial Facilities for Minuteman Solid Propellant Engines, Sep 30, 1958; memo, Donald A. Quarles, Secretary AF, to SAF, same subj, Oct 11, 1958.

126. Memo, Lt Gen Hewitt T. Wheless, DCS for Programs and Requirements, HQ USAF, to CSAF, no subj, Nov 6, 1958; memo, Brig Gen Charles M. McCorkle, Dep Asst VCSAF(GM), to SAF, subj: Minuteman Program, Dec 1, 1958; memo, William Holaday, Spec Asst for GM (OSD), to AF-BMC, same subj, Dec 8, 1958; Minuteman Development Plans, AFBMD, Nov 25, 1958; minutes, 27th AF-BMC Meeting, Dec 9, 1958; memo, Lyle S. Garlock, Assistant Secretary for Financial Management, to SECDEF, no subj, Dec 11, 1958; memo, R. E. Horner, Asst SAF

(R&D), to OSD-BMC, subj: Minuteman Development Plan, Dec 12, 1958; memo, Holaday to AF-BMC, subj: Minuteman Program, Jan 7, 1959; memo, AF-BMC to Holaday, subj: Fund Reservations for FY 1959 and Prior Air Force Ballistic Missile Programs, Jan 8, 1959.

127. JCS 1620/224, Jan 30, 1959; memo, Lt Gen Hewitt T. Wheless, DCS for Programs and Requirements, HQ USAF, to CSAF, subj: Minuteman Program, Feb 16, 1959; memo, JCS to SECDEF, subj: Minuteman Program, Feb 19, 1959; intvw, Maj Gen O. J. Ritland with Lt Col L. R. Officer, Mar 19-21, 1974, pp 199-200.

128. Minutes, 29th AF-BMC Meeting, Feb 25, 1959; ASSS, Brig Gen Charles M. McCorkle, Dep Asst VCSAF(GM), subj: Minuteman Program, Mar 13, 1959; memo, James H. Douglas, Secretary AF, to SECDEF, no subj, Apr 14, 1959; minutes, 33d AF-BMC Meeting, May 12, 1959; memo, William Holaday, Spec Asst for GM (OSD), to AF-BMC, subj: Minuteman Program, Jun 1, 1959.

129. Chavez Hearings, pp 1424, 1489, and 1567; AFC 13/3, subj: USAF Tasks and Objective Force Structure (1959-1970), May 15, 1959.

130. JCS 1620/193/1, Dec 1, 1958; memo, Maj Gen Jacob E. Smart, Asst VCSAF, to DCS/P&P, subj: Annual Commanders' Conference, Jan 17, 1959; msg, SAC to AFBMD, No. C-565, Jan 19, 1959; ltr, Maj Gen Joseph Ferguson, Dir/Reqts, HQ USAF, to CINCSAC, subj: Mobile ICBM Weapon System, Feb 24, 1959; msg, SAC to VCSAF, No. C-2233, Mar 3, 1959.

131. Memo, Lt Gen D. C. Strother, DCS/Opns, to CSAF, subj: Minuteman Mobility, Mar 3, 1959; msg, VCSAF to SAC, No. 57333, Mar 6, 1959; minutes, 31st and 33d AF-BMC Meetings, May 1 and 12, 1959; memo, William Holaday, Spec Asst for GM (OSD), to Chmn AF-BMC, no subj, Jun 1, 1959.

132. Edgar M. Bottome, *The Missile Gap* (Rutherford, NJ, 1971), Chapter 5.

133. Draft rprt, Review of the Construction of Certain Launch Facilities of Atlas and Titan ICBMs at Selected Department of the Air Force Bases, Compt Gen, nd, in OSAF Files.

134. *Ibid*; hist, SAC, Jul 1962-Jun 1963, pp 249-250.

135. Hist, SAC, Jul 1962-Jun 1963, pp 212-213; MR, Dir/Opns, HQ USAF, subj: ICBM Test and Evaluation Progam, ca Jan 1963.

136. Memo, SAF to Asst SAF (Mat), (R&D), (FM), subj: CINCSAC Briefing on Accelerated Missile Reliability Test Program, Mar 11, 1963; hist, Dir/Opnl Reqts, HQ USAF, Jan-Jun 1964, pp 51-52.

137. Hist, SAC, June 1958-Jul 1959, p 271.

138. Chronology, SAC Missile Chronology, 1939-1973.

139. Hist, SAC, Jun 1962-Jul 1963, III, p 187.

140. Rprt, Dir/Opns, HQ USAF, subj: Project 92A, Jun 1, 1962, in AFSC/HO; hist, USAFE, Jan-Jun 1963, frames 176-181, in Maxwell Microfilm K 570.01, I; hist, SAC, Jan-Jun 1962, I, p 207, in AFCHO K 416.01; hist, Dir/Opns, HQ USAF, Jul-Dec 1962, p 153, in AFCHO K 143.517.

141. Hist, Dir/Opns, HQ USAF, Jan-Jun 1963, p 94; hist, USAFE, Jan-Jun 1963, pp 158-163; memo, SAF to SECDEF, subj: Weekly Report on Withdrawal of Jupiter Missiles, ca. Apr 15, 1963, in Zuckert Papers, Maxwell Microfilm No. 1001753, frames 634-635.

142. Minutes, 61st AF-BMC Meeting, May 17, 1963, in OSAF Files; msg, CSAF to SAC, No. 93905, Apr 14, 1963; msg, SAC to CSAF, AFIN 44482, Apr 22, 1963; ltr, Dir/Plans to CSAF, subj: Phase Out of Ballistic Missiles, Jun 7, 1963; hist, SAC, Jul-Dec 1964, II, p 184.

143. Hist, SAC, Jul-Dec 1965, I, viii, II, p 189; Jan-Jun 1965, I, Chap III.

144. Bernard C. Nalty, *USAF Ballistic Missile Programs, 1962-1964* (Washington: USAF Historical Division Liaison Office, 1966), p 3.

145. *Ibid*, pp 1-3.

146. *Ibid*.

147. *Ibid*.

148. *Ibid*.

Epilogue

1. Futrell, *Ideas*, p 239.
2. *Ibid*, p 240.
3. Ernest G. Schwiebert, *A History of the United States Air Force Ballistic Missiles* (New York: Praeger, 1965), p 139.
4. *Ibid*, p 93.

5. Futrell, *Ideas*, pp 280–282.
6. The United States Air Force Summary: Fiscal Years 1988/1989, April 1, 1987, Economics and Field Support Division, Deputy Comptroller, Cost and Economics, Comptroller of the Air Force, p A–12.

Glossary

AAF	Army Air Forces
AAM	air to air missile
AEC	Atomic Energy Commission
AEF	Allied Expeditionary Force
AFLC	Air Force Logistics Command
AFSC	Air Force Systems Command
AF–BMC	Air Force Ballistic Missiles Committee
AGF	Army Ground Forces
AMC	Air Materiel Command
Anatol	ammonium nitrate and trinitrotoluene
ARDC	Air Research and Development Command
ARPA	Advanced Research Projects Agency
ARS	Advanced Reconnaissance System
ASF	Army Service Forces
ASM	air to surface missile
ATC	Air Training Command
ATSC	Air Technical Service Command
Azon	Azimuth only
BMD	Ballistic Missile Division
BSD	Ballistics Systems Division
Caltech	California Institute of Technology
CBR	Chemical, biological, and radiological
CEBMCO	Corps of Engineers, Ballistic Missile Construction Office
CEP	circular error probable
CIT	California Institute of Technology
Convair	Consolidated Vultee Aircraft Corporation
DASO	demonstration and shakedown operation
DCAS	Deputy Commander for Aerospace Systems

DCS/Development	Director of Research and Development
DDR&E	Director of Defense Research and Engineering
DOD	Department of Defense
DSMG	Designated Systems Management Group
EWO	Emergency War Order
FOT	Follow-on Operational Testing
GAL	Guggenheim Aeronautical Laboratory
GALCIT	Guggenheim Aeronautical Laboratory at the California Institute of Technology
GB	glide bombs
GMA-1	Guided Missile A-1
GMC	Guided Missiles Committee
GMIORG	Guided Missiles Interdepartmental Operational Requirements Group
GMRD	Guided Missile Research Division
GOR	general operational requirement
IBM	International Business Machines Corporation
ICBM	intercontinental ballistic missile
IGY	International Geophysical Year
IOC	initial operational capability
IRBM	intermediate range ballistic missile
JATO	jet assisted takeoff
JB-2	jet bomb
JCS	Joint Chiefs of Staff
JPL	Jet Propulsion Laboratory
JRDB	Joint Research and Development Board
LOX	liquid oxygen
MILS	Missile Range Impact Locator System
MIT	Massachusetts Institute of Technology
MRBM	medium range ballistic missile
MUL	Master Urgency List

GLOSSARY

NACA	National Advisory Committee for Aeronautics
NATO	North Atlantic Treaty Organization
NOA	new obligational authority
NSC	National Security Council
NSF	National Science Foundation
OMB	Office of Management and Budget
ORDCIT	Ordnance and CIT Project
OSD	Office of the Secretary of Defense
OSD–BMC	Office Secretary of Defense, Ballistic Missiles Committee
OSRD	Office of Scientific Research and Development
OSTF	operational systems test facility
OT	operational testing
QOR	qualitative operational requirement
RAF	Royal Air Force
Rand	Research and Development Corporation
Razon	range and azimuth
RDB	Research and Development Board
RFNA	red fuming nitric acid
RMI	Reaction Motors, Inc.
R–W	Ramo-Wooldridge
SAB	Scientific Advisory Board
SAC	Strategic Air Command
SAPO	Special Aircraft Projects Office
SDTAF	site deactivation task force
SIGMB	Special Interdepartmental Guided Missiles Board
SIOP	single integrated operational plan
SMS	strategic missile squadron
SMW	strategic missile wing
SSD	Space Systems Division
SSM	surface to surface missile

BALLISTIC MISSILES

STL	Space Technology Laboratories
Tarzon	Tallboy-Razon
TBM	tactical ballistic missile
TNT	trinitrotoluene
VB	vertical bombs
WADC	Wright Air Development Center
WDD	Western Development Division
WSEG	Weapon System Evaluation Group

Bibliographic Note

Governmental Sources

National Archives of the United States

The major collections concerning missiles are found in the Modern Military Branch of the National Archives, Washington, DC:

RG 18, records of the Army Air Forces. Especially useful are files 452.1, Radio-Controlled Planes, and 334, the Joint Research and Development Board. Also see files of the Office of the Chief of Air Staff, Scientific Advisory Group, NACA file 400.112, AAG 008 policy, AAG 350.6 Studies and Problems.

RG 218, records of the United States Joint Chiefs of Staff, file 334, the Guided Missiles Committee.

RG 340, records of the Office of Secretary of the Air Force. See Special Interest Files beginning 1948–1949; records of Under Secretary of the Air Force Arthur S. Barrows, and William A. M. Burden, Special Assistant for R&D, chronological files. Post-1950 records are housed at the Washington National Records Center, Suitland, Maryland. Entry to records is through Executive Services on the Air Staff. A complex subject and numerical system is used, with the suffix designating the year. For example, 1063–56 refers to ICBM/IRBM Guided Missiles for 1956; 97–56 Scientific Advisory Committee on Ballistic Missiles.

RG 341, records of Headquarters, United States Air Force. Particularly useful are the files of the Guided Missiles Branch (Directorate of R&D, Deputy Chief of Staff for Development); Guided Missiles Division (Assistant for Guided Missiles, Deputy Chief of Staff for Operations); decimal files 334.5 and 360.4.1. Also important are the correspondence files of the Special Assistant to the Chief of Staff, Lt Gen James H. Doolittle; files of the Assistant for Atomic Energy. Records beginning with the Korean War period are housed at the Washington Records Center, Suitland, Md.

Library of Congress

The Manuscript Division of the Library of Congress houses the papers of the Chiefs of Staff, USAF. For the most part, however, these papers are official documents, such as letters, messages, and reports, which are also located in the National Archives and elsewhere. The major collections consulted for this book were those of:

Henry H. Arnold (1907–1950)
Robert P. Patterson (1930–1952)
Vannevar Bush (1932–1960)
Carl A. Spaatz (1915–1953)
Hoyt S. Vandenberg (1948–1953)
Nathan F. Twining (1930–1960)
Thomas D. White (1952–1961)
Curtis E. LeMay (1961–1965)

USAF Historical Research Center

Formerly designated the Albert F. Simpson Historical Research Center at Maxwell AFB, Alabama, these archives house many documents cited in this work, including historical studies, reports, and interviews. Most of the holdings are on microfilm.

Office of Air Force History

The Office of Air Force History is located at Bolling AFB in Washington, DC. It has a copy of the microfilm collection of the USAF Historical Research Center. Currently, the office possesses the papers of Gen. Bernard A. Schriever (USAF, Ret), which have been microfilmed. The unclassified papers are periodically transferred to Texas A&M, College Station, Texas for permanent storage.

Another valuable holding is the multivolume *Atomic Air Force History* by Bowen and Little. Especially useful is Volume IV, Part 2. The Office of Air Force History has also published two important series of monographs on ballistic missiles and the Air Force in space. Finally, the holdings include notes on missile volumes, which include excerpts of numerous documents. The notes were taken by two former AFCHO staff members, Max Rosenberg and Jacob van Staaveren.

Air Force Systems Command

The History Office of the Air Force Systems Command at Andrews AFB, Maryland, is a valuable depository of missile documents. Available on microfilm or in "hard copy" are numerous histories, reports, letters, and memoranda. There are also some three dozen interviews with AFSC officials, conducted by former Chief Historian Ernest G. Schwiebert, which are not available elsewhere.

BIBLIOGRAPHIC NOTE

The history offices of the Ballistic Missiles Office at Norton AFB, California, and the Space Division at Los Angeles possess between them a collection called the Basic Documents. These are the files of the Western Development Division and Ballistic Missiles Division, which were assembled by their former historian, Alfred Rockefeller.

Other Collections

The Theodore von Kármán papers are in the Robert A. Millikan Library at the California Institute of Technology, Pasadena, California.
The papers of Donald A. Quarles (1952-1959) are housed in the Eisenhower Library, Abilene, Kansas.

Books

Craven, Wesley and James L. Cate, eds. *The Army Air Forces in World War II.* 7 vols. Chicago: The University of Chicago Press, 1948-1958. (Reprinted in 1983 by the Office of Air Force History.) See especially Vol III, Chapters 4 and 15 on Operation Crossbow; Vol VI, *Men and Planes,* Chapter 7, "The Quest for Better Weapons."

Durant, Frederick C. III, and George S. James, Eds. *First Steps Toward Space.* Smithsonian Annals of Flight No. 10 (final number in series). Washington: Smithsonian Institution Press, 1974.

Frisbee, John L., ed. *Makers of the United States Air Force.* Washington: Office of Air Force History, 1987. See Chapter 12, "Bernard Schriever: Challenging the Unknown" by Jacob Neufeld.

Futrell, Robert F. *Ideas, Concepts, Doctrine: A History of Basic Thinking in the United States Air Force, 1907-1964.* Maxwell AFB, Ala.: Air University, 1971.

Goldberg, Alfred, ed. *A History of the United States Air Force, 1907-1957.* Princeton, N.J.: D. Van Nostrand, 1957.

Hall, R. Cargill, ed. *Essays on the History of Rocketry and Aeronautics.* 2 vols. NASA Conference Publication No. 2014. Washington: NASA, 1977.

Hewlett, Richard G., and Francis Duncan. *A History of the United States Atomic Energy Commission.* University Park, Pa.: Penn State University Press, 1969. Vol II: *Atomic Shield, 1947-1952.*

——————. *Nuclear Navy, 1946-1962.* Chicago: University of Chicago Press, 1974.

—————— and Oscar O. Anderson, Jr. *A History of the Atomic Energy Commission.* University Park, Pa.: Penn State University Press, 1962. Vol I: *The New World, 1939-1946.*

Sturm, Thomas A. *The USAF Scientific Advisory Board: Its First Twenty Years, 1944-1964.* Washington, DC: USAF Historical Division Liaison Office, February 1, 1967. (Reprinted in 1986 by the Office of Air Force History.)

Swenson, Loyd S., James M. Grimwood, and Charles C. Alexander. *This New Ocean: A History of Project Mercury.* Washington: NASA, 1966.

BALLISTIC MISSILES

Historical Studies

The Aerospace Corporation: Its Work, 1960–1980. Los Angeles, 1980.

Bagwell, Margaret C. *Buying the USAF Aerospace Force.* Andrews AFB, Md.: Office of History, Air Force Systems Command, ca. 1962. Part of the History of AFSC. Reissued in 1980 as "Procurement of Air Force Systems, 1945–1961: AMC/ARDC Interface."

Baird, Virginia and Margaret Scriven, et al. *Controlled Missiles.* Historical Office ATSC, 1944–1945. A nine-volume work by various authors, detailing the remotely controlled aircraft and missiles employed in World War II by the Army Air Forces.

Berger, Carl. *History of the 1st Missile Division.* Vandenberg AFB, Calif.: Office of History, 1st Missile Division, 1960.

_____ and Warren S. Howard. *History of the 1st Strategic Aerospace Division and Vandenberg Air Force Base, 1957–1961.* Vandenberg AFB, Calif.: History Office, 1962.

Bickett, Robert D., comp. *Space and Missile Test Center Index of Missiles Launched on the Western Test Range, December 16, 1958 to December 31, 1969.* Vandenberg AFB, Calif.: Space and Missile Systems Organization (AFSC), nd.

Bowen, Lee. *An Air Force History of Space Activities.* Washington: USAF Historical Division Liaison Office, 1964.

_____ and Robert D. Little. *A History of the Air Force Atomic Energy Program, 1943–1953.* 5 vols. Washington: USAF Historical Division, nd.

Brassel, John C. *Jupiter Development Aspects—Deployment.* Mobile Air Service Command, 1962.

Christman, Albert B. *History of the Naval Weapons Center, China Lake, California.* Washington: Naval History Division, 1971. Vol I: *Sailors, Scientists and Rockets: Origins of the Navy Rocket Program and of the Naval Ordnance Test Station, Inyokern.*

Claussen, Martin P. *Materiel Research and Development in the Army Air Arm, 1914–1945.* Maxwell AFB, Ala.: AAF Historical Office, 1946. The best account available on this subject.

Clemmer, Wilbur E. *Phase-out of the Atlas E and F and Titan I Weapon Systems, November 1964–June 1966.* Wright-Patterson AFB, Ohio: Historical Research Division, Air Force Logistics Command, 1966.

Cole, Alice C. et al. *The Department of Defense: Documents on Establishment and Organization, 1944–1978.* Washington: Government Printing Office, 1978.

De Haven, Ethel. *Aerospace: The Evolution of USAF Weapons Acquisition Policy, 1945–1961.* 4 vols. Los Angeles: DCAS Historical Office (AFSC), August 1962. The first volume is narrative and the remaining three volumes contain 326 primary documents. Many of these documents are from Alfred Rockefeller's Basic Documents Collection.

_____. *Air Materiel Command Participation in the Air Force Ballistic Missiles Program Through December 1957.* Wright-Patterson AFB, Ohio: AMC, September 1958.

_____. *History of the Separation of Research and Development from the Air Materiel Command.* Wright-Patterson AFB, Ohio: AMC, 1954.

Del Papa, E. Michael. *From Snark to SRAM: A Pictorial History of Strategic Air Command Missiles*. Offutt AFB, Neb.: Office of the Historian, SAC, 1976.

Davis, Paul M. *The Problem of Organizing for Weapon System Management: An Historical Analysis*. Wright-Patterson AFB, Ohio: AMC, March 3, 1960.

Fletcher, Robert H. *The Signal Corps and the Air Service*. Army War College Monograph No. 16. Washington: Government Printing Office, 1922.

Forest, J. P. *SAC Studies: The Guided Missile through 1951*. Offutt AFB, Neb.: History Office (SAC), 1952.

Green, Constance M., et al. *The Ordnance Department: Planning Munitions for War*. Washington: Office of the Chief of Military History, 1955. British contributions to U.S. missile programs during World War II.

Greene, Warren E. *The Development of the SM-68 Titan*. Norton AFB, Calif.: Historical Office Deputy Commander for Aerospace Systems, 1962.

Grimwood, James M. and Frances Strowd. *History of the Jupiter Missile System*. Redstone Arsenal, Ala.: U.S. Army Ordnance Missile Command, July 27, 1962.

Hall, Edward N. "Epitaph." An unpublished personal statement on the ballistic missiles program, presumably written at BMD, August 29, 1958.

Harlan, Norman and Gene McConnell. *A Summary of German Guided Missiles*. Wright Field, Ohio: AAF Materiel Command, 1946.

Jordan, Harry C., and Doris E. Krudener. *Origins of Ballistic Missile Deployment Patterns*. Draft history. Norton AFB, Calif.: Historical Division, Office of Information, Ballistic Systems Division, 1964.

Klocko, Col Richard P. *The Impact of Guided Missiles Upon the USAF*. AWC Graduate Study Group. Maxwell AFB, Ala.: Air War College, March 1954.

Komons, Nick A. *Science and the Air Force: A History of the Air Force Office of Scientific Research*. Arlington, Va.: Historical Division, OAR, 1960.

Krudener, Doris E. *Site Activation: Plans, Policies, and Decisions, 1954–1961*. Norton AFB, Calif.: Historical Division, Office of Information, BSD, 1963. Revised 1964. (Volume 1A contains 50 documents, many of them duplicates of the De Haven collection. Also, Volume 2A contains 51 documents. Hundreds of additional supporting documents are preserved on microfilm, but these concern only minor program details.)

Kennedy, Margaret A., and Robert L. Perry. *The Establishment of Wright Air Development Center*. Wright-Patterson AFB, Ohio: WADC, 1953.

Little, Robert D. *Nuclear Propulsion for Manned Aircraft: The End of the Program, 1959–1961*. Washington: USAF Historical Division Liaison Office, 1963.

Littlefield, Clyde R. *The Site Program—1961*. Norton AFB, Calif.: Historical Office, Deputy Commander for Aerospace Systems (AFSC), 1962.

McIntyre, A. *Summary of AFCRL Rocket and Satellite Experiments (1946–1966)*. Hanscom Field, Mass.: Air Force Cambridge Research Laboratories, 1966.

McVeigh, Donald R. *Development of the Bomarc Guided Missile*. Wright-Patterson AFB, Ohio: WADC, 1956.

BALLISTIC MISSILES

Miller, Col Edwin B. *Guided Missiles and Pilotless Aircraft in Theater Operations*. Air War College Graduate Study Group Thesis No. 1, Maxwell AFB, Ala.: AWC, May 1953.

Minuteman Program Management Plan. Norton AFB, Calif.: Space and Missile Systems Organization (AFSC), 1972.

Nalty, Bernard C. *USAF Ballistic Missile Programs, 1962–1964*. Washington: USAF Historical Division Liaison Office, 1966.

_____. *USAF Ballistic Missile Programs, 1964–1966*. Washington: USAF Historical Division Liaison Office, 1967.

_____. *USAF Ballistic Missile Programs, 1967–1968*. Washington: USAF Historical Division Liaison Office, 1969.

Neal, J. Allen. *Development of the Navaho Guided Missile, 1945–1953*. Wright-Patterson AFB, Ohio: WADC, January 1956.

Neufeld, Jacob. "Atlas: The Race for Missile Supremacy." Paper presented at the Missouri Valley Historical Conference, Omaha, Nebraska, March 1979.

_____. "Bernard A. Schriever." Draft essay prepared for publication in an anthology of Air Force leaders by the Air Force Historical Foundation, 1983.

_____. *USAF Ballistic Missile Programs, 1969–1970*. Washington: Office of Air Force History, 1971.

New Developments: Guided Missiles. AC&SS Pamphlet No. 54. Maxwell AFB, Ala.: AC&SS (Air University), December 1948.

Organizational Evolution of DCS/Research and Development, September 1945–December 1964. Washington: Analysis Division, Assistant for R&D Programming (DCS/R&D), 1965.

Perry, Robert L. *The Development of the Snark Guided Missile, 1945–1953*. 2 vols. Wright-Patterson AFB, Ohio: Historical Branch, Wright Air Development Center (AFSC), 1956.

Piper, Robert F. *The Development of the SM-80 Minuteman*. Norton AFB, Calif.: Historical Office, Deputy Commander for Aerospace Systems (BSD), April 1962.

Rockefeller, Alfred. *Brief History of Air Force Ballistic Missile Developement, 1946–1955*. Los Angeles: Ballistic Missiles Division, October 1959.

Rosenberg, Max. *The Air Force and the National Guided Missile Program, 1944–1950*. Washington: USAF Historical Division Liaison Office, 1964.

_____. *Plans and Policies for the Ballistic Missile Initial Operational Capability Program*. Washington: USAF Historical Division Liaison Office, 1960.

_____. *USAF Ballistic Missiles, 1958–1959*. Washington: USAF Historical Division Liaison Office, 1960.

Schwiebert, Ernest G. *A History of the United States Air Force Ballistic Missiles*. New York: Praeger, 1965. Originally published in *Air Force Magazine,* May 1964.

Self, Mary R. *The Development of Guided Missiles*. 4 vols. Wright Field, Ohio: Air Materiel Command, June 1946. One narrative volume and three volumes of documents. Contains 128 documents, most of them duplicates of those at the National Archives.

_____. *History of the Development of Guided Missiles, 1946-1950.* 8 vols. Wright-Patterson AFB, Ohio: Historical Office, Air Materiel Command, December 1951. One narrative volume and seven volumes of documents. Contains 253 documents, most duplicates of those at the National Archives.

Smyth, H. D. *A General Account of the Development of Methods of Using Atomic Energy for Military Purposes under the Auspices of the U.S. Government.* Washington: Government Printing Office, July 1, 1945.

Sturm, Thomas A. *USAF Oversea Forces and Bases, 1947-1967.* Washington: USAF Historical Division Liaison Office, 1969.

Van Staaveren, Jacob. *USAF Intercontinental Ballistic Missiles, Fiscal Years 1960-1961.* Washington: USAF Historical Division Liaison Office, 1964.

Reports

Arnold, Henry H. *Third Report to the Secretary of War, November 12, 1945.*

Atlas Weapon System Final Report. Space Technology Laboratories, April 30, 1964.

Consolidated Guided Missile Report. Air Research and Development Command, 1954 through 1958.

Initial Report on Review of Administrative Management of the Ballistic Missile Program of the Department of the Air Force. Washington: General Accounting Office, 1960. A critique of Ramo-Wooldridge Corporation.

Report to the Congress of the United States: Initial Report on Review of Administrative Management of the Ballistic Missile Program of the Department of the Air Force. B-133042. Washington: Comptroller General of the United States, 1960. A GAO report on the Ramo-Wooldridge Corporation.

Report of the Secretary of the Air Force to the Secretary of Defense for Fiscal Year 1948. Washington: Government Printing Office, 1948.

Rockefeller, Alfred. *Historical Report, 1 July-31 December 1955.* Los Angeles: Western Development Division, 1956.

Survival in the Air Age: A Report by the President's Air Policy Commission. Washington: Government Printing Office, January 1948. Also called the Finletter Report.

The USAF Ballistic Missile Program. WDGP-60-25. 7 vols. Los Angeles: Ballistic Missile Division, 1960. Called the LeMay Report, it is an excellent source of missile descriptions, programming actions, and illustrations of Atlas, Titan, Thor, and Minuteman.

Histories

Historical Report, Western Development Division. Headquarters ARDC, July 1-December 31, 1955.

History, Assistant Chief of Staff for Guided Missiles. Various issues from April 1954 through June 1960.

History, 1st Missile Division. [April 15-December 31, 1957 under ARDC; January 1958-July

21, 1961 under SAC; then redesignated 1st Strategic Aerospace Division.] Various issues through December 1960.

History of Air Staff, Directorate of Operations.

History of the Engineering Division and Predecessor Organizations Covering the Early U.S. Army Corps of Engineers Support to the U.S. Air Force Ballistic Missile Program (IRBM/ICBM), 1955-1963. Los Angeles, Calif: U.S. Army Corps of Engineers Ballistic Missile Construction Office, nd.

History of Headquarters USAF, FY 1949 and FY 1950. Washington: U.S. Air Force Historical Division Liaison Office, 1955.

History of Office of Secretary of the Air Force.

History, 7th Air Division (SAC).

History of the Strategic Air Command.

A History of Strategic Arms Competition, 1945-1972. Washington: Directorate of Doctrine, Concepts and Objectives (AF/XOD, Brig Gen John E. Ralph), 1976.

History of Air Force Special Weapons Center, 1953.

Chronologies

Air Force Ballistic Missile Chronology [short title], *1946 to April 1, 1961*. Los Angeles: Historical Section, Executive Office, Air Force Ballistic Missile Division, nd.

OSAF Chronology: A Chronological Brief of Selected Guided Missile Projects. Washington: Office of the Secretary of the Air Force, February 1956.

Regulations, Circulars, Letters, Orders

Air Force Letter No. 136-3, Guided Missiles in USAF, April 18, 1952.

Air Force Manual 52-31, Guided Missiles Fundamentals, HQ ATC, July 1, 1972.

Air Force Regulation 58-1, Guided Missiles: Air Force Guided Missile Policy, August 15, 1955.

Papers

AGARD Guided Missiles Seminar Papers. NATO Advisory Group for Aeronautical Research and Development. Vol I, History of German Guided Missile Development; Vol II, Guidance and Control. Paris, April 1956.

Articles

Air University Quarterly Review, published by Air University at Maxwell AFB, Alabama, is the professional journal of the United States Air Force. Its summer 1957 issue, Vol IX, No. 3, was devoted to "The Air Force Ballistic Missile." Some of these articles were used in preparation of Kenneth F. Gantz (Ed.), *The United States Air Force Report on the Ballistic Missile* (New York: Doubleday, 1958). The winter 1957-58 issue, Vol IX,

No. 4, contains several articles on ballistic missiles. The winter and spring 1960–61 issues, Vol XII, Nos. 3 and 4, were devoted to "Aerospace Force in the Sixties."

Colopy, J. W. "Weapon Systems and the WS Concept." Air *University Quarterly Review* (Spring 1957).

de Seversky, Alexander P. "A Lecture on Air Power." *Air University Quarterly Review* (Winter 1947).

Glantzberg, Frederic E. "The New AF and Science." *Air University Quarterly Review* (Spring 1947).

Hall, Col Edward N. "Industry and the Military in the United States." *Air University Quarterly Review*, Vol. X (No. 3).

Mechling, Brig Gen E. P. "The Air Force and Guided Missiles." *Ordnance*, Vol. 37, No. 197. (March–April 1953).

Page, Jerry D. "Tooling Up for the Ballistic Missiles Training Program." *Air University Quarterly Review*, Vol. X, No. 4 (Winter 1958–59).

Schriever, Bernard A. Wrote numerous articles in the Air University Quarterly Review; some have been listed above as special issues.

_____. "The People behind the Ballistic Missile." *The Airman*, Vol. 8, No. 5. (May 1962).

Travis, Cliff. "Monikers for Missiles." *Airman*, Vol. 18 (June 1974). Tells how missiles are named.

Welling, Brig Gen Alvin C. "Constructing Missile Bases." *Army Information Digest* (April 1961).

Interviews

Selected oral history interviews were used in writing this book. Some were conducted by the author; many others are the product of the Oral History Branch of the USAF Historical Research Center, Maxwell AFB, Alabama. Typescripts and tapes of many interviews are available. The author has also consulted every interview in the collection with individuals who were associated in any way with R&D.

Alsop, Joseph with author. Washington, DC, September 7, 1977.

Anderson, Gen Samuel E. with Hugh N. Ahmann, Santa Monica, Calif., June 28–July 1, 1976.

Craigie, Lt Gen Laurence C. with Maj Paul Clark and Capt Don Beaufort, USAF Academy, Colorado Springs, Colo., September 24, 1971.

Doolittle, Gen James H. with Eugene M. Emme and William D. Putnam, Washington, DC, April 21, 1969. Other interviews with General Doolitle conducted by Arthur Marmor, June 23, 1965, and by instructors at the USAF Academy, September 26, 1971, are too general to be of use to this study.

Ford, Col Vincent J. with author Washington, DC, November 18, 1977. A personal friend, Col Ford graciously discussed his knowledge of the missile program on numerous occassions between 1977 and 1981.

Getting, Ivan A. In a letter to Secretary of the Air Force John L. McLucas, titled "Recollections of USAF in 1950-1951," March 12, 1971, Dr. Getting set down his recollections in writing. A copy of this document is available at the Office of Air Force History.

LeMay, Gen Curtis E. Four interviews were consulted: January 27, 1965; March 1965; March 9, 1971; and June 8, 1972.

McIntosh, Col Richard with author, Ft. Belvoir, Va. Colonel McIntosh worked with Col Jacobson in ICBM testing.

Murray, Peter R. with Hugh N. Ahmann, Andrews AFB, Md., February 28, 1973; and with Ahmann and author, July 10-11, 1973.

Partridge, Gen Earle E. with Thomas A. Sturm and Hugh N. Ahmann, Colorado Springs, Colo., April 23-25, 1974.

Putt, Lt Gen Donald L. with James C. Hasdorff, Atherton, Calif., April 1-3, 1974.

Ritland, Maj Gen Osmond J. with Lt Col Lyn R. Officer, March 19-21, 1974.

Rockefeller, Alfred with author, Los Angeles, August 16, 1977.

Schriever, Gen Bernard A. with Lt Col Lyn R. Officer and James C. Hasdorff, Washington, DC, June 20, 1973. Also with author September through December 1982. General Schriever was kind enough to take time from his hectic schedule to grant a series of seven interviews while the author was preparing a biographical essay for publication by the Air Force Historical Association.

Sessums, Maj Gen John with Hugh N. Ahmann, June 28, 1977.

Sharp, Dudley C. with Arthur Marmor, Washington, DC, May 29, 1967.

Soper, Col Ray E. with Harry C. Jordan, Norton AFB, Calif., November 29, 1966.

Twining, Gen Nathan F., November 3, 1967.

Zuckert, Eugene, several interviews: May 2-July 25, 1964; September 1, 1965; and July 19, 1973.

Reference Volumes

Air Force Pamphlet 190-2-1. Releasable Data on USAF Aerospace Craft. Washington: Department of the Air Force, June 1960.

Air Force Pamphlet 190-2-2. A Chronology of American Aerospace Events from 1903 through 1964. Washington: Department of the Air Force, 1965.

Air Force Historical Archives Document Classification Guide. Maxwell AFB, Ala.: Historical Research Division, 1971.

Air Force Manual 11-1. Glossary of Standardized Terms, Vol I. Washington: Department of the Air Force, January 1972.

Air Force Manual 11-2. Air Force Manual of Abbreviations. Washington: Department of the Air Force, March 1968-January 1975.

BIBLIOGRAPHIC NOTE

Ballistic Missile Familiarization Course. Vandenberg AFB, Calif.: Headquarters 1st STRAD, ca. 1963.

Ballistic Missile Staff Course: Study Guide. Vandenberg AFB, Calif.: Headquarters 1st STRAD, nd.

Creswell, Mary A., and Carl Berger. *United States Air Force History: An Annotated Bibliography.* Washington: Office of Air Force History, 1971.

DOD Fact Sheet. Washington: Office of Assistant Secretary of Defense, Public Affairs, 1976.

Department of Defense Model Designation of Military Aircraft, Rockets & Guided Missiles. Wright-Patterson AFB, Ohio: Deputy for Engineering, Aeronautical Systems Division (AFSC), January 1968.

Emme, Eugene M. *Aeronautics and Astronautics: An American Chronology of Science and Technology in the Exploration of Space, 1915-1960.* Washington: National Aeronautics and Space Administration, 1961.

Eppley, Charles V. *The Rocket Research Aircraft Program, 1946-1962.* Edwards AFB: Air Force Flight Test Center, 1963.

Estep, Raymond. *An Aerospace Bibliography.* Maxwell AFB, Ala.: Documentary Research Division, Research Studies Institute, Air University, 1962. [Previous editions, in 1956 and 1957, were titled *An Air Power Bibliography.*]

Goldberg, Alfred, et al., comp. *Organization of Headquarters USAF, 1945-58: With Particular Reference to DCS/Operations.* Washington: AU Historical Liaison Office, USAF Historical Division, July 1958.

Heflin, Woodford A., ed. *The Second Aerospace Glossary.* Maxwell AFB, Ala.: Documentary Research Division, Research Studies Institute, 1966.

_____. The United States Air Force Dictionary. Maxwell AFB, Ala.: Research Studies Institute, Air University, 1956.

History of the First Strategic Aerospace Division: Cumulative Index for Classified Histories Since 1957. Vandenberg AFB, Calif.: Headquarters 1st STRAD, nd.

History and Lineage, 1st Strategic Aerospace Division, 1943-1975. Vandenberg AFB, Calif.: The Office of History, nd.

Miller, Samuel D., comp. *An Aerospace Bibliography.* Washington: Office of Air Force History, 1978.

Neufeld, Jacob. "Key Personnel." [Looseleaf notebook of notable Air Force and DOD personnel.]

_____, et al, eds. *Guide to USAF Historical Literature, 1943-1983.* Washington: Office of Air Force History, 1985.

Paszek, Lawrence J., comp. *United States Air Force History: A Guide to Documentary Sources.* Washington: Office of Air Force History, 1973.

Strategic Air Command Missile Chronology, 1939-1973. Offutt AFB, Neb.: Office of the Historian (SAC), 1975.

Snyder, Thomas S., et al, comps. *Space and Missile Systems Organization: A Chronology 1954-1976.* Los Angeles: Office of History (SAMSO), 1978.

BALLISTIC MISSILES

U.S. *Air Force Oral History Catalog.* Maxwell AFB, Ala.: Albert F. Simpson Historical Research Center, 1977.

Whipple, Marven R., comp. *Index of Missile Launchings by Missile Program: July 1950–June 1960, First Ten Years of Effort by the Atlantic Missile Range.* Patrick AFB, Fla.: Historical Branch, Office of Information, Air Force Missile Test Center (ARDC), 1960.

Congress

The hearings and reports of the 84th through the 86th Congresses were most important to this history. Also useful is *Congress and the Nation, 1945–1964: A Review of Government and Politics in the Postwar Years.* Washington: Congressional Quarterly Service, 1965.

House. Hearings before the Committee on Appropriations, Subcommittee on DOD Appropriations. *Department of Defense: The Ballistic Missile Program.* [November 1957] 85th Cong, 1st sess. Washington: Government Printing Office, 1958.

House. Hearings before a subcommittee of the Committee on Government Operations. *Organization and Management of Missile Programs.* [February and March 1959] 86th Cong., 1st sess. Washington: Government Printing Office, 1959.

House. Eleventh Report by the Committee on Government Operations. *Organization andMan-agement of Missile Programs.* [House Report No. 1121, September 1959] 86th Cong, 1st sess. Washington: Government Printing Office, 1959.

House. Subcommittee on Manpower and Utilization of the Committee on Post Office and Civil Service. *Preliminary Report on the Aspects of the Missile Program in the Departments of the Navy and the Air Force.* [April 1959] 86th Cong, 1st sess. Washington: Government Printing Office, 1959.

House. Hearings before the Committee on Science and Astronautics. *Progress of Atlas and Polaris Missiles.* [Brooks Committee] 86th Cong, 1st sess. Washington: Government Printing Office, 1959.

House. Hearings before the subcommitteee of the Committee on Appropriations. *Department of Defense Appropriations for 1960.* [Mahon hearings] 86th Cong, 1st sess. Washington: Government Printing Office, 1959.

House. Report of the Committee on Science and Astronautics. *Space, Missiles, and the Nation.* [Brooks Committee] 86th Cong, 2d sess. Washington: Government Printing Office, 1960.

House. Subcommittee on Manpower Utilization of the Committee on Post Office and Civil Service. *Survey of Certain Aspects of the Ballistic Missile Program of the Department of the Air Force.* [Davis Committee.] 86th Cong, 2d sess. Washington: Government Printing Office, 1960. [Deals primarily with Ramo-Wooldridge.]

House. Third Report of the Committee on Government Operations. *Air Force Ballistic Missile Management: Formation of Aerospace Corporation.* 87th Cong, 1st sess. Washington: Government Printing Office, 1961.

House. Hearings before the subcommittee of the Committee on Appropriations. *Air Force Ballistic Missile Construction Program.* [Sheppard Committee] 87th Cong, 1st sess. Washington: Government Printing Office, 1961.

House. Report by the Committee on Appropriations. *Air Force Intercontinental Ballistic Missile Construction Program*. [No. 51] 87th Cong, 1st sess. Washington: Government Printing Office, 1961.

House. Report of the Committee on Science and Astronautics. *A Chronology Of Missile and Astronautic Events*. [Brooks Committee, Report No. 67, compiled by Charles S. Sheldon] 87th Cong, 1st sess. Washington: Government Printing Office, 1961.

Senate. Hearings before the Committee on Armed Services. *Nomination of Trevor Gardner*. 84th Cong, 1st sess. Washington: Government Printing Office, 1955.

Senate. Hearings before the Subcommittee on the Air Force of the Committee on Armed services. *Study of Airpower*. [Symington Committee, April 16–July 19, 1956] 84th Cong, 2d sess. Washington: Government Printing Office, 1956. [A report was issued on January 25, 1957.] 85th Cong, 1st sess. Washington: GPO, 1957.

Senate. Hearings before the Preparedness Investigating Subcommittee of the Committee on Armed Services. *Inquiry into Satellite and Missile Programs*. [Lyndon B. Johnson Committee] 85th Cong, 1st and 2d sess. Washington: Government Printing Office, 1958. [These hearings ran from November 25, 1957 until July 24, 1958 and produced nearly 2,500 pages of testimony. They represent what is undoubtedly the most extensive Congressional inquiry into the subject.]

Senate. Joint hearings before the Preparedness Investigating Subcommittee of the Committee on Armed Services and the Committee on Aeronautical and Space Sciences [both chaired by Lyndon B. Johnson]. *Missile and Space Activities*. 86th Cong, 1st sess. Washington: Government Printing Office, 1959.

Senate. Preparedness Investigating Subcommittee of the Committee on Armed Services. *The United States Guided Missile Program*. [Lyndon B. Johnson Committee] 86th Cong, 1st sess. Washington, DC: GPO, 1959. [This is a study by Charles H. Donnelly.]

Senate. Hearings before the subcommittee of the Committee on Appropriations. *Department of Defense Appropriations for 1960*. [Chavez Committee] 86th Cong, 1st sess. Washington: Government Printing Office, 1960.

Senate. Joint Committee on Defense Production. *Deterrence and Survival in the Nuclear Age*. 94th Cong, 2d sess. Washington: Government Printing Office, 1976. [This is the first publication of the famous Gaither Report of 1957.]

Non-Governmental Sources

Books

Abel, Elie. *The Missile Crisis*. Philadelphia: Lippincott, 1966.

Alsop, Joseph and Stewart Alsop. *The Reporter's Trade*. New York: Reynal and Co., 1958.

Armacost, Michael H. *The Politics of Weapons Innovation: The Thor-Jupiter Controversy*. New York: Columbia University Press, 1969.

Arnold, Henry H. *Global Mission*. New York: Harper & Brothers, 1949.

Atlas Intercontinental Ballistic Missile: United States Air Force WS 107A-1. San Diego, Calif.: Convair Astronautics, 1959.

BALLISTIC MISSILES

Augenstein, Bruno W. *A Revised Development Program for Ballistic Missile of Intercontinental Range.* RM–1191. Santa Barbara, Calif.: The RAND Corp, February 8, 1954.

Baar, James, and William E. Howard. *Combat Missileman.* New York: Harcourt, Brace & World, Inc., 1961.

——————. *Polaris!* New York: Harcourt, Brace, 1960.

Beard, Edmund. *Developing the ICBM: A Study in Bureaucratic Politics.* New York: Columbia University Press, 1976.

Bergaust, Erik. *Rockets and Missiles.* New York: G.P. Putnam's Sons, 1957.

——————. *Reaching for the Stars.* Garden City, N.Y.: Doubleday, 1960.

Bottome, Edgar M. *The Missile Gap.* Rutherford, N.J.: Farleigh Dickinson University Press, 1971.

Boyce, Joseph C., ed. *New Weapons for Air Warfare: Fire-Control Equipment, Proximity Fuzes, and Guided Missiles.* Boston: Little, Brown and Co, 1947. [Part of the Science in World War II Series of the Office of Scientific Research and Development.]

Brodie, Bernard. *Strategy in the Missile Age.* Princeton: Princeton University Press, 1959.

Burchard, John E. *Rockets, Guns and Targets.* Boston: Little, Brown and Co, 1948. [Part of the Science in World War II Series of the Office of Scientific Research and Development.]

Burgess, Eric. *Guided Weapons.* London: Chapman and Hall, 1957.

——————. *Long Range Ballistic Missiles.* London: Chapman and Hall, 1961.

Bush, Vannevar. *Modern Arms and Free Men.* New York: Simon & Schuster, 1949.

Caidin, Martin. *Countdown for Tomorrow.* New York: E.P. Dutton & Co, Inc, 1958. [Caidin is a prolific writer with a large number of books on missiles and space to his credit.]

Chapman, John L. *Atlas: The Story of a Missile.* New York: Harper & Brothers, 1960.

A Comparison of Long Range Surface to Surface Rocket and Ramjet Missiles. R–174. Santa Barbara, Calif.: The RAND Corporation, May 1950.

Dornberger, Walter. Trans. by James Cleugh and Geoffry Halliday. *V–2.* New York: The Viking, 1954.

DuPre, Flint O. *U.S. Air Force Biographical Dictionary.* New York: Franklin Watts, Inc, 1965.

Emme, Eugene M., ed. *The History of Rocket Technology.* Detroit, Mich.: Wayne State University Press, 1964.

Eisenhower, Dwight D. *Crusade in Europe.* Garden City, N. Y.: Doubleday & Co, Inc, 1948.

——————. *The White House Years: Mandate for Change, 1953–1956.* Garden City, N.Y.: Doubleday & Co., 1963.

——————. *The White House Years: Waging Peace, 1956–1961.* Garden City, N.Y.: Doubleday & Co., 1965.

Gantz, Kenneth F., ed. *The United States Air Force Report on the Ballistic Missile: Its Technology, Logistics, and Strategy.* Garden City, N.Y.: Doubleday, 1958.

Gavin, James M. *War and Peace in the Space Age.* New York: Harper & Brothers, 1958.

BIBLIOGRAPHIC NOTE

Gibbs-Smith, Charles H. *The Aeroplane: An Historical Survey*. London, 1960.

Gilpin, Robert. *American Scientists and Nuclear Weapons Policy*. Princeton, N.J.: Princeton University Press, 1982.

Hartt, Julian. *The Mighty Thor: Missile in Readiness*. New York: Duell, Sloan and Pearce, 1961.

Lapp, Ralph E. *The Weapons Culture*. New York: W. W. Norton, 1968.

Lasby Charles G. *Project Paperclip: German Scientists and the Cold War*. New York: Atheneum, 1971.

Ley, Willy. *Rockets, Missiles, and Men in Space*. New York: The Viking Press, 1968.

Mallan, Lloyd. *Men, Rockets, and Space Rats*. New York: Messner, 1961.

McGovern, James. *Crossbow and Overcast*. New York: Morrow, 1964.

Medaris, John B. with Arthur Gordon. *Countdown for Decision*. New York: Putnam, 1960.

MX-774 Ground to Ground Missile: Summary Report. San Diego, Calif.: Consolidated-Vultee Aircraft Corp, December 1, 1949.

Neal, Roy. *Ace in the Hole: The Story of the Minuteman Missile*. Garden City, N.Y.: Doubleday and Co, 1962.

Ordway, Frederick I., and Ronald C. Wakeford. *International Missile and Spacecraft Guide*. New York: McGraw-Hill, 1960.

Parson, Nels A. *Missiles and the Revolution in Warfare*. Cambridge, Mass.: Harvard University Press, 1962.

Peck, Merton, and Frederick Scherer. *The Weapons Acquisition Process*. Cambridge, Mass.: Harvard University Press, 1962.

Pendray, G. Edward. *The Coming Age of Rocket Power*. New York: Harper Brothers, 1945.

Perry, Robert L. *The Ballistic Missile Decisions*. P-3686. Santa Monica, Calif.: The RAND Corp, 1967.

_____. *System Development Strategies: A Comparative Study of Doctrine, Technology, and Organization in the USAF Ballistic and Cruise Missile Programs, 1950-1960*. RM-4853-PR. Santa Monica, Calif.: The RAND Corp, 1966.

Putnam, W. D. *The Evolution of Air Force System Acquisition Management*. R-868-PR. Santa Monica, Calif.: The RAND Corp, 1972.

Rosen, Milton W. *The Viking Rocket Story*. New York: Harper & Bros, 1955.

Ross, Frank. *Guided Missiles: Rockets & Torpedoes*. New York: Lothrop, Lee & Shepard Co, Inc, 1951.

Schilling, Warner R., et al. *Strategy, Politics, and Defense Budgets*. New York: Columbia University Press, 1962.

Scoville, Herbert, and Robert Osborn. *Missile Madness*. Boston: Houghton Mifflin, 1970.

Seifert, Howard S., and Kenneth Brown, eds. *Ballistic Missile and Space Vehicle Systems*. New York: John Wiley & Sons Inc., 1961.

Stewart, Irvin. *Organizing Scientific Research for War: The Administrative History of the Office of Scientific Research and Development*. Boston: Little, Brown and Co, 1948.

Taylor, Maxwell D. *The Uncertain Trumpet*. New York: Harper and Bros., 1959.

Truman, Harry S. *Memoirs of Harry S Truman*. Garden City, N.Y.: Doubleday, 1956.

Twining, Nathan F. *Neither Liberty Nor Safety: A Hard Look at U.S. U.S. Military Policy and Strategy*. New York: Holt, 1966.

von Braun, Wernher, and Frederick I. Ordway. *History of Rocketry and Space Travel*. New York: Thomas Y. Crowell Co, 1975.

von Kármán, Theodore, with Lee Edson. *The Wind and Beyond: Theodore von Kármán, Pioneer in Aviation and Pathfinder in Space*. Boston: Little, Brown and Co, 1967.

Winterbotham, F. W. *The Ultra Secret*. New York: Harper & Row, 1974.

Who's Who in America. 32d edition, 1962-1963. Chicago: Marquis.

York, Herbert. *The Missile Race—Destination Unknown*. Phonorecord # 576. Santa Barbara, Calif.: Center for the Study of Democratic Institutions, 1972.

——————. *Race to Oblivion: A Participant's View of the Arms Race*. New York: Simon & Schuster, 1970.

Articles

Air Force Magazine is a monthly magazine published by the Air Force Association. The September 1956 issue, Vol. 39, No. 9, featured a section on "Guided Missiles—A Conference," pp 97–130, which included articles by Secretary of the Air Force James H. Douglas, Lt Gen Thomas S. Power, CINCSAC, and other USAF leaders. These authors discussed missile R&D status and expectations of the future employment of these weapons.

The April 1958 issue of *Air Force Magazine*, Vol. 41, No. 4, pp 49–80, also discussed USAF missiles and included articles by General Schriever and Richard E. Horner, Assistant SAF for R&D, among others. The Army and Navy missile programs were discussed by service spokesmen.

Air Force and Space Digest, May 1964.

American Aviation, May 7, 1956, p 42.

Angell, Joseph W. "Guided Missiles Could Have Won." *Atlantic*, December 1951, Vol. 188, No. 6, pp 29–34; January 1952, Vol. 189, No. 1, pp 57–63.

"A Noble Experiment?" *Forbes*, September 15, 1968, p 75. Discusses Bernard A. Schriever's work after his retirement.

Aviation Week and Space Technology, a McGraw-Hill publication, devotes a portion of most issues to missile development. It is an indispensable source of general information. The June 20, 1960 issue, pp 101–144, contains a special report on Strategic Air Command's adaption to the new missiles, entitled "SAC in Transition."

Baldwin, Hansen. "Rocket Program Splits Services: Army Air Forces Seeking Control." *New York Times*, May 12, 1946, p 1.

Bergaust, Erik, and Vincent B. Hackett. "USAF's Long Range Missile Program." *Missiles and Rockets*, April 1957. This magazine also published a very useful "First Annual Guided Missile Encyclopedia, 1957" in its July 1957 issue.

"Brain to Guide an ICBM Gets Its I.Q. Tested." *Business Week*, September 14, 1957.

"Builder of the Atlas." *Time*, January 20, 1958.

"Can U.S. Still Win the Missile Race? Interviews with Top Experts." *U.S. News and World Report*, November 15, 1957.

Donnelly, Ralph W. "Rocket Batteries of the Civil War." *Military Affairs*, XXV (May 1961).

"Does the U.S. Lag Behind USSR in Missiles?" *Foreign Policy Bulletin*, May 15, 1956.

Elliott, J. Richard Jr. "Deadly Birds: A Flock of New Guided Missiles Is Being Hatched." *Barron's*, December 10, 1956.

Emme, Eugene M. "Space and the Historian." *Spaceflight*, Vol 15 (November 1973).

Gaddis, Paul O. "The Project Manager." *Harvard Business Review*, May–June 1959.

Gardner, Trevor. "But We Are Still Lagging: Reasons Why, What We Can Do About It." *Life*, November 4, 1957.

_____. "How We Fell Behind in Guided Missiles." *Airpower Historian*, Vol 5, No. 1 (January 1958).

_____. "Must Our Air Force be Second Best?" *Look*, May 1, 1956.

_____. "Our Guided Missile Crisis." *Look*, May 15, 1956.

Greenwood, John T. "The Air Force Ballistic Missile and Space Program (1954–1974)." *Aerospace Historian*, Vol. 21, No. 4 (Winter/December 1974).

Hotz, Robert. "Gardner Quits, Starts USAF R&D Fight." *Aviation Week*, February 13, 1956.

Jacobs, Paul. "Pilots, Missilemen and Rockets." *The Reporter*, February 6, 1958.

"J.R. Dempsey, Ex-Light Colonel Runs Atlas Project at Convair." *Air Force Times*, April 5, 1958, p 38.

Keenan, Francis J. "Congressional Leaders Call for More Emphasis on ICBM." *American Aviation Historical Society Journal*, Vol 19, No. 20 (February 27, 1956).

Keller, Charles L. "The First Guided Missile Program: The Aerial Torpedo." *American Aviation Historical Society Journal*, Winter 1975. Reprinted from *Sperry Engineering Review*. March 1961.

Kimball, Dan A. "Effective Organization for Missile Supremacy." *Vital Speeches*, February 1958.

LeMay, Gen Curtis E. "United States Air Force: Power for Peace." *National Geographic*, September 1965, Vol. 128, No. 3 (September 1965).

Leviero, Anthony. "An Aide Resigns on Missile Rift." *New York Times*, February 8, 1956, p 1.

_____. "President Disputes Aide on Missile Lag." *New York Times*, February 9, 1956, p 1.

BALLISTIC MISSILES

Leavitt, William. "How USAF's Missile Program Helped the Nation Off the Pad." *Air Force Magazine*, Vol 47, No. 5 (May 1964).

"Man in the News." *New York Times*, December 1957.

Mullen, Donald E. "Missile Guidance—Steel Nerves, Steel Muscles." *General Electric Review*, May–July 1956.

Murray, Russ. "The Navaho Inheritance." *American Aviation Historical Society Journal*, Vol. 19 (Spring 1974) pp 17–21.

"New Look—ICBMs Rise on Prairie." *Missiles and Rockets*, January 11, 1960, pp 15–20.

Olejar, Paul D. "Rockets in Early American Wars." *Military Affairs*, Vol. X (Winter 1946).

Perkins, Donald T. "Dropping the Pilot." *Annals of the American Academy of Political and Social Science*. Vol. 299, May 1955.

Pike, Iain. "Atlas: Pioneer ICBM and Space Age Workhorse." *International*, January 18, 1962; February 1, 1962.

Ramo, Simon. "ICBM: Giant Step Into Space." *Astronautics*, August 1, 1957.

Ridenour, Louis. "Pilot Lights of the Apocalypse." Vol 33, (January 1946).

Rollefson, R. "Why So Many Missiles?" *Bulletin of the Atomic Scientists*, Vol. 13 (October 1957).

Schriever, Bernard A. "AFBMD: Catching Up with the Soviets." *Missiles and Rockets*, July 28, 1958.

_____. "Ballistic Missiles: Springboard to Space." *Air Force Magazine*, Vol. 41, No. 3 (March 1958). Also: The article on pp 76–95, written by John F. Loosbrock, discusses the organization of the missile program.

_____. "The Battle for 'Space Superiority." *Air Force Magazine*, Vol. 40, No. 4 (April 1957).

Symington, Stuart. "The Intercontinental Ballistic Missile." *Vital Speeches of the Day*, Vol. 20, No. 23, September 15, 1954.

"The Man Who Differed and the Reasons Why." *Time*, August 30, 1963. About Thomas S. Power.

Twining, Nathan F. "Report From Moscow." *Air Force Magazine*, Vol. 39, No. 8 (August 1956).

Weaver, Kenneth F. "Of Men and Planes." *National Geographic*, Vol. 128, No. 3 (September 1965).

"What it Takes to Make an Atlas." *Business Week*, June 10, 1959.

"Where Services Test Missiles." *Aviation Week*, Vol. 55, No. 16, October 15, 1951.

Wood, Robert H. "Those 'Fantastic' Weapons." *Aviation Week*, Vol. 55, No. 17, October 22, 1951.

York, Herbert F., and G. Allen Grebb. "Military Research and Development: A Postwar History." *The Bulletin of the Atomic Scientists*, Vol. 33, No. 1 (Janaury 1977).

BIBLIOGRAPHIC NOTE

Ph.D. Dissertations

These Ph.D. dissertations were especially helpful in the writing of this study:

Clark, Paul W. "Major General George Owen Squier: Military Scientist." Case Western Reserve University, 1974.

Evans, Eugene E. "Dispute Settlement and Hierarchy: The Military Guided Missile Controversy, 1955–1960." University of Illinois, 1963.

Johns, Claude Jackson. "The United States Air Force Intercontinental Ballistic Missile Program 1945–1959: Technological Change and Organizational Innovation." The University of North Carolina, 1964.

Parrish, Noel F. "Behind the Sheltering Bomb: Military Indecision from Alamogordo to Korea." Rice University, 1968.

Index

Aberdeen Proving Ground, MD, 38
A.C. Spark Plug Company, 126, 132, 148
Advanced Research Projects Agency
    (ARPA), 210
AEC. *See* Atomic Energy Commission
Aerial torpedo, 8, 9
Aerojet General Corporation, 40, 48n, 96n,
    122, 122n, 130
    and propulsion system, 126, 143
    and Titan contract, 132
Aeronautical Division (Signal Corps), 8n
Aerospace Corporation, 212, 221, 238
Air defense, 27, 89. *See also* Missiles,
    air-to-air; Missiles, anti-missile
Air Force Ballistic Missile Program, 288
Air Force Ballistic Missile and Space
    Committee, 137, 138, 212n. *See also*
    Ballistic Missiles Committee (Air
    Force)
Air Force Budget Advisory Committee, 310
Air Force Council, 138, 158, 179, 221, 297,
    310
    and missile designations, 67, 85
    and Atlas missiles, 105
    and ICBMs, 94, 155, 157
    and Thor missile, 162
Air Force Flight Test Center, 130
Air Force/Air Corps Headquarters, positions
    See also specific individuals in each
    position
Air Communications Officer, 13, 13n, 17
Asst. Chief of Staff, Guided Missiles,
    107, 139, 140, 278, 285, 286, 310,
    313, 315, 316, 317, 318, 319, 320,
    321, 328
Asst. Chief of Staff, Installations, 139,
    310
Asst. Chief of Air Staff, Materiel and
    Services, 13, 17, 18
Asst. Chief of Staff, Operations,
    Commitments, and Requirements,
    13, 17, 25, 25n, 82, 83
Asst. Chief of Staff, Plans, 13
Asst. Deputy Chief of Staff, Operations
    (Guided Missiles), 83
Chief of Staff, 57, 138, 278, 310, 312,
    327
Dep. Chief of Staff, Comptroller, 139,
    310
Dep. Chief of Staff, Development, 2, 66,
    67, 74, 82, 139, 310, 328
Dep. Chief of Staff, Materiel, 67, 68, 82,
    138, 295, 310
Dep. Chief of Staff, Operations, 83, 138,
    310

Dep. Chief of Staff, Personnel, 139, 310
Dep. Chief of Staff, Research and
    Development, 24
Office of the Asst. for Guided Missiles,
    83
Vice Chief of Staff, 327
Air Force Installations Board, 311
Air Force Letter 136-3, 89, 90
Air Force Logistics Command (AFLC), 4,
    186, 222, 237, 238
Air Force Missile Test Center, 76, 126, 130
Air Force Plan for Simplifying
    Administrative Procedures, 136. *See
    also* Gillette Procedures
Air Force Special Weapons Center, 117
Air Force, Office of the Secretary, positions
    in. *See also* specific individuals in
    each position
    Asst. Sec., Applications Engineering, 277
    Asst. Sec., Financial Management, 138,
        278, 285, 310, 312, 313, 320, 321
    Asst. Sec., Manpower & Personnel, 138,
        310
    Asst. Sec., Materiel, 138, 278, 285, 310,
        312, 320
    Asst Sec., Properties & Installations, 277
    Asst. Sec., R&D, 133, 138, 274, 277,
        278, 285, 310, 312, 313, 320, 321
    Comptroller, 277
    Secretary of the Air Force, 138, 274,
        297, 305-6, 310
    Special Assistant for Research and
        Development, 2, 93, 327
    Undersecretary, 327
Air Force Systems Command (AFSC), 4, 44,
    186, 194, 194n, 219, 222, 328
Air Forces (numbered)
    Fifth, 108
    Eighth, 10
    Fifteenth, 11
Air Materiel Command, 9, 26, 26n, 32, 42,
    56, 58, 61, 62, 139, 140, 180, 201-2,
    209
Air Proving Ground Command of, 11n
    and Air Research and Development
        Command (ARDC), 77n, 123, 221,
        277
    and Atlas missiles, 113, 217
    and contracting authority, 3, 109
    and ICBMs, 152, 278, 288, 311
    and "insurance missiles," 27
    and loss of R&D responsibilities, 65, 67
    and missile complex construction, 201-
        202, 209
    and Ramo-Wooldridge, 126

389